WATER, HEALTH AND SOCIETY

Caricature
of Dr. Abel Wolman
Baltimore, Maryland
1952
May 10

WATER,
HEALTH
AND
SOCIETY

Selected papers by ABEL WOLMAN

Edited by GILBERT F. WHITE

INDIANA UNIVERSITY PRESS   *Bloomington and London*

TO ANNE

Inspiration and Mentor

Contents

The Search for Standards

Water Planning and Policy

Comprehensive Planning for Human Environment

The Role of the Engineer

Introduction

The channeling and storage of water to meet human needs has a long history of skillful design for single purposes showing little regard for its effects upon other parts of environment. In this, it is like much engineering dealing with transport or energy or industrial processing. However, in recent decades, while engineering has greatly improved design, construction, and operation of works for water management, it also has broadened its aims to deal with multiple purposes. Projects with single aims have given way to ones with multiple objectives as exemplified by multipurpose dams. Increasingly, attention is given to the interaction of manipulation of one sector of the earth upon other sectors. Sanitary engineering becomes environmental management.

With the widening of areas of interest has come a deepened concern for the responsibility of individual engineers as they shape the actions of society. Engineers have tended to exercise their competence and experience in reaching limited goals which they accept from society and to hold themselves somewhat aloof from the making of public policy or the assessment of human values. A new city water supply or a waste disposal plant is viewed as a task deserving application of the best scientific knowledge and the most prudent judgment to satisfy its purpose with a reasonable minimum of cost and risk. It has been more difficult to recognize that engineers in effect define community goals by the way they

present projects or establish standards of quality or organize studies
and operations. To take that influence into account is to enlarge the
scope of considerations engineers feel obliged to assess.

To a remarkable degree the writings of Abel Wolman reflect this
broadening stream of thought. They also record his contributions to it,
for he opened the way in several sectors and interpreted and clarified
it in others.

His published papers over half a century show a series of original
concepts which Wolman helped develop and give wide application.
Elementary notions of the rational loading of water filter plants were
stated in his 1917 paper on bacterial removal. A year later his work on
chlorine absorption became the basis for chlorination practice, a technique which probably has had a more profound effect upon public health
than any other single device in water management. His scheme for supply
of municipal waste effluent to the Sparrows Point steel plant pioneered
efforts to find opportunities for reuse of waste water.

In the field of public organization to deal with water problems
Wolman was associated with a series of ventures that shaped later action.
The analyses of municipal water supply needs in Baltimore were exem-
plary. At the state level, the Maryland agencies were among the first to
attempt to integrate conventional sanitary engineering with wildlife,
recreation, and public-works construction in a statewide plan. The first
serious efforts at coordination of federal and state activities in water
planning were undertaken by the Water Resources Committee of the
National Resources Board under Wolman's chairmanship in 1935. The
financing of water supply in developing countries felt the pervasive
impact of his suggestions, particularly in Latin America. The Water Resources Board Act of 1964 bears the mark of his analysis of Ceylon's
water problems. Israeli strategy in developing water has benefited from
his imagination and critical analysis over a long period.

Wolman's involvement in community efforts at all levels gives him
a special base from which to appraise the role of his profession. He has
had a vigorous and constructive hand in university policy, municipal
planning and operation, state organization, interstate negotiations, federal
policy and coordination, programs of foreign governments, and the
methods of international agencies. At all levels he has commanded the
respect of his peers, and his association with the activities of the American Water Works Association and the American Public Health Association has been perennial. To a young engineer the papers may be a
demonstration of what one man who remains solidly grounded in his
professional art can do as a citizen of the world.

Probably Wolman's most pervasive influence is in a genre of thought
and presentation that shines only partly on the printed page. Rare is the

national organization or conference touching on water and environmental engineering that has not felt the charm of his analysis of an issue of policy and responsibility. Usually extemporaneous, always felicitous in expression, and punctuated with gentle wit and a soft-spoken sarcasm, the typical Wolman talk sums up the problems in a lucid framework and sends his audience away smiling, a bit puzzled by some of the generalizations, and refreshed by a train of thought that leads to a new perspective. A gift for asking the pertinent but disarming question and for illuminating it in a sharp and faintly ludicrous light has given both direction and relief to countless administrative sessions, and has enlivened seminars and consulting boards. Technical precision and insight blend with cultured urbanity. Some of this shows in the papers, but the ones selected for publication in this volume are not intended primarily to present his activities and achievements.

A biographical account would examine Wolman's part in the life of the Johns Hopkins University and his native city of Baltimore. It would review the evolution of sanitary and environmental engineering, the impact of an American engineer who is concerned with overseas environments rather than with impressing American methods on them, and the mounting complexity of public management of water around the globe. It would recognize the influence of Abel and Anne Wolman as they have moved gracefully across academic, professional, and political boundaries. The more notable professional experience is presented in outline at the end of the papers for the reader who would like to see where a specific technical contribution fits into a complex human career.

An adequate assessment of the influence of Wolman's thought and action would go far beyond his papers or those of others who quote and build on his work. This selection is arranged according to the principal problems to which he has addressed himself, ranging from the broad field of water resources through questions of technology, policy, and organization to the ethics of a profession. Because water has been the principal substantive theme, the selections begin with Wolman's review of water resources in the United States. And because his continuing concern has been the role of the engineer in society, they conclude with his latest views on the problem. Intervening items are chosen to illustrate the quality of his thought as applied to issues having continuing relevance. Certain of the earlier ones, such as the discussions of environmental management, record the beginnings of now prevalent ideas. A few represent positions on which he has changed his views. Others, such as the appraisal of standards of water quality, are contemporary in import and apply to any aspect of environment for which society attempts to establish canons of preference.

Taken together, the papers present not only a man of rare intellectual strength and vision, but also the unfolding of a point of view as to human capacity and responsibility in shaping environment. In that direction, more than a chronicle of accomplishment, they are a chart of aspiration.

GILBERT F. WHITE

The University of Chicago

WATER RESOURCES

Water Resources
A Report to the National
Academy of Sciences*

I. *Outline of the Problem*

Next to oxygen, water is perhaps the most important single element for human existence. Despite this fact, relatively few citizens fully recognize the pricelessness of water and its vital role in our expanding economy. The average American takes for granted an adequate water supply upon which he may draw at will to meet his manifold needs in every aspect of life. Moreover, although there has been much public discussion over the nation's water-resources picture and its problems in this area, there have also been wide differences of opinion as to the nature of such problems and the best means of overcoming them.

Today, the nation is faced by a number of water problems, the urgency and gravity of which vary from one area to another. Although the total amount of water available in the United States today is sufficient, it is highly variable in distribution, both spatially and temporally. Unfortunately, an excess of water in one area is not often of more than limited assistance to other areas suffering from water scarcity. So it is that, while one region may be struggling with the limitations imposed by insufficient water supply, another may be facing serious problems of flood control.

---

* "Water Resources," A Report to the Committee on Natural Resources by Abel Wolman, National Academy of Sciences—National Research Council Publication No. 1000B, 1962.

Moreover, it is clear that within about 20 years, the full potential development of some of our big river basins will have been reached—the Colorado, for example. This will mean that there will be no more water attainable in those areas, and the whole field of water management will assume major importance. At the same time, many of the nation's existing rivers and streams are becoming seriously polluted, and the outlook for the future indicates that this problem will continue to grow.

On the other hand, ever-expanding demands on our nation's water resources have resulted not only from the greater absolute number of people and the continued population increase, but also from the growing and varied uses we make of our water resources. The need for water to support our continued growth and progress is magnified when a close look is taken at the vital role played by this resource in our industrial, agricultural, and municipal life. If America is to maintain the way of life and aspirations of her people in this rapidly changing world, then it is essential that the nation so manage its resources that these values can be protected and enhanced.

Because the entire hydrological system is so directly interconnected, we must be able to measure the effect of the actions we take on specific parts of the overall system. Unfortunately, although we know a great deal about certain of the critical elements of the system, we are quite ignorant in other crucially important areas. The fact is that at present, less than one-fourth of one per cent of the total funds spent on water-resources development is allocated for basic research in water. So it is that years after an action is taken, effects occur that were not foreseen and are often more important than the advantages offered by the development itself.

Here we must also recognize that the whole question of water-resource development involves, in addition to such fundamental scientific knowledge, basic economic and social issues as well. These become apparent in deciding between alternative uses, for example, or, in planning for maximization of benefit in water-development projects, trying to evaluate the needs of the people, when and if they can be defined. We need a much broader understanding of the social implications of our actions in the water-resources area if we are to get wise public decisions on such programs.

It is clear that complex areas such as water resources can no longer be approached in the compartmentalized way that they have been in the past. Recognizing this fact, we run into the human difficulty of translating knowledge into action. Unfortunately, at present, we have no institutional structure in the United States to take care of multidisciplinary research in such areas as water. There is a complacency in this regard, a lag in recognition of the need to invest the time, resources, and funds necessary to develop a new structure and a new generation of well-rounded water scientists, ready and able to approach the nation's water resources problems from a unified, multidisciplinary standpoint. In contrast to the heavy emphasis placed upon development of water supplies, there has been comparative disregard for the improvement of our understanding of physical and chemical processes, which is so urgently needed if we are to foresee the results of that development. On the whole, we find that it is, in fact, far easier to get approval for new, costly projects than for education or research.

With this in mind, it is the primary purpose of this report to identify both the more significant problems in the water-resource field and the areas of physical science research which will contribute to the understanding and more effective use of this resource. This study is undertaken with the hope that it will emphasize and indicate the basic scientific research needed in order to provide a better basis for water-resource planning and policy formulation.

In Section II, we begin by reviewing the general aspects of the behavior of water in the hydrosphere, and identifying some general problems which arise from the physical characteristics of water supply and the nature of man's demand for it. In this section, the availability of water resources in the United States today will be discussed and evaluated briefly with respect to the demands for its use. Some general problems having to do with water-resource development and allocations will be highlighted in terms of both their physical and their social aspects. Here, in order to present a balanced appraisal of the field, certain unique conditions that govern the administration and use of water, such as economic evaluations and the legal structure of water use, will be reviewed, and some areas in need of total socio-economic-technological research indicated.

With this overall picture in mind, Section III will deal specifically with the areas in need of basic research. This chapter will concentrate almost exclusively on the physical aspects of water research. Specific problems in need of further investigation will be discussed and research proposals made in order of priority.

Section IV will present a summary of some of the recommendations made with respect to basic research in this report.

II. *The Nature of the Problem*

The Supply of Water in the United States

Of all the water in the world, 97 per cent, or one quadrillion (10^{15}) acre feet, is contained in the oceans. If the world were a uniform sphere, this quantity would be sufficient to cover it to a depth of 800 feet. The total amount of fresh water, on the other hand, is estimated at about 33 trillion acre feet. It is distributed roughly as follows:

75 per cent is contained in polar ice and glaciers.
11 per cent is ground water at depths less than 2,500 feet.
14 per cent is ground water at depths greater than 2,500 feet, but less than 12,500 feet.
0.3 per cent is in lakes.
0.03 per cent is in rivers.
0.06 per cent is soil moisture.
0.035 per cent is in the atmosphere.

These are static estimates of distribution, however. While the water content of the atmosphere is relatively small at any given time, immense quantities of water pass through it annually. For example, the annual precipitation on land surfaces alone is 7.7 times as great as the moisture contained in the entire atmosphere at any one time; that is, about 30 times as great as the moisture in the air over the land.

We can think of the hydrologic cycle as beginning with the evaporation of fresh water, largely from the oceans, into the atmosphere by means of the sun's energy. This fresh water is carried in the atmosphere until eventually, as precipitation, it falls to earth either on land or in the oceans.

The natural, continuously renewed source of fresh water potentially beneficial to man is precipitation occurring over land surfaces. There are two principal sources of moisture for the United States. The first is the Pacific Ocean, from which the air masses move inland; the second is the Gulf of Mexico. Although the average annual precipitation for the continental United States is about 30 inches, sufficient to cover the whole country to a depth of about two and a half feet,[1] there are wide fluctuations in terms of distribution. On the whole, the East receives two-thirds of the nation's rainfall and the West the remaining third. Within any given area, there are seasonal fluctuations in precipitation. Moreover, although there is little evidence of any significant change in average annual precipitation (at least over large areas) during modern times, there are non-cyclical secular changes. The distribution of precipitation over land areas is influenced by geographical features (latitude, topography, etc.), however it is generally independent of what man does with his land and water resources by way of patterns of cultivation, creation of artificial lakes, and similar manipulations.

Figure 1 represents the overall features of what happens to water that falls as precipitation. Numerical values correspond to estimates for the continental United States. In interpreting the numbers given in the diagram, it is important to remember that they are averages over the entire country. Although figures for total water supply seem quite impressive at first glance, they do not reflect the fact that neither precipitation nor the flow of streams is distributed either geographically or temporally in a manner which matches man's needs and wishes.

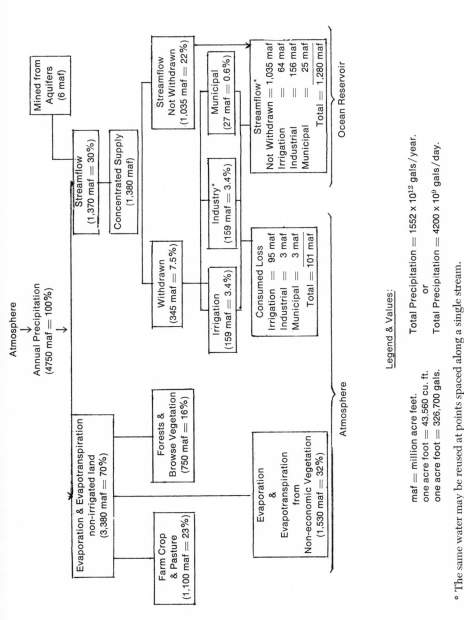

Fig. 1 Overall distribution of precipitation in the United States

Legend & Values:

maf = million acre feet.
one acre foot = 43,560 cu. ft.
one acre foot = 326,700 gals.

Total Precipitation = 1552 x 10^{12} gals/year.
or
Total Precipitation = 4200 x 10^9 gals/day.

* The same water may be reused at points spaced along a single stream.

Atmosphere

Annual Precipitation
(4750 maf = 100%)

Mined from
Aquifers
(6 maf)

Streamflow
(1,370 maf = 30%)

Concentrated Supply
(1,380 maf)

Evaporation & Evapotranspiration
non-irrigated land
(3,380 maf = 70%)

Forests &
Browse Vegetation
(750 maf = 16%)

Farm Crop
& Pasture
(1,100 maf = 23%)

Evaporation
&
Evapotranspiration
from
Non-economic Vegetation
(1,530 maf = 32%)

Atmosphere

Withdrawn
(345 maf = 7.5%)

Streamflow
Not Withdrawn
(1,035 maf = 22%)

Irrigation
(159 maf = 3.4%)

Industry*
(159 maf = 3.4%)

Municipal
(27 maf = 0.6%)

Consumed Loss
Irrigation   =   95 maf
Industrial   =   3 maf
Municipal   =   3 maf
          Total = 101 maf

Streamflow*
Not Withdrawn = 1,035 maf
Irrigation   =   64 maf
Industrial   =   156 maf
Municipal   =   25 maf
          Total = 1,280 maf

Ocean Reservoir

The rain and snow which wet the soil seep into underground water-bearing strata (aquifers) and run off saturated soil surfaces into streams, lakes, and rivers. About 70 to 75 per cent of this precipitation is returned to the atmosphere by evapotranspiration from growing plants and direct evaporation from moist soils, lakes, and streams. This water, at least under the limitations of present scientific, technological, and economic knowledge, is not available for man's volitional use or manipulation. Slightly over half of it produces beneficial results, however, since it sustains the growth of forests, grasslands, and non-irrigated farmlands.[2] The portion of precipitation which seeps into underground aquifers is particularly important because the gradual overflow from full aquifers accounts for most of the regular streamflow (as distinct from that resulting from surface runoff after rainstorms or from runoff of snow melt). Theoretically, streamflow is a measure of the maximum amount of water that man could withdraw and use up on a steady-state continuing basis before producing net depletion. By virtue of the hydrologic interdependency of ground waters and streamflow, this flow can be tapped either by direct diversion of stream water or by pumping from aquifers, and thereby reduce their overflow into streams.[3]

In summary, the fresh-water cycle may be described as a closed flow circuit containing two branches. The combined annual flow through the two branches equals annual precipitation. Seventy per cent of the flow goes through the first branch: precipitation–land surface–atmosphere. Although, to date, man can exercise very little control over this process, nevertheless about half produces beneficial results. The remaining 30 per cent goes through the second branch of the circuit as streamflow, the concentrated supply which man can potentially control, manipulate, and use. It is this portion upon which water-resources planning and development has focused. Actually only one-fourth of this streamflow is diverted and about two-thirds of that is fed back into the stream whence it, like the undiverted flow, goes to ocean storage before returning to the atmosphere. The remaining one-third of that diverted from the branch is consumed and returns to the atmosphere directly.

The Demand for Water in the United States

Much has been written on the elements that have contributed to the nation's increase in per capita water use. Growing urbanization and the rapid industrial and agricultural expansion of this country are certainly significant factors in this regard. At current rates of growth, it seems that the population of the United States will have doubled within the next 40 to 50 years. At the same time, production will be four or five times bigger while per capita income will be two or three times greater. Such figures spell out the broad implications of water-resource requirements.

Moreover, the fact is that water-using activities have grown more rapidly in the past decades than the total economy. Although the water used for irrigation has increased substantially, agricultural production has grown at a considerably lower rate. Similarly, the growth of the manufacturing industries that use large quantities of water has been greater than that of total manufacturing. Household water use has increased more rapidly than population growth. Per capita urban use exceeds per capita rural use, and our population is becoming increasingly urbanized. The American standard of living has risen sharply and is expected to continue to rise. At the same time, together with growing industrialization has come greater usage of water-connected devices.

In addition to these general areas of increased water demand, the rapid change in the structure of American society and the coming of mass production have contributed to a growing demand for recreational facilities. Water resources play a tremendously important role in the recreational life of the nation.

Despite such indications of constantly increasing demand for water use, we may reasonably assume that for many years beyond the year 2000, *total* water shortages for the United States as a whole are improbable. This conclusion may be quantitatively illustrated by the following data presented in Table 1 which indicates the present and projected withdrawal and consumptive use of water in the United States. The figures given should be compared with the average annual runoff of 1,200 billion gallons per day.

Table 1
Present and Projected Withdrawal and Consumptive
Use of Water in the United States*
(In billion gallons per day)

Year	Withdrawal	Consumptive Use
1960	300	120
1980	600	190
2000	900	255

* These figures are based on numerous assumptions, some even controversial, and can be applied only as rough guideposts for this report. Among these assumptions are the following: (1) There will be no technological change; (2) pricing policies will remain unchanged; (3) present inefficient methods of using water will remain the same; (4) industrial expansion will create corresponding quantities of wastes. It is possible, however, to change all of these conditions by such activities as scientific and technological development, pricing policies, and improvement in the application of available technologies.

On the other hand, although overall water shortages are not anticipated, it is true that the increased demands for water supplies in some areas of the country will pose problems, largely fiscal in nature, in making available low-cost water supplies of satisfactory quality. Spatially, or regionally, the problem is this: the population is not evenly spread, and the prospects are that this density problem will become greater. At the same time, the resources needed by these clusters of population are not evenly spread either. The problem, of course, becomes one of matching population needs with the supply of resources on a regional basis both within a region and among regions, as, for example, in Southern California where 75 per cent of the population of the state is clustered around an area that contains only about 25 per cent of the state's water supply.

At the present time, the limited pure-water resources of the arid West are almost at an end. Several states, such as Arizona which draws 60 percent of its water supply from overpumped wells, have cause for real concern at this point. Some states in the manufacturing belt of the East are beginning to find themselves faced with the possibility of deterioration of their fresh-water resources.

On the other hand, the fact remains that probably half of the states could afford to double their water withdrawal, and the cost involved would be relatively low. Still, the water problem is essentially a regional one. The total national supply of water is not generally a helpful factor in solving a regional or area supply problem. With some resources which can be transported easily and cheaply, the problem can be approached on a national basis. With water, however, very long-haul distribution may be so costly that a surplus of water in the northeastern United States, for example, would not be very helpful, under present economic conditions, in augmenting a scarcity in the Southwest. At the present time, the techniques available for solving a problem of this type are not adequate. It is apparent that the growing demands for water and the increasing per capita consumption will add to the pressures felt in those areas which are already facing water shortages.

Some General Considerations in Water-Resource Development

Problems such as those cited above point to the need for more refined and empirically valid techniques in all the social sciences. In general, the analyses applied in these spheres are essentially economic techniques.

Unlike the physical sciences, economics is a science of human behavior. Its primary concern is with human beings in their social relationships rather than with the natural laws affecting objects. Individuals function within a social framework. Their economic transactions necessarily involve relations with many persons, groups, and classes. The agents involved may be independent producers or consumers, or they may be powerful groups representing differing interests and objectives.

A market economy depends primarily upon competition between economic units to achieve resource allocation. In such a setting, planning for efficient use and development of water can be conducted most effectively only by an organization (or organizations) representing primarily the public interest and having jurisdiction beyond individual economic and local political units. This, as implied above, is in large measure because the manner in which man uses water resources or influences the hydrologic cycle through control activities at one point intimately and importantly affects the range and character of opportunities for use and control at other points. Examples are easily cited. Flow regulation may benefit a wide range of activities over extensive areas, surface water used for irrigation often incidentally recharges ground water aquifers, and cool water released from the bottom strata of reservoirs may have a beneficial effect on game-fish population. On the other hand, wastes introduced into a stream at one point affect the cost, if not the feasibility, of downstream activities; artificial recharge of an aquifer raises the water table and may cause land-drainage problems at another point; and hot water effluent from a power plant may reduce the oxygen saturation level of the water downstream and make it a less efficient assimilator of organic wastes. Small economic or political units with a limited purview cannot be expected to act optimally with respect to major water-resources planning. For many small water developments for domestic or industrial uses, these dicta are, of course, less applicable.

Society may not have fully utilized, as yet, all possible guides to water-resource allocation in the market. There is a frequent tendency to overemphasize the separation of public from private decision-making when considering water-resource management problems. In point of fact, there is actually a continuum between the two areas, with a great deal of intermingling of public and private interest, influence, and effect. In practice, *private* decisions are always made within a publicly established decision framework, and *public* decisions are always subject to private pressure. In fact, in the United States, the whole private decision-making process in water-resource management is carried on within a framework set by society and operated by the government at various levels. We have much direct government involvement in the resource-management field throughout the whole political structure—federal, state, county, city —concerned with such elements as flood-control districts, irrigation districts, and the like. And at all these levels of government we certainly have private pressure groups seeking to influence government.

Planning for the optimum development and use of the nation's water resources presents many difficult problems. From its very nature, water-resource planning demands not only continued progress in relevant aspects of the physical and social sciences, but also serves as a sort of barometer to their development in this area and to the correlation and coordination prevalent among them.

An ideal evaluation technique should make it possible to appraise accurately the relative advantages and disadvantages of the proposed project with regard to the alternative means available, together with the effects of such a project. Both of these considerations would definitely require a higher level of scientific knowledge together with down-to-earth recognition of the social structure in line with the practices and limitations in the field of water-resource development.

Recognition of the need for planning on a relatively extensive level has posed the difficult problem of defining an appropriate planning unit. Perhaps the basin is the best general unit. Many important interdependencies of a hydrological-economic character are incorporated within a basin, as are aspects of the hydrological cycle over which man can presently exercise at least limited discretion. It is apparent, however, that rigid adherence to a pre-determined basin or any other unit can be misleading in regard to planning and development as well as research. For example, an optimum program might and often does require inter-basin transfers of streamflow. Moreover, since only a small portion of the total hydrological cycle is comprehended in a basin, undertakings which have a rather fundamental effect upon other parts of the cycle (rainfall augmentation, for example), would require extension of the planning unit beyond the basin. In some cases the service area of a natural water system is the best planning unit. The planning unit for a basin like the Delaware is a case in point, since it obviously includes not only states drained by the Delaware River system, but also the city of New York and other areas outside the basin.

Despite these qualifications and limitations, however, the basin has become increasingly recognized as a meaningful planning unit.[4] Basin-wide planning for productive water-resource development and use is significantly inhibited, however, by the great conceptual and computational complexity which approximating optimum water-resource systems poses. At the same time, even if and when optimal determinations have been reached, there are still other factors in our social structure which must be taken into consideration in working in connection with water development. Given physical and economical feasibility, it is still the legal aspects of the water-resource problem that finally control the enactment of measures found to be both physically and economically practical. The legal limitations are composed of laws, customs, and other forms of group control. They may facilitate enactment of water-resource policies; on the other hand, they may block them completely.

For example, the changing pattern of water use coupled with changing value standards requires shift of emphasis from activities of less need and value to the opposite. Unfortunately, such shifts come slowly and will depend on laws, institutions, customs, and enterprises as well as other factors. New value standards are not always appropriate in monetary terms, usually because the market does not function effectively with regard to them. Studies on some basic questions relative to water-resource institutions may stimulate the adjustment and assist in obtaining an optimum pattern of water use. Such studies should consider how existing institutional arrangements influence realization of specific objectives and social values and how these arrangements may be improved. The question of how such changes can be brought about in a manner consistent with the basic value standards of American society should be studied carefully.

It is clear, then, that the whole question of resource management within a social framework is in need of research in order to understand and evaluate the nature and effects of the complex decision-making processes operating in our society, as well as to provide a better basis for intelligent policy formulation and planning. Admittedly, it is difficult to do this kind of research. Man always seems to have trouble studying man. Often we become too involved emotionally, and it is easy to lose perspective. Nevertheless, there are real possibilities for research progress both in the domestic and international areas. Such research must be well led with the best capabilities we can muster; it must be properly organized and objective; it must be well-financed, and it must be carefully reported and presented.

Conclusion

From the information available, it seems clear that if scientific and technological improvements in our knowledge and management of water resources are forthcoming at a sufficiently high rate, we can expect to cope successfully with these and other problems which will multiply as demands for water increase. Should they not be forthcoming, we can look forward to greater restriction of economic and demographic growth and to constraints on the improvement of the amenities of life, not only in areas of the United States currently experiencing water problems, but in others as well. As important examples, we can cite the increased costs for flow control of streams, for transportation of water over greater and greater distances, and, as water quality deteriorates with increasing use, for treatment and quality control. Less direct but equally important effects are increased risks to public health from greater introduction of pollutants, decreased opportunities for and increased costs of outdoor recreation, and forced shift of population and production from one area to another as governed by availability of water supplies rather than desirability of other conditions.

To decide how to prevent or mitigate such situations or to plan how to encourage development, we need more knowledge, not only about the hydrology of water and about potential demands, but also about the interaction between our efforts to satisfy these demands and the hydrologic cycle. Understanding is required in order that we may have freedom in choosing the means of attacking particular problems and in order to put them in proper perspective. Only after we have put each problem into perspective with others and have identified possible alternatives can we make an informed decision, first as to whether a given problem is worth attacking at all, and second how to allot resources of money and research talent for its solution.

The most critical shortage by far in the area of water resources is the very real shortage of broadly trained people capable of planning and executing effective research programs. It seems that it is far easier to get approval for new, costly projects than for basic research or education. Again, the segmented fashion in which water-resource development has been approached and the lack of an institutional structure conducive to a multi-disciplinary attack upon the nation's water problems have been significant factors in this regard. The fact is that at the present time the number of research people working in the pollution field, for example, is a few hundred; the number of hydrologists is a mere handful. Less than a thousand practitioners in the hydrosciences are available in this country. Of these, the large majority are in government service, with some 75 per cent in federal service. This meager complement of investigators is most distressing in view of past and projected capital investments in water resources. Over the next 25 years it is anticipated that the dollars expended for these purposes alone will run into the hundreds of billions. To accomplish this major task well, the most urgent need is the establishment of a program to enlist and train new people in virtually all disciplines relating to water resources. To strengthen the whole hydrosciences field, now pathetically limited for the tasks involved, will require immediate provision for major expansion in specialized education and training programs and facilities, both within the government and within the universities. Such a program must include a strenuous attempt to increase the tiny fraction of teachers now in this field and to understand the reasons for this lag, as well as to expand teaching and research on a basic science multi-disciplinary front.

III. *Planning a Research Program for Water Resources*

The Need for Research in Water Resources

Keeping in mind the overall water situation in the United States as presented in Section I, it is clear that water-resource planning cannot proceed and intelligent guidance to research cannot be given on the basis of a static view of problems and possibilities. The recent studies of the Senate Select Committee on Water Resources and other similar investigations have shown that rapid technological progress based upon fundamental scientific understanding is an essential prerequisite to unencumbered national development within the next several decades.

In areas of water scarcity, advanced technological knowledge and skills may often be used to compensate and substitute for shortage of the resource itself. We know, in fact, that economically this is an accepted means of dealing with such problems, as has been well demonstrated by the tremendous progress of our own and other countries.

Essentially, most water problems may be put into two broad categories. First one can attempt to increase the total supply potentially available for all uses; second, one can seek ways to increase the beneficial use of supplies already available. The former might be done by such means as reduction of evapotranspiration in storage or in transit, reduction of evapotranspiration by useful vegetation and by useless water-loving plants and trees, climate control, and artificial rainmaking or long-distance transportation of large quantities of water. The latter approach might accomplish its end by such means as better control of flow rates (both surface and underground), or by increased efficiency in use and re-use of water (to be achieved by such methods as better pollution control and demineralization of brackish and saline water).

Examining some of these problems, we find lack of basic research and understanding on all levels. For example, at the present time some feel that it is possible to effect an increase in rainfall by artificial stimulation; the difficulty here is that, during a drought, when water is badly needed, conditions are least propitious for rainmaking. Unfortunately, we do not yet understand how rain forms in the atmosphere—the action of nuclei, stability, and similar factors. With regard to evapotranspiration, the crucial problem is how to increase the efficiency of this natural phenomenon and reduce losses. In general, water loss from the soil is around 50 per cent. Of the water used for irrigation, again about 50 per cent is lost en route, and only about 25 per cent of the balance is used by the plant. The potentials are great; it has been estimated that if we were to reduce evapotranspiration or evaporation from reservoirs in the Western States alone, we could save enough water to suppy municipal and household water for a population equal to the present total for the entire country. In order to solve some of these problems, however, we need better knowledge of how and why water enters the soil and how to effect more efficient water utilization by increasing the water-holding power of the soil, and increased understanding of the permeability of soils and similar factors.

With respect to improvement of water quality, it seems clear that if society would not only guard its present sources of supply but also facilitate the natural processes working to make this resource usable once again, we should be able to make greater and more efficient use of what we already have. Our problem in this regard is greatly increased by the growing complexity and variety of the pollutants being disposed into our streams. Some pollutants, such as those which are radioactive, take a very long time to decay. In addition, other organic chemicals may adversely affect the natural processes of stream self-purification, may cause harmful reactions when in combination, and are difficult to treat. Here again, we find that our purification processes, for example, may require major adjustments and improvements. We know too little about the self-purification of streams or how much pollution a stream can stand. Although we can estimate these things, we do not really understand them fully. As far as salt-water conversion is concerned, the prevailing feeling is that this is not likely, for some time to come, to be of general use. At the present time, it appears that desalted water composes a relatively unimportant source of water supply for the United States, even though brackish waters may be increasingly demineralized. Fundamental physical-chemical research in the properties of sea water and the phenomena of their separation are, however, prime necessities for moving forward in the whole field of demineralization.

The foregoing discussion has served merely to indicate the present status of investigation into some of the areas of greatest concern to scientists in the water-resources field. The best method or combination of methods used to deal with water resources in a given region will be determined as much by the relative magnitudes of the several problems, present and anticipated, as by the best "handle" offered by the flow circuit of the hydrologic cycle.

Potential sources of difficulty in arid and semi-arid basins are somewhat different, at least in priority of importance, from those in humid basins. In both instances, however, areas of investigation can be identified which show great promise of at least averting and quite possibly reversing the undesirable effects—which in some cases are already in view—of man's changing relationship to his water environment.

Identification of critical informational requirements for effective water-resources system planning, and projections of demographic-economic trends, can greatly aid in identifying broad areas of research capable of contributing directly to substanially improved water-resources development and use. It would, however, be a disservice to base research recommendations solely upon the orientation provided by problems currently existing or clearly in view. A major reason for the support of research is to widen the effective area of social choice by calling upon and expanding basic scientific knowledge in ways which are not clearly foreseeable. Knowledge acquired in this way may alter the context of water-resources planning and development in fundamental ways. The effect of this can be to expand greatly man's ability to control and derive benefits from the water environment. Consequently, attention must be given to research justified only by the educated judgment, or perhaps even the intuition, by competent scientists, rather than by its role in currently known methods of analysis and design.

In accordance with the above reasoning, we classify our suggested areas of research into four categories:

A. Research directed toward problems existing or in view, and particularly urgent with respect to improved and more productive water-resources development and use in arid and semi-arid basins.

B. Research directed toward problems existing or in view, and particularly urgent with respect to improved and more productive water-resources development and use in humid basins.

C. Research directed toward problems existing or in view, and of great importance to improved and more productive resources development and use in all areas.

D. Longer-range and more speculative research areas, but with potentially large payoffs.

We are aware, of course, that when dealing with an interdependent system, any categorizing will contain arbitrary elements, produce overlaps, and neglect interdependencies. Moreover, it is to be expected that research undertaken with one end in view will have payoffs in other, perhaps unanticipated, directions. This is particularly probable when so-called "basic" scientific principles are being explored. It is our view, however, that the suggested structuring of research areas can aid in organizing thought and can ultimately help in assessing priorities. The importance of the latter step cannot be overemphasized since, as pointed out in Section I, undoubtedly the scarcest of all our resources is trained research talent.

The following section is devoted to a further development of the framework just outlined. Selected broad areas of highly important research are also identified.

Areas of Research

Arid and Semi-Arid Basins

General Characteristics Affecting Research Needs. One approach to the specification of the more critical information gaps in regard to optimum planning, to the anticipation of developing stringencies, and to the identification of potentially productive areas of research, is to look rather closely at an actual arid or semi-arid basin. For the purposes of this report, it appears more desirable to think in terms of a prototype arid basin which synthesizes some of the major characteristics typical of such basins. Among these characteristics are the following:

a. Rainfall is low and is to one or another degree (often greatly) exceeded by potential evapotranspiration.

b. Orographic precipitation is a major source of fresh water.

c. By far the largest proportion of streamflow and recharge of aquifers is accounted for by snow melt in mountain ranges.

d. Streamflow is comparatively fully controlled by existing or planned surface structures. Yield from additional storage is severely limited by high rates of evaporation.

e. By far the largest current, and projected, diversion and depletion of water is for irrigation purposes. A very high percentage of water diverted for irrigation is returned to the atmosphere via evaporation and transpiration.[5]

f. Major and widespread current and prospective sources of water-quality problems are salinity and suspended sediment. Salinity is substantially increased by the return flow from irrigation. Salinity increases irrigation requirements, makes some water completely unsuitable for irrigation, damages equipment, and reduces potability. Suspended sediment deposits in reservoirs and eventually fills them, damages equipment, increases treatment costs, and reduces the esthetic appeal of water. Sediment entrainment and deposition can also substantially alter the conformation of stream beds.

g. There is a heavy draft on ground water, with instances of "mining" (i.e., pumping rates exceeding recharge) and generally the water level in ground-water aquifers has been lowered by pumping. The basin is relatively well supplied with areas where natural recharge, or recharge by artificial surface spreading, can occur. Despite this, there is relatively little planned conjunctive use of ground and surface supplies. In some areas, compaction of aquifers and salinity intrusion are already problems.

h. A substantial part of the water depleted in the area is transpired by useless phreatophytic plants.

i. The area has, in recent years, experienced a relatively (but not necessarily absolutely) large increase in urban population and in industrial activity. So far this has largely been accomplished by the use of unappropriated water or interbasin transfers of water. Unless research leads the way to large-scale increases in natural water supply, future large-scale economic and demographic growth will be accompanied to a greater degree by diversion of water from presently irrigated acreage.[6]

Recommended Research. The following are examples of broad research areas of most urgent importance in arid areas, to provide information for improved and more productive basin planning and development or to help deal with foreseeable stringencies. With the exception of example 7, the sequence in which these areas of investigation is presented is indicative of their relative importance.

1. *Research having relevance to conjunctive ground-surface water management.* This will include research on improved means of ground-water exploration, better means of tracing and predicting ground-water movement and quality, improved techniques for forecasting the capacity of aquifers and recharge areas, and study of possible use of treated waste water for artificial ground-water recharge. The payoffs in terms of water saved and more effective streamflow control could be highly significant, especially in light of the fact that additional surface storage in some arid areas may be incapable of increasing usable yield from streams. Research in this area is relatively neglected, but is of great importance.

2. *Research with regard to evaporation suppression and transpiration control.* Phreatophyte control studies are the element of major importance in this category. Other elements include investigation of the suppression of evaporation from reservoirs and soils, study of transpiration control and drought tolerance of plants, and investigation of the influence of alternative plant populations on the yield of water from watersheds. Some idea of the possible water saving which successful research in this general area might produce is given by the fact that *evaporation* from reservoirs and *transpiration* by phreatophytes in the 17 western states is more than twice the amount of water *withdrawn* for public supplies in the entire United States.

3. *Research in salinity control and use of saline water.* This will include studies of ocean water but, more importantly, research on the conversion and/or use of moderately saline water as well, including the use of such water for irrigation. Investigation leading to prediction of effects of irrigation on water quality would fill a significant gap for system planning. A large proportion of the streamflow in arid and semi-arid areas is slightly to moderately saline. Vast quantities of saline water—currently useless or of limited usefulness—are stored in underground aquifers. Effective use of saline water could vastly increase the scope for development in arid areas. Desalination of ocean water, however, is *not* regarded as a solution for some time to come.

4. *Research concerning factors which govern the entrainment, transport, and deposition of suspended sediment.* Deposition of sediment is beginning to limit the capacities of some of the most important reservoirs. This endangers the usefulness of vast public investments. In addition, sediment can have a profoundly unfavorable effect upon the stream beds themselves, causing water-treatment problems, damaging equipment, and reducing esthetic qualities. Improved understanding of the physical principles involved in this important area is a necessary prerequisite for devising effective remedial measures.

5. *Research on the factors which govern snow melt.* Since much of the streamflow in arid areas arises from snow melt, control over melting could substitute to some degree for reservoir storage. The resultant reduction of evaporation and better river control could be highly important in arid areas. Forest-management practices do not provide the only means for altering the rates and timing of snow melt. In Scandinavia, for example, some attempt has been made using alcohol or hexadecanol on the snow itself. The potential beneficial effects of control over snow melt are not as large as those available from conjunctive ground and surface water management, but would be of an analogous type.

6. *Research on induced rainfall.* This area of investigation is included here because of its potential importance for increasing flow and adding to water storage in arid basins. Its limited but significant promise appears to be with respect to orographic areas which are frequently contiguous to arid basins. One of the major research needs in this area is understanding of the mechanisms governing rainfall.

7. *Research relevant to the Great Plains, which share some of the attributes of both arid and humid areas.* In this category, projects such as those applicable to improved watershed management and for the development of drought-resistant crops bear greater emphasis than they would in regard to truly arid areas. Examples of this kind of research would involve problems such as how to increase the capacity of the soil-moisture reservoir. Almost all the research areas listed above are relevant, however, since most of the major plains rivers have their origin in mountain snow melt, salinity of ground and surface water is often a problem, sedimentation of reservoirs and other sediment problems are common, reservoir evaporation depletes supplies substantially, and there appear to be opportunities for conjunctive management of ground and surface waters.

Humid Areas

General Characteristics Affecting Research Needs. A rough but useful definition of a wet or humid area is one in which precipitation exceeds potential evapotranspiration. If this criterion is used, that part of the United States east of about the 97th meridian would qualify as humid.[7] This area currently contains about three-quarters of the nation's population and the higher proportion of industrial output. Projections for 1980 and 2000 typically indicate that only a small loss of relative position is anticipated with regard to population and industrial growth. In other words, while the humid basins are expected to grow relatively somewhat less than the arid areas, projection of current trends indicates that a very large proportion of *total* growth will occur in these already populous and industrially developed basins. Some typical characteristics of the humid basins are as follows:

a. Rainfall is such that, by the standard of potential evapotranspiration, there is generally little or no water deficiency in any season.[8]

b. As implied by Point a, precipitation is generally comparatively well distributed throughout the year. Streamflow, however, varies considerably, and opportunities exist for attaining desirable effects by means of flow regulation. By the same token, flood control (i.e., dealing with the effects of periodic excesses of water) is a major problem.[9]

c. While the water is already re-used to some extent in some sub-basins (i.e., withdrawal exceeds low-flow), depletion (evapotranspiration resulting from use) is generally a minor proportion of available flow.

d. The comparatively modest amount of depletion results from the fact that only a minor percentage of cropland is currently under irrigation. While projections indicate some increase in supplemental irrigation, water depleted by agricultural use will probably continue to be only a minor proportion of available streamflow.

e. As implied by Point c, almost all water withdrawals are for industrial use (including steam electric power) and domestic purposes which deplete only a small portion—less than 10 per cent—of water withdrawn.

f. Where large municipal and/or industrial supplies are withdrawn, or special and highly atypical irrigation circumstances exist, ground-water aquifers have generally not been drawn down.

g. The major present and expected future water-quality problems result from the domestic and industrial activities of man. Domestic sewage and industrial-waste effluents delivered to streams consist heavily of degradable and persistent organic substances, inorganic chemicals, and heat. These wastes, combined with the increasing necessity for water re-use, pose the most significant and difficult problems for improved planning of water-resources systems and for the physical and biological sciences addressing themselves to water-resources issues in humid basins. In the absence of significant advances in these fields, projections suggest that among the important reasons for streamflow control might be the augmentation of low flows for dilution purposes. Since immense investments in flow-control structures are implied, it is doubly important to increase the pace of scientific understanding and technological improvement of treatment processes. Large volumes of valuable regulated flows should not be permanently consigned to low economic dilution purposes. Such volumes will ultimately have a much higher priority for other more productive purposes.

h. The quality and character of recreation opportunities are intimately associated with waste disposal due to the effects of oxygen-demanding, plant-nutrient, bacterial, and toxic wastes upon recreational and esthetic amenities. In the future, issues surrounding the value and cost of maintaining these amenities in the face of competing demands will pose some of the most difficult issues of social decision with respect to water resources.

Recommended Research. The following are broad areas of research most urgently required to improve water-resources planning to meet developing problems in humid basins. The order in which the areas of investigation are presented is indicative of their relative importance.

1. *Research aimed at developing water-purification methods.* Traditional waste-treatment measures are now old and at times ill-suited for dealing with plant nutrients, persistent organics, and other pollutants of increasing importance. New separation techniques are urgently needed. Fundamental research in physics, chemistry, and biology of water and waste water (including the phenomena of adsorption, absorption, and association) should yield returns in this regard. Because of its direct bearing upon the potentialities of water re-use, discovery of greatly improved means of separating a wide variety of substances from water is the most important water-resources research problem in humid areas. The alternative is the investment of billions of dollars in flow-control facilities, which would result in increasing the water available for all economic uses as well as for waste disposal.

2. *Research directed toward discovering means of forecasting the effect of wastes on receiving water and toward quantifying pollution damages.* Remarkably little basis exists for precise prediction of the waste-degradation, plant-nutrient, algae-growth-and-decay sequence, and its effect upon dissolved oxygen and other desirable characteristics of water. Prediction of waste effects on long stretches of streams and on estuaries is especially circumscribed. Knowledge of such effects is essential to evaluation of alternative methods of dealing with wastes and to the design of optimum waste-treatment systems. For a similar reason, it is highly important that means be developed for predicting the costs associated with a wide variety of pollutants at various levels of loadings, treatment, and dilution. Presently, only limited information is available which would permit systematic inclusion of waste disposal in planning for optimum integrated water-resources systems. Reliance on rules of thumb, such as arbitrary stream-flow and stream-water quality criteria as a basis for design of treatment facilities, could add greatly to future cost of waste disposal.

3. *Research on means for the detection and identification of traces of pollutants and toxicological research on their possible chronic effects on public health.* There are thousands of distinct organic substances presently known. Of these, a substantial and variable number are found in water bodies. Detection and identification of minute, but possibly harmful, amounts of these is currently an immensely difficult, expensive procedure. Indeed, the vast majority of such trace pollutants occurring in public water supplies are not identified. Moreover, the chronic physiological effects of minute amounts of chemical substances are almost completely unknown. Some public health authorities suspect that a number of the newer synthetic chemicals may have a harmful long-term influence, but there is no real basis for evaluating the risks involved. A substantial expansion of research effort in this field is merited, especially in view of the fact that chemical production and use is increasing much faster than population and economic activity.

All Areas

1. *Research Directed Toward Forecasting and Controlling Channel Modifications.* In large measure man's efforts to use rivers in such a way as to yield maximum benefits is accomplished by alterations of the natural flow. Wherever the natural pattern of flow is changed, the channel, left to itself, readjusts to the new regimen. The readjustment may take several forms and each is apt to be troublesome and costly. Stabilization of the flow through reservoir regulation, for example, may lead to sedimentation of the channel, realignment of the meander pattern, and downcutting and erosion of banks. The limited research which has been done in the field of what might be called stream morphology has paid off. Certainly this is an area basic to planning, meriting efforts to replace current trial and error approaches with the orderliness of science.

2. *Research Directed Towards Improving the Process of Approximating Optimum Water Resources Systems.* While deficiencies of data and scientific understanding present major obstacles to improved water-resources system planning, such planning also poses complex problems in the actual implementation of optimizing procedures. Determining the combination of systems elements and operating procedures which will maximize net benefits obtainable from a multi-purpose, multi-unit system with a complicated hydrology is an extremely demanding task. To do so, aggregate benefits should outweigh aggregate costs of such projects examined in view of the alternatives. To achieve this goal, precise definition, quantification, and a well-balanced evaluation based on better knowledge and application of the related fields are necessary. Promising initial steps have been made in the application of simulation, mathematical programming, and other methods of operations research to simplified problems of water-resources system design. These formal

optimization methods should be adapted specifically to comprehend water-quality problems, such as the effects of waste on long stretches of streams, and the complex interrelations of surface and ground waters.[10] It is important that such methods be developed for actual application to complex planning problems.

Certain values of multi-purpose development are extremely difficult, or impossible, to measure by means of the market system valuation process (aspects of esthetics, recreation, and public health fall into this category). Accordingly, they cannot be included in the objective function of optimization problems, except by arbitrary weighting procedures. As a consequence, optimum solutions are prevented. Ingenious methods of tapping market-generated information, cost-sensitivity analysis, and studies aimed at better use and understanding of political processes are possible approaches to improved handling of these valuable aspects of water-resources development. Research in these areas is urgently required.

Finally, the validity of results of precise and powerful optimizing procedures is somewhat mitigated by various conceptual problems of evaluation. Among the most important of these are market imperfections outside the water-resources sector, income distribution, questions with respect to the appropriate discount for time, and the problem, so far intractable, of taking explicit account of uncertainty in the design procedure. Study and clarification of these matters are extremely important.

3. *Investigations to Improve Streamflow Forecasting.* Reservoirs are built to store water during periods of surplus for use during periods of deficiency. Artificial recharge of ground-water aquifers is usually undertaken for the same purpose. Coordinated planning for the use of surface and ground-water storage presents the greatest opportunity for improved water-resources systems in arid basins. Among the reasons for this is the fact that water stored underground is not subject to evaporation, and often underground storage provides a built-in distribution system. Planning and operation of systems of storage in order to yield maximum benefit is heavily dependent on forecasts of short- and long-term hydrological variation. Moreover, preliminary study shows that more accurate knowledge of the nature and variability of streamflow can add greatly to the usefulness of existing storage.

Quantitative characterization of land-use and land-cover parameters that affect relationships between rainfall and streamflow is needed to predict streamflow as a result of a given kind of storm. Evaluation of the influence of terrain, antecedent moisture, stratigraphy, ground-water regime, snow cover, and frost prevalence is also needed. Similarly, and more importantly, there is little firm basis for forecasting the full hydrological effects of streamflow-control structures under widely varying conditions of soil and geological structure, bank conformation, etc. Since such forecasting is fundamental to all planning for streamflow control, improvement in this area is essential. Its importance will increase as more and more precise stream control becomes required.

4. *Research to Improve Weather Forecasting.* More acccurate weather prediction could greatly improve short-term streamflow forecasting and yield valuable benefits in other respects. Consequently, it is highly desirable to extend our knowledge of how phenomena in global air masses predicate forthcoming weather conditions in a given area. Furthermore, virtually nothing is known about the scientific laws governing longer-term weather phenomena, and research should be encouraged in the whole area of thermodynamics of the atmosphere.

5. *Investigation of Physiological Aspects of Water.* Few, if any, sophisticated statistical studies of the physiological aspects of water quality have ever been made. Such studies would be valuable in their own right, and, perhaps even more importantly, they would point to more fundamental scientific studies which deserve emphasis. Such studies should undertake to find significant differences in general health and in degenerative and other diseases between different communities and population groups. Where differences appear, they may be due to age, heredity, or environment. If environmental effects can be segregated it would be possible to discover which factors are responsible for differences in health. Natural or introduced differences in water quality might be one of these.

Longer-Range or More Speculative Research Areas with Potentially Large Payoffs

Any attempt to specify a research program is, in essence, an effort to deal with a very difficult problem in resource allocation, for it is an effort to determine the optimal allocation of research funds and talent. In large measure the complications which arise in this undertaking are due to the inherent uncertainties of research endeavors. If the outcome were not uncertain, the undertaking would not be research. By relating research recommendations to existing or clearly emerging problems, payoffs can be foreseen, at least in a general way. However, after the results are known, the most valuable single research project may turn out to be one for which the character and timing of the payoff was anything but obvious at the planning stage.

Research planning should perhaps take as a rough model the stock market investor who deals with the inevitable uncertainty of his activity by putting most of his funds in fairly secure investments, but designates a portion of his available funds for playing the long shots. Investments or research projects which are both highly uncertain and promise only a small return should be identified and evaluated carefully together with a selected group which is uncertain but may yield potentially large returns. Such projects should find a place in the optimum portfolio. Since a deterministic function describing "trade-offs" between comparatively certain but lower-return and relatively uncertain but higher-return projects cannot be specified, the continuing exercise of scientifically informed judgment and review is a necessary part of implementing a research program. Moreover, the less well defined the objective and procedures of a research project, the greater the emphasis that must be placed upon the general competence and judgment of the investigator.

International Implications

Water circulates on the whole planet. In any one country or region, the occurrence and distribution of water are the direct consequences of global phenomena. In some countries, sufficient observational data are at hand for ad hoc water-plan decisions. In no country, however, does there now exist anything approaching an understanding either of the gamut of the parameters involved in the hydrologic cycle or of their joint global behavior and interaction.

The scope of scientific study, therefore, cannot be delineated by the phenomena, natural or man-made, occurring only within the United States or even within the Americas. A recent study has properly emphasized the fact that most hydrologic studies hitherto have proceeded as though each problem were an isolated case, rather than one affected by multiple parameters operative, in fact, throughout the globe. Scientific inquiry hence should not be the province only of the United States, England, France, India, and others; a mechanism for global exploration in hydrosciences is long overdue. Thoughtful workers in this field are well aware of this necessity and opportunity. They wait upon militant government interest and support to give a major impetus to this kind of international effort. We cannot overemphasize the necessity for early action on this.

Aside from the strictly scientific and technologic implications of this activity, many strong socio-political reasons exist for focusing prompt and extensive emphasis on fundamental water research. One of the major contributions we can make to the less-favored countries lies in research and development of improved, less costly and more easily adapted water programs and procedures. Our studies, both in field and laboratory, hence should not and cannot be restricted to the search for answers only to our immediate and perhaps sophisticated problems. It is fortunately true that a great number of the physical problems of the United States in water-resources development traverse the whole spectrum of water use on a global basis. We are plagued by many of the same difficulties, and the same ignorances, which beset the rest of the world in arid, semi-arid, and humid regions. We are less "crisis-pressed," but water research has global applications, and even some of the same relative priorities suggested in this discussion.

In this regard, it might be wise to correlate and encourage, even perhaps to subsidize partially, the research of other countries with problems similar to ours, especially if this research is of the kind which promises a comparatively high return, and thus could have a cumulative effect on the development of water resources in this country and/or in other areas of the world. In considering such a program, it would be well to keep in mind the priorities indicated in this section together with the present and future plans being undertaken in the United States with respect to water-resources development. A program of this sort must be planned and supervised wisely, taking into consideration its overall effects.[11] Following this line of thought, perhaps the United States should take the lead in world analysis of water availability and use while, at the same time, enabling other countries to help themselves in their own development.

IV. *Summary of Priorities in Water Research*

The task of estimating, measuring, and describing the water supplies in the United States is reasonably well in hand. It still needs, and will continue to require, expanded coverage, budgets, and manpower in a rapidly growing country. The dramatic lack, however, is in thorough scientific exploration of water-waste behavior complexes, which have been amply probed in shallow depths. One can depend upon private and public agencies to continue, albeit stumblingly, on the road of orthodox data-collection and partial interpretation. These proceed because action programs press for them or move forward, too often, without them. Fundamental hydrosciences research, however, is minimal at the federal level and nearly non-existent at the other levels of government. For the most part, applied research, reflecting the immediate requirements of action programs, has been the characteristic effort. There are exceptions, of course, but the total outlay for these in annual dollars is relatively small.

Government must take steps now to correct the imbalance of emphasis between action, applied research, and research directed toward opening new vistas and new understanding. The areas for multi-disciplinary investigation, with some suggestions as to priority, are listed herewith. They have equal significance, with similar priorities, for our international obligations.

A. Improving Present Practices
  1. Increasing the production of skilled professionals in the hydrosciences, by development of programs and facilities within government and universities.

2. Ground-water exploration, with special reference to research in the physics, chemistry, and biology of ground-water behavior and the more efficient management of ground-water use and storage.

3. Techniques of water management
    a. Agricultural use and misuse of water.
    b. Analysis and appraisal of management practices.
    c. Hydrologic forecasting, weather analysis, statistical diagnosis.
    d. Behavior of watersheds.
    e. Control of evaporation and evapotranspiration.

B. Increasing Scientific Understanding
    1. Thermodynamics of water cycle—water in atmosphere, distribution, cloud physics.
    2. Pollutants—treatment processes, stream and lake behavior, physics, chemistry, and biology of surface and ground waters, dilution mechanisms, physiological effects.
    3. Demineralization of brackish and sea waters—physical chemistry of sea water.

Since the primary restraint on the speed with which research may go forward lies in the limited number of competent investigators, immediate support must be provided for university education and in-service training. These, in turn, wait upon the creation of laboratories, office, and classroom facilities.

v. *Summary (Conclusion)*

The need for water to support the continued growth and progress of our nation is magnified when a close look is taken at the vital role played by this resource in our industrial, agricultural, and municipal life. Although the *total* amount of water available in the United States today is sufficient, it is highly variable in distribution, both spatially and temporally. Unfortunately, an excess of water in one area is not often of more than limited assistance to other areas suffering from water scarcity.

Because the entire hydrologic system is so directly interconnected, we must be able to measure the effects of the actions we take on specific parts of the overall system. Although we know a great deal about certain of the critical elements, we are quite ignorant in other crucially important areas. So it is that years after an action is taken, effects may occur that were not foreseen and are often more important than the advantages offered by the development itself. It is clear that complex areas such as water resources can no longer be approached in the compartmentalized way that they have been in the past.

In light of these considerations, the following areas of research deserve urgent consideration:

A. *Interdisciplinary training of personnel.* The most critical shortage in the field of water resources by far is the very real shortage of broadly trained people capable of planning and executing effective research programs. At present, we have no institutional structure in the United States to take care of multi-disciplinary research in water. The whole hydrosciences field is now pathetically limited for the tasks involved. To strengthen it will require immediate provision of a program to enlist and train new people in a great many of the disciplines relating to water resources. The ultimate objective should be the development of a new structure and a new generation of well-rounded water scientists ready and able to approach the nation's multi-disciplinary water-resources problems in a unified manner as "hydrosciences."

B. *Research having relevance to ground-water supplies.* Ground water at depths of less than 12,500 feet represents approximately 24 per cent of the nation's total fresh-water supply. Research in this area has been relatively neglected to date but is of great importance. Such studies should include research on improved means of ground-water exploration, better means of tracing and predicting ground-water movement and quality, improved techniques for forecasting the capacity of aquifers and recharge areas, and study of possible use of treated waste water for artificial ground-water recharge.

C. *Research in systems for development of water resources.* Research is greatly needed in techniques, such as systems analysis, which will enable simultaneous evaluation of a large number of combinations of alternative uses, operating procedures, and structures for the development and management of specific water resources. Such techniques have the capacity to use much greater amounts of technical and economical information than are presently available on the several uses of water resources. Thus, research should be undertaken simultaneously on the technological relationships[12] and on the costs and benefits of the many purposes of water-resource development. Among other studies, this will require additional research on projections, national and regional, of water needs and of the basic demographic and economic components of these needs.

D. *Research with regard to evaporation suppression and transpiration control.* Some idea of the possible water saving which successful research in this general area might produce is given by the fact that *evaporation* from reservoirs and *transpiration* by phreatophytes in the 17 western states is more than twice the amount of water *withdrawn* for public supplies in the entire United States. Phreatophyte control studies are the element of major importance in this category. Other elements include investigation of the suppression of evaporation from reservoirs and soils, study of transpiration control and drought-tolerance of plants, and investigation of the influence of alternative plant populations on the yield of water from watersheds. Such studies must consider the entire hydrological system, its interdependencies and equilibrium.

E. *Research aimed at developing water-purification methods and forecasting the effects of pollution damage.* Traditional waste-treatment measures are at times ill-suited for dealing with plant nutrients, persistent organics, and other pollutants of increasing importance. New separation techniques are urgently needed. Fundamental research in the physics, chemistry, and biology of water and waste water should yield returns in this regard. It is also highly important that means be developed for predicting waste effects on long stretches of streams and the costs associated with a wide variety of pollutants at various levels of loadings, treatment, and dilution.

It is clear that scientific inquiry in areas such as those mentioned above should not be the province only of the United States, but a mechanism for global exploration in the hydrosciences. Thoughtful workers in this field are well aware of this necessity and opportunity. They wait upon militant government interest and support to give a major impetus to this kind of international effort. In this regard, it might be wise to correlate and encourage, perhaps even to subsidize partially, the research of other countries with problems similar to ours. Moreover, if this research is of the kind which promises a comparatively high return, it could very well facilitate the development of water resources in this country and/or in other areas of the world. Thus, the United States could take the lead in world analysis of water availability and use while, at the same time, enabling other countries to help themselves in their own development.

NOTES

1. However, not all of the precipitation is available for man's use. Evapotranspiration takes 21 inches. The remaining nine inches is our manageable supply. Three of the nine inches are now being used by man. After use, two of the three inches reach the rivers and flow into the oceans; the other inch returns to the atmosphere by evaporation.

2. We exclude irrigated crops here as water used for them is used volitionally, even if not always economically.

3. In some areas of the United States, withdrawal from aquifers is far greater than recharge, thereby causing a serious deficit in those regions. If the rate of withdrawal from an aquifer exceeds the rate of recharge, the water table will fall until eventually the stock is exhausted.

4. Formation of interstate compacts of various types, interagency committees, U.S. study commissions, and the establishment of comprehensive planning by the Public Health Service attest to this fact.

5. This has the result that most of the water *used up* in withdrawal uses (domestic, industrial, irrigation), in the United States is used up in the driest areas.

6. Such reallocation permits expansion, since water used for municipal and industrial purposes is capable of supporting much higher levels of populations and economic activity than equivalent amounts used for irrigation.

7. I.e., roughly east of a line through Omaha, Nebraska, and Houston, Texas. The northern Pacific coast and limited islands of moisture in the Rocky Mountains would also qualify.

8. This statement, by and large, would hold true over the average monthly and yearly rates. On the other hand, daily for particular years there could be periods of water deficiency.

9. It should be noted that flood control is also a problem in arid basins.

10. See page 22, paragraph 2, for research along this line and the place of such knowledge with regard to the optimum waste-treatment system.

11. Possible negative effects should also be carefully considered, such as the possibility of overdependency upon the research work of other countries and/or the creation of barriers to proper research development and progress in the United States.

12. An example of such technological relationships is the application of different quantities of water to different crops.

WATER QUALITY
AND
TREATMENT

A Preliminary Analysis of the Degree and Nature of Bacterial Removal in Filtration Plants*

The determination of a law of bacterial removal by rapid sand water filtration plants is of great practical importance and utility. Such determinations of plant efficiencies are valuable as indicators not only of present but also of future performance. The objection is, however, often justly raised against the attempt to predict quantitatively the possibilities of bacterial removal, that existing numerical measures of performances are misleading and in some cases even harmful. The calculation of percentage removal from raw water to effluent is an illustration of the type of measure which has arithmetical accuracy, but little logical basis. It is quite evident, however, that it would be desirable to measure quantitatively the performance of a plant in such a way as to obtain a comparative conception of how well or how badly it is being operated.

Since at present no agreement exists among operators, designers, or public health officials as to a standard of "good performance," because, in the past, agreement has been prevented by the interminable search for a "standard effluent," itself the subject of disagreement, it becomes necessary to attack the problem of rating or standardizing plant accomplishment from another angle. In this discussion, an initial search is

* Reprinted from the *Journal of the American Water Works Association*, Vol. 5, No. 3 (September, 1918). Copyright 1918 by the American Water Works Association, Inc. Read before the St. Louis Convention, May 15, 1918.

made for certain basic characteristics of rapid sand filtration. The term, rapid sand filtration, is here used more broadly than usually, to describe the entire process from preliminary coagulation through sedimentation or settling, filtration, and disinfection.

The measure of variable phenomena by comparison with ideal or "normal" conditions is a procedure common to scientific analysis. The application of this method offers here a fruitful means of testing our ideas of filtration efficiency. The first problem obviously consists in the attempt to determine a possible correlation between the number of bacteria in the final effluent of a filtration plant and the number in the raw water. A numerical statement of the problem should be clearer. If a plant uses a raw water containing 500 bacteria per cubic centimeter and produces an effluent containing 10 per cubic centimeter, will the same plant produce an effluent of 20 per cubic centimeter when the raw water content is 1000 per cubic centimeter? Can one predict, in other words, with any degree of precision, what effluent counts should be normally attainable with varying raw water counts?

The use of a "percentage efficiency" is of but little value in the solution of this problem, since that measure is predicated upon the very assumption that the effluent •counts vary directly, rather than more complexly, with raw water counts. The fallacy in this view need hardly be demonstrated at this late period in the development of filtration practice.

The norm or ideal performance from which it is possible to obtain hypotheses as to standard empirical accomplishment is not difficult to deduce. The "normal empirical performance" may be defined as the accomplishment of a filtration plant which is known to be operating successfully. Successful operation can be said to exist wherever there is an unquestioned superior bacteriological and physical quality of effluent, consistent performance, excellent control, and scientific observation of operating details. Plants whose performance may be used as the basis for comparison and for the derivation of the law of bacterial removal are not at all rare. In this analysis, the operating statistics of the filtration plant at Avalon, Maryland, owned by the Baltimore County Water & Electric Company and operated by S. T. Powell, were used.

This plant obtains its raw water from the Patapsco River, a highly polluted stream, ranging in turbidity during the year from 0 to 5000 parts per million and in bacterial content (20°C. gelatine—48 hours), from several hundred to 150,000 per cubic centimeter. The watershed of the stream is composed largely of cultivated areas, with no large sewage polluting influences. This water is treated with aluminum sulphate, at an average rate of 0.8 grain per gallon, and is then allowed to settle for four hours. After leaving the sedimentation basin it is treated with calcium hypochlorite with an average dose of 0.34 part per million, and then passes through the rapid sand filters which have a capacity of 2,500,000 gallons per day.

The plant is controlled scientifically by a trained operator with the aid of modern equipment and laboratory observation. During several years of operation the bacterial content of the effluent has not exceeded, at any time, 20 bacteria per cubic centimeter. Presumptive tests for B. coli in lactose broth have indicated positive tests in 1 cc. less than 2 per cent of the time during any year. The number and kinds of bacteria are determined in raw water and final effluent every day and general experimental data are constantly collected.

It is clear, therefore, that the plant in Baltimore County approaches so closely, from the standpoint of operating results, the ideal plant as to justify the use of its performance as the basis of a law of filtration.

In order to determine with some degree of accuracy the form of a characteristic empirical performance curve, the results of raw water and final effluent counts of the Avalon plant were plotted in figure 1. In order to avoid plotting a mass of points which would tend to confuse the reader, seven-day averages of both stations, rather than daily results extending over a period of nineteen months in 1915, 1916, and 1917, were used. In plotting these values, approximately 520 daily analyses were summarized. These were obtained in consecutive months and under every phase of operating conditions. No counts were discarded as being unfair or incorrect. Figure 1 represents, therefore, the normal daily performance of the plant for more than a year and a half.

A study of the samples plotted on figure 1 reveals at once a consistency of arrangement. It is clear, too, that the performance of this normal plant is represented by the curves shown on figure 1. Inasmuch as these curves are practically straight lines, within the limits shown, the derivation of their equation is simple. The equation of a straight line, when the results have been plotted on a logarithmic basis, is given by: $c = \log y \div \log x$, where c is a constant for this particular plant, and y and x are respectively the raw water and final effluent counts.

It would appear, therefore, that the "normal empirical performance" is represented by a curve having the equation: $y = x^c$. A tentative hypothesis, with regard to bacterial removal by filtration action, may be promulgated, therefore, as follows: The final effluent count, under normal operating conditions, is an exponential function of the raw water count. This hypothesis provides a means of determining whether or not a plant under scrutiny is, at least, "performing normally," where normal performance would be interpreted as conformity to the logarithmic curve of filtration. Figure 2 illustrates, for instance, the failure of plant A to perform its function efficiently. By comparing the points on figure 2 showing the operating statistics of plant A with the points and the form of resultant curves in figure 1, it becomes clear that the plant A is erratic

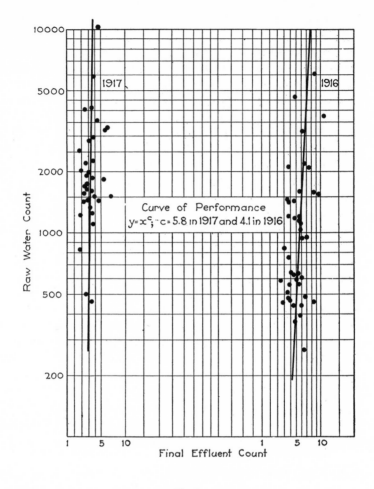

Fig. 1

Bacterial Removal by the Avalon Rapid Sand Filtration Plant During 1916 and 1917; 20°C. Bacterial Counts Used

in performance in so far as the graphic representation of its operation departs from what we have reason to believe is a characteristic form of ideal curve of bacterial removal.

The "normal performance" curve demonstrates the fallacy of assuming that the *difficulty* of removal of bacteria is relatively the same regardless of the number of bacteria in the raw water. Although this assumption is rarely publicly proclaimed, it is usually summoned, however, to the aid of those plants which, for one reason or another, are so unsuccessful as to require a specious hypothesis, fairly reasonable to the layman, to support their claims to maximum efficiency of 99 per cent plus. The practical results of a scientifically controlled plant certainly

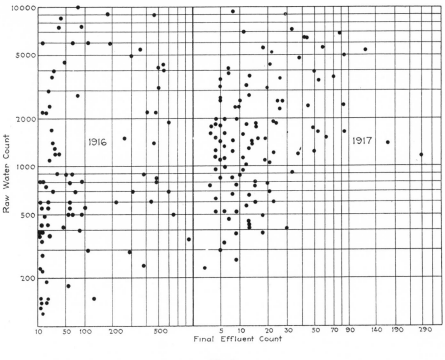

Fig. 2

Inconsistency of Performance of Plant A as Indicated by 20°C. Counts

seem to lead to the conclusion that increases in raw water bacterial content decrease the corresponding bacterial content *interval* in the final effluent.

It should be added, too, that the equation of normal performance, $y = x^c$, offers a new quantitative measure of the efficiency of any plant, obtained by evaluating in any case the constant, c. Such a measure, among other qualities, has the advantage of a rational basis and of a practical significance. Its use has been discussed elsewhere by the author.[1]

What absolute value this constant, c, or the so-called "coefficient of efficiency," should attain is dependent upon individual opinion of "good performance." It is of interest to note, however, that, in a survey of 19 rapid sand filtration plants, varying in size from 2.2 to 80.0 million gallons filtered per day, the coefficient of efficiency of these plants has attained an annual average of over 2.5. The raw waters which these plants had to treat contained turbidities ranging from an annual average of 1 to 561 parts per million, and average bacterial contents from 350 to 16,500 per cubic centimeter. The 19 plants chosen, therefore, for the evaluation of c, are representative, in their initial conditions, of rapid sand filtration.

The probable existence of the law of filtration, $y = x^c$, combined with known values of c, practically attainable, gives the investigator of filtration plant accomplishment the fundamental criteria with which to measure both the character and the amount of removal in any particular plant. The objection may be raised to the above method of critical standardization of plants, that all do not function in a similar manner, on account of differences in raw water, resulting from peculiarities of suspended matter, variations in resistance of bacteria, and other similar factors. This objection does not seem to the author to be entirely valid, since peculiar characteristics of raw water are usually provided for by variations in design, such as increased periods of sedimentation and greater doses of disinfectant. It is reasonable to suppose, therefore, that given plants, initially properly designed for local conditions, should function according to some common law, since death rates under disinfection, devitalization, sedimentation, and filtration of bacteria differ in the degree, but not in the kind, of changes effected.

The preliminary theory of bacterial removal by filtration is supported by the curves shown in figure 3, where are plotted the average monthly

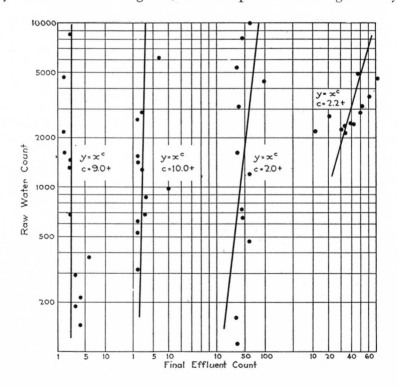

Fig. 3

Performance Curves of Four Large Rapid Sand Filtration Plants

results from several large rapid sand plants in the United States. The monthly, instead of the weekly, results are used since the latter were not obtainable. The form of curve would be the same in both instances, while the value of the constant may change. It is quite obvious that each plant follows in its performance the characteristic $y = x^c$ curve.

Since the death-rate of bacteria under the action of disinfectants, and under well defined conditions, has been shown,[2] to follow in general the law: $c = \dfrac{1}{t_2 - t_1} \log \dfrac{y}{x}$, it will be necessary to look for the causative factors of the $y = x^c$ law in other phases of the system of rapid sand filtration. It is the author's purpose to study further the bacterial removal in the individual and distinct processes of coagulation, sedimentation, and filtration proper, with a view to throwing further light on the problem of causation.[3]

NOTES

1. *Jour. Amer. Pub. Health Assoc.*, November, 1916.

2. H. Chick, *Jour. of Hygiene*, Vol. 8, 1908; Vol. 10, 1910.

3. Strictly speaking, the equation of a straight line curve plotted on logarithmic axes is: $y = bx^c$, where b is the intercept on the y axis. In that case, c becomes $\dfrac{\log y - \log b}{\log x}$ rather than $\dfrac{\log y}{\log x}$. Log b is infinitely small in our particular problem, since b, the intercept on the y axis, would be equivalent to those raw water counts which produce resultant final effluent counts of one. Since zero counts are rarely obtained in filtration plants, even with extremely low raw water counts, it is conceivable that the performance curve in the "normal operation" described above would intercept the y axis at some point approaching unity. Log b, therefore, would approach zero and could be neglected in the evaluation of c. It is evident, therefore, that $c = \dfrac{\log y}{\log x}$ measures in each case, with sufficient accuracy, the slope or inclination of the performance curve, the significant index to the efficiency of bacterial removal.

Chlorine Absorption and the
Chlorination of Water*
with Linn H. Enslow

Introductory

The disinfection of waters by means of various forms of chlorine has been practiced in this country and abroad for many years. During this period a general theory of chlorination has grown up, particularly on this side of the water, which has had little or no scientific basis. The general hypothesis concerning the effects of chlorination, the proper dosage, and the nature of the chemical and biological reactions have been deduced from a few well-controlled experiments on waters of certain characteristics. The results of these experiments, however, have led to the universal adoption of chlorination for waters differing materially from those upon which earlier experimental data were made available. When, therefore, a number of water supplies were treated with standardized doses of chlorine, or its compounds, failures in performance were soon recorded.

In the supervision and control of a single water supply, the problem of chlorination offers far less difficulty than in the case of a group of water supplies, all of which have distinctive and disconcertingly variable qualities. The control of disinfection of a city water supply, supported

* Reprinted from the *Journal of Industrial and Engineering Chemistry*, Vol. 11, No. 3, p. 209. Copyright 1919 by the American Chemical Society. Reprinted by permission of the copyright owner.

by daily chemical and bacteriological examinations, may at least approach a scientific procedure, although surprisingly few cities even at this late date actually do more than a superficial dosing at a more or less constant rate. The supervision of chlorination becomes, however, a problem of major importance where a large series of supplies are to be treated under the direction of some central authority, like a State Department of Health. With 10 or 15 water supplies—inadequately sampled, some in the raw state, some just after coagulation, some filtered, ranging through every degree of color and turbidity, now free from organic material and an hour later loaded with surface wash—what form of control should be adopted? Here a speedy, safe, easy method of antecedent control, rather than of subsequent failure, is essential. On this phase of chlorination, the preliminary routine control of widely different types of waters, scientific literature, with some few exceptions, is silent.

In the State of Maryland, as in other States, experience indicates that, in general, chlorination control has been inadequately studied. When we bear in mind that a number of supplies are under the supervision of laymen, it becomes clear that consistently good results in disinfection are hardly attainable without the use of some presumptive indicator of an efficient chlorine dose. Presumptive tests of chlorine efficiency have been discussed by various students of the problem; but their contributions, although suggestive, have been based upon such meager experimental evidence that they cannot yet be considered definitive.

The present brief discussion is the result of a study, carried on during the past 18 months, of the application of chlorinators under variable conditions. The data here set forth are fragmentary. They are reported in order to invite attention to the extreme intricacy of the whole problem rather than as the basis of a formula designed to furnish the proper doses of chlorine and its alllied compounds. It may be stated, however, that observation of the conditions in this State has served to point out a wide field for further intensive experimentation and, in this respect, the material here presented may be of some little value.

Absorption of Available Chlorine

The importance of the absorption of so-called "active chlorine" by different waters is somewhat ill-defined in its relation to disinfection or the elimination of objectionable bacterial life. Some experimenters assert that the amount of absorption discloses little concerning the destruction of bacteria, while others assume that the chlorine consumed in "oxidizing organic matter and sometimes ferrous salts or sulfides will not effect sterilization."[1] Since the latter assumption necessarily permits an increased factor of safety in the control of the chlorination, it is probably advantageous to use the hypothesis as a base until the collection of adequate data indicates what quantitative variations therefrom may be necessary.

In order to study the significance of the absorption of chlorine by waters, it is of interest for scientific and practical purposes to obtain some idea of the factors which influence or predetermine the losses of chlorine in different waters. Owing to the complexity of conditions under which the action of chlorination proceeds, such data as the above and any conclusions pertaining thereto may be ascertained in only an empirical manner. A few apparently elementary features of chlorine absorption, therefore, are described briefly in order to establish at least some salient characteristics of the phenomenon of the disappearance of the active agency in chlorination.

The Rate of Chlorine Absorption. A few experiments were tried to determine the velocity of absorption of available chlorine by the same water during varying time intervals. The data were collected in order to compare with simliar work reported by Race.[2] The results are set forth in Table 1. A comparison of these findings with the values reported by Race indicates that K, the velocity constant, in general, decreases with the time of contact. These values are in agreement with

Table 1
Absorption of Chlorine by Waters at 20°C. Variations in K with Time.

		Values of $K = \dfrac{1}{t_2 - t_1} \log \dfrac{N_1}{N_2}$ for time intervals of		
Sample		5 min.	30 min.	60 min.
1	Surface	0.052	0.009	0.005
2	Surface	0.069	0.012	0.006
3	Surface	0.032	0.013	0.007
4	Surface	0.041	0.013	....
5	Surface	0.082	0.018	....
6	Surface	0.066	0.017	0.009
7	Surface	0.071	0.013	0.013
8	Surface	0.082	0.023	0.015
9	Surface	0.032	0.011	0.007
10	Surface	0.099	0.026	....
11	Surface	0.036	0.015	....
12	Surface	0.017	0.007	....
13	Filtered	0.007	0.004	....
14	Well	0.014	0.005	0.003
15	Well	0.007	0.008	0.006
16	Well	0.013	0.003	0.002
17	Well	0.009	0.009	....
18	Surface	0.104	0.018	0.010
19	Surface	0.036	0.007	....
20	Surface	0.044	0.004	....
21	Surface	0.026	0.014	0.010
22	Surface	0.120	0.023	0.014

Table 1a
Summary of Data in Table 1.

Initial Chlorine Absorbed in 5 min.	Ratio K_5/K_{30}	Ratio K_5/K_{60}
0.08	1.8	1.1
0.08	1.1	...
0.10	1.0	...
0.14	4.3	6.5
0.15	2.8	3.3
0.18	2.4	...
0.26	1.8	1.3
0.31	2.5	4.6
0.31	2.9	4.6
0.34	2.8	...
0.34	5.1	...
0.38	3.2	...
0.40	11.0	...
0.45	5.9	10.4
0.53	3.9	7.3
0.55	5.6	11.5
0.56	5.5	5.5
0.61	4.6	...
0.61	3.5	5.5
0.68	3.8	...
0.70	5.8	10.4
0.75	5.2	8.6

the conclusions noted by Race. It should be pointed out, however, that the value of K approaches a constant for different time intervals in those waters whose organic content is low. It appears, therefore, that the rate of chlorine absorption deviates from the ideal monomolecular law of chemical reaction in an increasing degree with waters of increased organic content. In other words, the monomolecular law with K constant is fairly well typified in those few waters which have only slight organic content, such as well and filtered waters, Nos. 13, 15 and 17. This is to be expected, since it is only in these latter waters that the compounds acted upon are probably of such simple chemical structure as to result in a constant reaction velocity.

Color and the Rate of Chlorine Absorption. The use of color readings as a presumptive indicator of the amount of chlorine which would be absorbed by a water in a given period has been suggested as a convenient procedure for routine operation of disinfectant plants. To be of any value, such readings should be the result of a long series of correlated experimental observations. Such continuous series have not been developed, it is believed, for many individual water supplies, while still less has been done in the way of comparative readings on different water supplies. Data upon this question are now being collected in this department. They are not reported in this paper on account of their insufficient number, but the evidence from the observations now available would seem to indicate that for the *same* water supply, changes in color are not necessarily concomitant with variations in chlorine absorption during a constant time interval, while for different water supplies the same conclusion is indicated as far as interdependent chlorine absorptions are concerned. It would appear, from the evidence now at hand, that color readings in different water supplies cannot be adapted to the prediction of chlorine absorption readings, because of the absence of any adequate conversion factor.

Turbidity and the Rate of Chlorine Absorption. In order to study the variation of chlorine absorption in a surface water within different ranges of turbidity, a series of 350 samples of the Potomac River water at Luke, Md., were examined during June and July, 1918. A study of turbidity readings and the chlorine absorption tests indicates practically no correlation whatever between these two phenomena, although the turbidities ranged from 0 to 90 parts per million. The Potomac River water at the above station offers an interesting illustration of the necessity for guarding against unwarranted correlations between the physical property of a water and its biochemical conduct. In the case of the above water, the chlorine absorption values (during five minutes) showed no increase whatever with increases of turbidity, but rather a slight decrease. That the absorption remained almost constant and even decreased, in a degree, with an apparent physical degradation of the water is probably explained by the fact that the Potomac River at the point under discussion contains considerable oxidizable mine wastes. Sudden rainfalls create dilutions of these wastes, but at the same time raise the turbidity readings on the river. It comes about, therefore, that the increased muddiness in the water is in reality accompanied by a reduction in oxidizable material, without a consequent increase in chlorine absorption values. The situation is somewhat analogous to the reductions in alkalinity frequently observed with rises in turbidity. It is clear from the above situation that the direct variation of dosage with increase of turbidity would have been fallacious and contrary to the demand of the water. When the attempt is made to correlate turbidities of *different* waters with their corresponding chlorine absorptions, even less success is experienced. This situation is to be expected in different supplies, because of the variance in character and degree of watershed pollution. It may be postulated, as a preliminary conclusion, that turbidity readings are not a safe index of chlorine absorption for different water supplies, but may be adapted, with sufficient precautionary measures, to use for an individual supply. Even in the latter case, the conversion of turbidity to chlorine absorption is accomplished only after long studies of widely varying phases of the same supply.

Oxygen Consumed and the Rate of Chlorine Absorption. Inasmuch as the oxygen-consumed values of waters represent approximately the oxidizable compounds present in such supplies, it would seem that this chemical index should bear some relation to the complex action of chlorine absorption, of which some portion at least partakes of the nature of an oxidation. In order to study this phase of absorption, a series of widely varying waters, of surface and underground types and of different ranges of pollution, were examined during portions of 1917 and 1918. In all of these waters the oxygen-consumed and the chlorine-absorbed (5 min.) values were obtained. These readings are graphically shown on Chart 1, where the individual and average values have been plotted, in order to permit the construction of an empirical curve. The data there shown apparently disclose a fairly close variation of chlorine absorption with the oxygen-consumed values of different supplies. This correlation, it should be emphasized, is independent of the source or nature of the water, since the 45 waters tabulated include those from raw surface streams, deep wells, and filtered supplies.

Table 2
A Comparison between Chlorine Absorption Intervals
and Equal Oxygen-Consumed Intervals

Oxygen Reading.	Consumed Interval.	Chlorine Reading.	Absorbed Interval.
0.5	..	0.117	....
1.0	0.5	0.211	0.094
1.5	0.5	0.290	0.079
2.0	0.5	0.350	0.060
2.5	0.5	0.402	0.052
3.0	0.5	0.449	0.047
3.5	0.5	0.488	0.039
4.0	0.5	0.520	0.032
4.5	0.5	0.550	0.030
5.0	0.5	0.577	0.027
5.5	0.5	0.600	0.023
6.0	0.5	0.620	0.020
6.5	0.5	0.635	0.015
7.0	0.5	0.652	0.017

The empirical curve indicates at once that the amount of chlorine absorbed in a definite time interval does not increase in direct proportion with the increase in pollution of the water (as measured by the oxygen-consumed test), but that the 5 minute rate of chlorine absorption shows a decreasing acceleration with increases in pollution. In other words, increases in oxygen-consumed values appear to result in *relative* decreases in the intervals between successive chlorine absorption values. This phenomenon is made clearer by reference to Table 2, wherein are compared certain values obtained from the empirical curve shown in Chart 1.

The apparent correlation discussed above has considerable practical importance aside from its use in the chlorination of water supplies.

Its probable existence may result in the development of an extremely rapid presumptive indicator of the quality of a water, namely, its chlorine absorption in a definite time interval. It has been found comparatively simple, in this laboratory, for instance, to differentiate between an underground supply of good quality and a comparatively poor surface supply, simply by means of a chlorine absorption test made in 5 minutes. The information gained would seem to be capable of wider application to the entire field of water treatment. As a rapid diagnostic index of changes in quality of water supplies, the chlorine absorption test appears to offer a fruitful field for investigative effort.

Chlorine Absorption and Effective Disinfection Dosage

The practical effectiveness of any chlorine treatment is necessarily measured and conditioned by its ability to eliminate the significant bacterial life in the water. The preliminary determination of a dose which may be subsequently found to be effective has been the primary objective of past investigations in this field. In practically all of these methods of presumptive testing for effective dosage, chlorine absorption tests have played an important role. It is of interest, therefore, at this point to review briefly several of the methods of chlorine control now in use and to discuss the principles underlying their application.

American practice in the chlorination of water supplies has always been sharply differentiated from the foreign. In general, the foreign sanitarians have employed chlorine doses appreciably higher than those in use on this continent. This policy has been the resultant of a conservative conception of the whole question of chlorination and has therefore left its impress upon the modern systems of chlorination control. A study of the various methods of presumptive tests for the effective doses discloses the common assumption, independently promulgated, that the chlorine absorption in definite intervals bears some definite but apparently unknown relation to disinfection accomplishment. This definite relationship is, however, the subject of a wide difference of opinion among individual sanitarians, with always the sharp demarcation between the foreign and domestic viewpoints.

The principle underlying practically all of the chlorination control procedures is that of measuring the amount of available chlorine absorbed by the water to be disinfected in a given period of time. To this amount a factor of safety is usually added, giving a resultant so-called effective chlorine index. It is clear that the important element in the above procedure is the time element. The time interval taken for the measurement of the chlorine absorption is dependent upon the consideration of the death rate of the bacteria under the particular conditions. A dose measured in the light of the above principle is a safe dose only if the time interval used in its evaluation is amply sufficient to provide for adequate bacterial destruction. The problem of measurement of chlorine dosage resolves itself, therefore, into the question, "What is the safe time interval for the chlorine absorption test?"

The literature of chlorination suggests various answers to this question. Adams,[3] in his discussion of the chlorination of the water for Toronto, Canada, seems to assume that 3 minutes (plus a factor of safety) is a sufficient time interval for such a test. The basis for his criterion is not apparent. He states, however, that "by conducting a series of tests it was determined that Color No. 2 represented a surplus of chlorine in the finished water that would guarantee efficiency in bacterial destruction at all times, and in the great majority of cases would not give taste or odor, and under no circumstances a bad taste or odor." Color No. 2 was equivalent to the intensity of color existing with a definite excess of available chlorine.

That such a short time interval as the above is not universally applicable is evidenced by a survey of the data reported by Race.[4] It would appear from a number of the experiments there cited that effective sterilization or even approximately fair destruction is frequently not obtained even after a 60-minute interval. The application of a 3-minute absorption test to such a condition would demand, of course, an auxiliary factor of safety of high proportions in order to eliminate the danger of ineffective dosage.

Dienert,[5] of the city of Paris, France, approaches this problem in the conservative manner suggested in the preceding statement. He not only stipulates factors of safety abnormally high in comparison with American practice, but uses in addition a chlorine absorption time interval of 15 minutes. His procedure of presumptive testing is of sufficient interest to quote at length in this discussion. His statements follow:

> For the treatment of water we use always a quantity of available chlorine equal to that absorbed in a quarter of an hour increased by 0.5 p. p. m. We estimate that to sterilize a clear water with a quantity of chlorine determined as we have just said, 3 hours' contact are necessary. If, for certain reasons, we are obliged to distribute water before this delay, we must increase the quantity of chlorine and bring it up to 1.00 instead of 0.5 p. p. m.
>
> Thus, let us take a water whose absorption of available chlorine in a quarter of an hour is equal to 0.2 p. p. m. If the water must be distributed in a very short time we would add 1.2 p. p. m. in order to sterilize it. If we should store the water longer than 3 hours, we would use only $0.2 + 0.5 = 0.7$ p. p. m. of available chlorine.
>
> We have established, in following the bacterial content of river or turbid waters treated with doses of free chlorine of from 1.00 to 1.5 p. p. m., that at certain moments *B. coli* was not destroyed. Safety in

treatment demands the use of a dose of free chlorine a little higher than the doses given above.

Professor Santoliquido,[6] of Italy, adds to the general theory by stating that "the bacterial action of chlorine is not instantaneous for any particular bacterium; in order that the action should result, there is always necessary a contact period, which, at a minimum, must be from 10 to 20 minutes."

Costa and Pecker[7] modify somewhat the system of presumptive test for chlorine dosage by eliminating the factor of safety and using their so-called "chlorine index." The index appears to differ but slightly, in its evaluation, from the usual chlorine absorption tests reported by other authors in our own discussion. They establish as a principle or hypothesis that the useful dose for the purification of water is determined by the total quantity of chlorine fixed by the water in a given time and under definite conditions. They have determined, as a result of experience, that the initial dose of chlorine to be used in evaluating their index should be 5 p. p. m. As to the period of contact for the test, the authors have

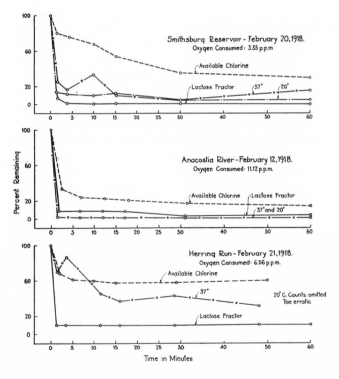

Chart 2

A Comparison of the Rates of Chlorine Absorption
and Bacterial Destruction

taken the figure of 30 minutes, which they state "is generally adopted for the purification of water by chemical substances."

These authors declare further, that they have been able to decide after more than 2 years' experimental work that the sterilization of water is not very often obtained if the quantity of chlorine used does not reach the figure fixed by the index, and that these latter figures give quantities sufficient for purification.

The foregoing discussion seems to indicate the absence of any general agreement either as to the necessary time interval for the chlorine absorption test or the relative scale of factor of safety. The evidence as to the velocity of bacterial destruction under widely varying conditions is far from complete. If the rates of disinfection on Chart 2 (experimental data) are approximately as shown, it would seem that a 30-minute absorption plus a high factor of safety is hardly necessary. It is doubtful, too, whether such factors of safety as 0.5 to 1.00 can be universally employed under such conditions as exist in Maryland, where frequently the period of contact before consumption is so brief as to preclude a dose which would result in such excessive amounts of free chlorine at the tap.

A general survey of this phase of chlorination discloses a need for additional data regarding the velocities of disinfection under actual operating conditions. That the conceptions of this phase are inadequately developed is evidenced by the wide discrepancy in the phenol coefficients of chlorine, for example, quoted in current literature.[8]

Five or Thirty Minute Absorption Test?

For practical purposes, any rapid method of presumptive indication of efficient dosage is particularly valuable. It remains to be determined, however, whether the substitution of a rapid 5- for a safer 30-minute test will result in any practical diminution of a necessary safety factor. The demonstration of such an effect either in the positive or negative direction would demand manifestly far more experimental proof than the present writers are in a position to adduce.

It is of interest, however, in connection with this problem, to refer to the experimental data shown in Table 3 and Chart 3. These experiments[9] were designed to answer in a preliminary manner the question as to the effect of increased time intervals upon the total amounts of available chlorine absorbed by different waters. In other words, what additional information is gained by extending absorption tests from 5 to 30 or 60 minutes? Chart 3, with its few empirical values, seems to suggest that the importance of increasing the period of test decreases materially with the increased values of the initial 5-minute absorptions. The evidence in Table 3 would appear to point to the conclusions that increased safety in dosage is occasioned by the 30-minute test in those waters where the

Table 3
Showing the Additional Percentages of Available Chlorine Absorbed
by Different Waters in Increased Time Intervals.

Sample		Initial Dose of Chlorine = 1.00 p. p. m. Per cent. of Initial Chlorine Absorbed in			Temperature 20°C. Ratio of Per cent. Chlorine Absorbed.	
		5 min.	30 min.	60 min.	30 min. to 5 min.	60 min. to 5 min.
1	Surface	45	47	50	1.04	1.12
2	Surface	55	57	58	1.04	1.06
3	Surface	31	60	62	1.95	2.00
4	Surface	38	60	..	1.59	...
5	Surface	61	71	..	1.17	...
6	Surface	53	70	72	1.32	1.36
7	Surface	56	61	84	1.09	1.50
8	Surface	61	79	88	1.21	1.44
9	Surface	31	53	63	1.71	2.02
10	Surface	68	84	..	1.24	...
11	Surface	34	59	..	1.74	...
12	Surface	18	39	..	2.15	...
13	Filtered	08	25	..	3.22	...
14	Well	15	30	38	2.00	2.53
15	Well	08	42	56	5.25	7.00
16	Well	14	18	24	1.29	1.71
17	Well	10	45	..	4.50	...
18	Surface	70	72	75	1.03	1.08
19	Surface	34	37	..	1.09	...
20	Surface	40	40	..	1.00	...
21	Surface	26	64	75	2.48	2.90
22	Surface	75	80	85	1.07	1.14

factor of safety is least essential, whereas little additional safety is gained in waters of higher initial absorption or in those where it is most necessary.

If the 5-minute chlorine absorption test is at all indicative of the pollute content of a water, then the evaluation of a 30-minute test seems to add but little necessary information as to effective dosage. It would hardly be advantageous to use a 30-minute test, in preference to a 5, when the former increases greatly the dosages for good waters and affects but little those of poorer waters. The addition of a constant factor of safety, as, for instance, 0.2, to the 5-minute absorption value would apparently accomplish the same result in the routine control of chlorination as the use of a longer absorption time interval.

NOTES

1. Dakin and Dunham, Handbook of Antiseptics, 1918, p. 106.

2. "Some Aspects of Chlorination," J. Am. Water Works Assoc. June, 1916.

3. "Water Chlorination Experiences at Toronto, Canada," Am. J. Pub. Health, August, 1916.

4. "Some Aspects of Chlorination," J. Am. Water Works Assoc. June, 1916; "Chlorination and Chloramine," ibid., March, 1918.

5. "New Perfections in the Chlorination of Waters," La Technique Sanitaire et Municipale, February, 1917.

6. "Note on the Purification of Potable Water by Calcium Hypochlorite," Office International d'Hygiene Publique, May, 1918.

7. "The Determination of the Useful Dose of Chlorine for the Purification of Water: The Chlorine Index," Compt. rend., February, 1918.

8. Rideal, J. Roy. San. Inst., 31 (1910), 33–45, gives 2.2. while Schneider, Bacteriological Methods—Food and Drugs, p. 200, gives 12.5.

9. The determinations were all made according to the 1917 A. P. H. A. Standard Method of Water Analysis. The oxygen-consumed readings were obtained in acid digestion, with a period of digestion of 30 minutes at a boiling temperature. No corrections for oxidizable mineral substances were applied to the oxygen-consumed values, since these latter were to be used to represent the *total* oxygen demand of the water supply. In the measurement of available chlorine in the different experiments the temperature used was 20° C.

The Statistical Method in Problems
of Water Supply Quality*

Introductory

The concept of water supply quality has the simplicity of the un-known to the layman, but the complexity of the universe to the sanitarian. If one uses the mathematician's measure of the complexity of a function —the number of its attributes—the problem of water supply quality, a function dependent upon mutually active natural, physical, chemical, and biological phenomena, offers an attractive field of·study to the statistician. For the professional statistician has been concerned always with "quantitative data affected by a multiplicity of causes"[1] and with their elucidation. In considering the causes operating to produce relatively good or bad waters, such as rainfalls, pollution, purification, etc., and their interpretation upon the basis of laboratory findings and personal surveys it becomes manifest that problems of water supply quality fall well within the scope of statistical method. Just as in all statistical problems, so in that of water supply quality, the investigator is confronted with the two-fold task of determining the method of evaluating the units of interpretation and of defining the limiting values of such units. The method of approach to each problem involves a statistical viewpoint, as well as a quantitative methodology. The present paper has been prepared

* Reprinted from the *Quarterly Publications of the American Statistical Association*, New Series No. 130, June 1920, 188–202.

in order to illustrate, in as brief terms as possible, this statistical method of approach, by developing therein a few examples of its application to the question of water supply quality. The writer plans to trace the evolution of the concept of water supply quality in the sanitarian's mind and to point out in such a development the function which the statistical art has performed or may be expected to supply in the future. The discussion appears to be a necessary one since hitherto the water supply investigator has been accused of an aversion for the quantitative sciences, while, on the other hand, the professional statistician has shown a neglect of a field which perhaps did not appear to be worthy of his mettle. The present study may serve to remove this friendly distrust which retards in a degree progress in critical studies of water supply quality.

1. *The Laboratory Examination of Water Supplies*

The sanitary quality of water supply must be predicated necessarily upon the demonstration of its relative inability to produce disease. With the present germ theory of disease, such a demonstration resolves itself into the laboratory problem of enumerating the number and types of pathogenic organisms in stated quantities of water. It is apparent, therefore, that the technique in this instance is largely bacteriological, and the discussion, for purposes of simplicity, may be restricted to the problems of the evaluation of bacterial units, as illustrative of the statistical method.

It is manifestly impossible and impracticable to examine an unknown water in such manner as to determine its content of all kinds of bacteria or even of those relatively few classes of specific organisms which it is known are both disease-producing and capable of living in water. It is more desirable as well as convenient, therefore, to choose one family or group of micro-organisms whose natural habitat and life history are similar to the variety of pathogenic organisms and whose detection by laboratory methods is most simple and speedy. Bacteriologists have concluded that a particular class of bacteria serves as the most convenient index to water supply quality or contamination. They have chosen as this index class or type the so-called colon or bacillus coli group. The B. coli group has been so selected, because its origin is in general the colon or digestive tract of man and its presence is usually indicative of human sewage pollution (the possible and probable existence of colon types in other environments need not concern us at this point).

One of the primary objects of the bacteriologist, therefore, is to differentiate the bacterial species present in a water supply, so as to demonstrate the presence or absence of members of the B. coli group. In addition, it is necessary to obtain some idea of the relative frequency of such a group, since smaller numbers naturally connote a more remote pollution, due to the dying off of bacteria in the unfavorable environment of water, to the presence of antagonistic life, and to other natural and artificial barriers to its development. The problems arising in the laboratory differentiation of bacterial varieties offers, therefore, material for an initial example. Two general methods of distinguishing groups of bacteria are available. Both are based upon the method of differences. In the one case, morphological or structural characteristics, and in the other, metabolic distinctions control. Various classifications of the colon group, for instance, are based upon its ability to produce acid and gas from fermentable substances. Investigators have observed that certain types of B. coli ferment such complex organic compounds as sucrose, dulcitol, and raffinose while others do not. Differences in the amount and character of gas formation from certain substances distinguish other types of bacteria. In all classifications, however, it has been recognized that the same group may have a variety of reactions which overlap partially those of other groups. Two types of bacteria, for instance, may both ferment sucrose, but may differ in their effect upon a second or third compound. This gives rise naturally to a vast amount of possible combinations between characters and Levine[2] points out that "as the number of fermentable substances increases, the number of varieties increases geometrically approaching infinity. The number of 'varieties' is given by the formula 2^n where 'n' is the number of characters studied. Thus with 8 characters there are 256 possible combinations; this number rises to 1,024 with 10 characters and to 65,536 when 16 characters are observed. The absurdity of regarding each character as of similar and equal differential value is thus evident."

Levine, as well as other more recent investigators, has concluded that the principle of the correlation of characters should be emphasized in the attempt to distinguish bacterial species. He points out that certain properties have been universally accepted, after long checking, as reliable evidences of bacterial differences. Among such properties, he enumerates the selective dyeing of bacteria, their powers of spore formation, and their adaptation of aerobic or anaerobic development. The taxonomic value of the characters of motility, indol formation, and fermentation of certain compounds, on the other hand, he assumes to be still debatable. In order to avoid the adoption of a confusing classification of bacteria upon the basis of every character studied (of which we have indicated only a few) he has recourse to a basis of subdivision "on that character which gives the greatest amount of information as to the manner in which the resulting sub-groups react with respect to other characters."[2] By making use of the above principle Levine evolves a classification of coli-like bacteria which is based almost completely upon statistically evaluated correlated characters. For the purpose of this study, he recognizes two main strains of bacteria, the B. coli and the B. aerogenes-cloacae group, which earlier investigations have shown to be distinguishable most often by their reactions to methyl-red and to the Voges-Proskauer reagent. The first strain is usually methyl-red positive and Voges-Proskauer negative, while the second strain shows the reverse. The justification of this initial subdivision into two main groups consists in the fact that the strains thus subdivided show end products of carbohydrate fermentations of two entirely distinct kinds.

Levine's procedure consists in tabulating all of the reactions of the organisms studied in each of the above two groups in two different tables, from which are calculated the coefficients of correlation for each pair of characters. He selects, then, for subdivision that character which gives the highest coefficient of correlation with the greatest number of other characters. For these resulting sub-groups new correlation tables are prepared and further subdivision is made. These sub-groups are regarded as species and each is assigned its name.

In order to illustrate Levine's use of the coefficient of correlation for taxonomic purposes, let us follow his procedure in the subdivision of the B. coli, or methyl-red positive and Voges-Proskauer negative, group of bacteria. For the 182 strains of this group that were studied by means of microscopic and metabolic methods, the coefficients of correlation shown in Table 1 were obtained.

Table 1
Coefficients of Correlation Obtained from Pairs of Characters among 182 Strains of the B. Coli Group

	Motility	Indol	Sucrose	Raffinose	Dulcitol	Glycerol	Salicin
Motility		−.39	+.53	+.43	+.53	+.18	+.40
Indol	−.39		+.08	+.00	+.02	−.28	+.76
Sucrose	+.53	+.08		+.99	+.58	−.38	+.20
Raffinose	+.43	+.00	+.99		+.58	−.29	+.27
Dulcitol	+.53	+.02	+.58	+.58		−.21	+.60
Glycerol	+.18	−.28	−.38	−.29	−.21		+.52
Salicin	+.40	+.76	+.20	+.27	+.60	+.52	

Since Levine's criterion for the choice of a character for subdivision is that that character should give the highest coefficient of correlation with most other characters, it is apparent, from an inspection of Table 1, that sucrose, raffinose, dulcitol, and salicin meet this criterion more completely than do other properties. For special technical reasons, Levine chooses sucrose for primary division of the B. coli group and obtains by differentiation on sucrose ninety-three strains of the sucrose positive and eighty-nine strains of the sucrose negative groups. These two groups combined form, of course, the total of 182 strains initially chosen for study. Further study of the sucrose positive strains discloses a series of coefficients of correlation of characters as shown in Table 2.

Coefficients of Correlation for Pairs of Characters among 93 Sucrose
Positive Strains of the B. Coli Group

	Motility	Indol	Dulcitol	Glycerol	Salicin
Motility		−.27	+.67	+.40	+.54
Indol	−.27		+.05	−.42	+.28
Dulcitol	+.67	+.05		−.32	+.39
Glycerol	+.40	−.42	−.32		+.32
Salicin	+.54	+.28	+.39	+.32	

Table 2 indicates that motility is the best correlated character and this property provides, therefore, for two further sub-groups, a sucrose-postive motile sub-group and a sucrose-positive non-motile group. These sub-groups are treated in the manner already illustrated and the coefficient of correlation for different characters provide for further subdivision. With the aid of this statistical interpretation of his studies of 333 coli-like bacteria, isolated from various sources, Levine suggests a classification of bacterial varieties. The summary of this classification need not be repeated here, since the reader is interested more in his method of attack than in the resulting bacteriological findings.

Such classifications as Levine's supply the sanitarian with the qualitative information necessary for the interpretation of one phase of the water supply quality problem.* The analyst dealing with waters is concerned not only with the nature of the bacterial types present therein, but also in the magnitude of their content, since it is the latter which indicates the degree and the remoteness of pollution. In the search for a potable water, it is often useless to seek that water which has no possible source of contamination, but it is always necessary to determine the quantiative bacterial importance of the latter. The methods so far described answer only one question, that is, what types of bacteria are present in the water. In the solution of the second inquiry, regarding the number of a particular type in a stated quantity of water, statistical method has played recently an important part.

In the simpler tests for the B. coli group in waters, the so-called fermentation tubes are used. These tubes contain the medium selected for most efficient differentiation of the B. coli group from other kinds of bacteria and are inoculated with specific quantities of the water to be tested. The production of gas in the tubes after stated periods of incubation indicates the presence of the B. coli group. Our knowledge that of five tubes, each inoculated with 0.1 c.c. of the water, four show the presence of the organism, is of value, but more important is the additional

* The subdivisions Levine develops have their importance to the investigator in the fact that species or varieties appear to be somewhat correlated with habitat or source of pollution.

fact that such a series of findings indicates that the probable number of organisms in the sample tested is about 1,600 per 100 c.c. This conversion of qualitative fermentation-tube results into quantitative values is of special interest to the statistician.

In 1915, McCrady[3] showed that "the frequency of the appearance of the fermenting organism in the volume drawn from the sample for the test is an exponential function of the number of such organisms in the sample," and that "every fermentation-tube result, whether simple or compound, corresponds to one most probable number of organisms." By employing the theory of probabilities, he demonstrates that, given the result "$\dfrac{p}{p+q}$ in 1 volume," for instance, the corresponding most probable number is given by the solution for x of the equation

$$1 - \left(\frac{V-1}{V}\right)^x = \frac{p}{p+q}.$$

Thus, for the result "five out of ten tubes positive in 1 c.c.," the most probable number is given by solution of the equation $1 - .99^x = 5/10$, since $V = 100$ c.c., assumed as the original quantity of water sampled. The equation being solved, $x = 69$ or the most probable number of B. coli in the sample, per 100 c.c.

For compound results, such as $\dfrac{p}{p+q}$ in 10 c.c., $\dfrac{r}{r+s}$ in 1 c.c., a more complicated formula is employed which is built up, as follows:[3]

For the result $\dfrac{p}{p+q}$ in 10 c.c. the equation becomes $(p+q)\,(\log .9)$

$= \dfrac{p\,(\log .9)}{1 - .9^x}$ which is obtained by differentiating for a maximum the equation given in the earlier paragraph for the probability of the results.

If the result is $\dfrac{p}{p+q}$ in 10 c.c., $\dfrac{r}{r+s}$ in 1 c.c., the equation stands

$$(p+q)\,(\log .9) + (r+s)(\log .99) = \frac{p\,(\log .99)}{1 - .9^x} + \frac{r\,(\log. .99)}{1 - .99^x}$$

where $(p+q) =$ number of tubes inoculated with 10 c.c. of sample
$(r+s) =$ number of tubes inoculated with 1 c.c. of sample
$x =$ number of fermenting organisms in 100 c.c. of sample
p and $r =$ number of tubes giving positive results in 10 and 1 c.c. respectively.

If lower additional quantities of water are tested, extra similar terms are added to each side of the above equation. This equation has been modified by Wolman and Weaver[4] into

$$100\,(p+q+10(r+s) = \frac{100p}{1 - .9^x} + \frac{10r}{1 - .99^x}$$

since, approximately, $\log .9 = 10 \log .99 = 100 \log .999$.

McCrady published later[5] a series of tables for the rapid interpretation of these results which makes the standardized use of the probable numbers of B. coli possible for the water supply investigator.*

The work of McCrady was followed by other investigations dealing with the numerical interpretations of B. coli tests, of which the more important are Stein,[6, 7, 8] Greenwood and Yule,[9] and Wells.[10, 11, 12] The results of Stein and Greenwood and Yule, although differing in technique and in additional interesting viewpoints, are in substantial agreement with those obtained by McCrady. Stein[8] adds considerable interesting statistical material to the B. coli problem by introducing the so-called B. coli factor method, in which he considers the most probable number of B. coli per c.c. from the percentage of positive tests, the expected error of results, the study of the distribution of coli during a series of tests, and the "coli characteristic" which attempts to show by one figure, the average coli, the expected error, and the variable distribution.

The discussion of the problem by Greenwood and Yule[9] has all the intricacy and mathematical complexity usually associated with Yule's contributions. Their findings, however, agree with those of McCrady and Stein. Greenwood and Yule, for instance, give as their formula for the number of B. coli per cc., when using several tubes with 1 c.c. each

$$x = \text{B. coli per c.c.} = 2.3 \log \frac{p+q}{q}$$

whereas McCrady gives for the same condition (using an original size sample of 1,000 c.c.)

$$x = \frac{\log \frac{q}{p+q}}{1,000 \log .999} = \frac{\log \frac{q}{p+q}}{-1,000(.0004344)} = \frac{\log \frac{q}{p+q}}{-.4344} = -2.3 \log \frac{q}{p+q}$$
$$= 2.3 \log \frac{p+q}{q}$$

Perhaps the mathematician's interest may be aroused to the sanitarian's problems of water supply by the mere examination of Greenwood and Yule's discussions, while the bacteriologist may view with some alarm the same paper. It should be postulated in either case, however, that superficial considerations should not prevent the mutual aid which these two branches of science may extend to each other. While such complexity of treatment of the numerical interpretation of fermentation tube tests as is indicated by the formula

---

* The assumption of McCrady that the distribution of B. coli is similar to that in a mixture of a few red balls with many white balls is to be contrasted with the hypothesis of other workers that bacteria are uniformly distributed in water (G. C. Whipple[13]). More recent independent investigators, however, confirm McCrady's assumptions.

$$P = \frac{\int_0^k \left[e^{-ha_1n_1}\left(1-e^{-ha_1}\right)^{m_1} \cdot e^{-ha_2n_2}\left(1-e^{-ha_2}\right)^{m_2} \cdots e^{-ha_nn_n}\left(1-e^{-ha_n}\right)^{m_n}\right] dh}{\int_0^w \left[e^{-ha_1n_1}\left(1-e^{-ha_1}\right)^{m_1} \cdot e^{-ha_2n_2}\left(1-e^{-ha_2}\right)^{m_2} \cdots e^{-ha_nn_n}\left(1-e^{-ha_n}\right)^{m_n}\right] dh}$$

may attract the statistician, it is hoped that it may not at the same time deter the laboratory technician from the adoption of devices which provide for more adequate solutions of his problems. Emphasis must be placed upon the fact that the mental attitude resulting from the adoption of statistical method has much promise in a field of endeavor where laboratory findings are too infrequently tested for accuracy of interpretation and rarely treated as examples of mass phenomena. The work of such men as Stein and McCrady has done much to introduce such methods by clarifying our concepts of fermentation-tube results and their relative significance.

That the statistical method is an important asset in the exposition of laboratory findings is illustrated in another series of studies of various phases of water supply. Whipple,[13] for instance, has demonstrated that "if, in a series of daily observations of the number of bacteria in a filter effluent extending over a year the deviation of any determination from the mean should be found to be more than five times as much as the probable error, to use a round number, this should be rejected from the series as being, for some reason or other, abnormal." He has made important contributions to the study of the frequency distributions of measures of various bacteriological, biological, and chemical characteristics of water, such as the preliminary finding that extended series of filter effluent results follow definite statistical laws in their distribution. His conclusion has been further substantiated by the more recent study of Wolman[14] of thousands of laboratory findings, in which it is indicated that the logarithms of bacterial counts, through long periods of time, have the characteristic normal probability distribution of more familiar biological statistical data.

It is of considerable interest to refer at this point to a form of graph presentation of data developed by a sanitary engineer which may be unfamiliar to most statisticians. Allen Hazen[15] in 1914 devised a form of chart ruled with a horizontal scale so divided that the curve of probability would plot thereon as a straight line. Any series of observations, therefore, which varied in accordance with the probability law would plot also as a straight line. Illustrations of the use of such paper in water supply problems may be found in the original paper of Hazen[15] and in subsequent discussions by Whipple[13] and Wolman.[14]

Stein,[16] in his study of the bacterial count in water and sewage, has added considerable material to our conceptions of the variability of laboratory findings and their importance in practical studies. He has concluded, after an interesting detailed analysis of the problem, that:

(a) For platings of a single sample of water, the mean error is equal to the square root of the number of colonies on a single plate, or the square root of the average number of colonies on several plates.

(b) The variations to be expected for careful and accurate work with bacterial counts are indicated by:

(1) Standard Deviation of $\pm$ 12%

(2) Deviation (1 in 10 times) of $\pm$ 25%

For ordinary routine work:

(1) Standard Deviation of $\pm$ 25%

(2) Deviation (1 in 10 times) of $\pm$ 50%

His comparison of the characteristics of bacteriological data with certain mathematical series should be of interest to the reader, since he shows, for example, that for daily tests of Lake Erie water for one month the Lexian Ratio is 29.00 and the Disturbancy Coefficient 124.00, while the corresponding values for a normal mathematical series (Bernouilli) are given as 1.00 and 0.00 respectively.

II. *The Interpretation of the Quality of Water Supplies*

In the preceding paragraphs the writer has indicated a few of the problems encountered in the laboratory technique of water supply examination, which lend themselves to statistical treatment. It has been impossible to include in the present brief paper any complete survey of such applications to other phases of laboratory procedure, but sufficient material has been presented, to demonstrate that the data in the field of laboratory technique have considerable to offer to the professional statistician as bases for the development of interpretative principles of quality.

The writer believes that some mention should be made briefly of certain interesting possibilities of development in the application of statistical method to general problems of laboratory procedure. The use of the coefficient of partial correlation, for instance, does not appear to have been introduced widely in the interpretation of laboratory findings, yet the necessity for its application is most apparent. Often investigative work in water supplies is carried out on a large or plant scale with the aid of analytical laboratory methods. In the study of the chlorination of a water supply, for example, a number of different variable quantities such as turbidity, color, organic content, and bacterial densities have their effect in modifying the efficiency of the disinfection process. In practically all conclusions from such studies no attempt is made to determine mathematically the effect of such variables, other than by mere inspection of tabulated data. There is little doubt that erroneous conclusions are often obtained through the failure to evaluate quantitatively the importance of fluctuations in the various characteristics of waters subject to chlorination. It is almost impossible to determine by qualitative inspection of a series of daily observations, over an entire year, of temperature, turbidity, color, organic content, and bacterial density in a water supply, whether the effect of a constant dosage of chlorine is influenced more greatly by any one of the above characteristics or by a combination of several or all of them.

The same problem arises, of course, in the study of any phenomena associated with the purification of water supplies. In the coagulation of suspended matter in water, for instance, all the variables such as time, agitation, temperature, hydrogen-ion concentration, nature of suspended matter, and character of coagulant play an interconnected part. The principle of partial correlation could be adapted with profit to these problems of associated phenomena.

The application of such a statistical principle as pointed out above is complicated, however, by the fact that the more simple statistical coefficients usually cannot be directly applied to the problems encountered, on account of the fact that such measures presuppose the use of data having a symmetrical or Gaussian distribution, while the phenomena with which the sanitarian has to deal often are characterized by asymmetrical distributions.[17, 18]

Michael[18] has discussed in this connection the determination of the most probable number of bacteria present in a sample and has demonstrated that it is not permissible to apply the probable error in the usual manner on account of the fact that the logarithms of the plate counts, and not the counts themselves, show a Gaussian frequency distribution.[19] McEwen and Michael[17] in another field of investigation have been confronted with the same problem of determining the "functional relation of one variable to each of a number of correlated variables" where such variables do not show the usual symmetrical frequency distribution. It is manifestly impossible to extend in this paper the elucidation of these applications of statistical method to problems of laboratory and plant, but the reader may find profitable data in the original papers already noted.

The opportunity for the application of statistical tests to problems of water supply quality is not restricted, however, to the materials of the analyst. The consideration of the potability of a supply involves always a series of mutually active attributes, each of which has its importance in determining the character of the water. The concept of quality connotes, therefore, a composite of properly weighted individual and fundamental units, in the evaluation of which statistics again comes to the fore.

It is unfortunate, however, that in the field of interpretation of quality statistical method has been even slower of application than in the corresponding study of laboratory data. The quantitative evaluation of sanitary data has always given way to the liberal exercise of expert personal judgment. Where a multiplicity of causes predetermines a phenomenon, such as quality, it was thought that a proper perspective was possible only through the development of a maturity of judgment in which the play of the manifold effects was qualitatively summarized rather than quantitatively analyzed. As the methods of diagnosis of quality developed, however, the opportunity for the fruitful application of the principles of mass phenomena gradually becomes apparent. With this development of a new viewpoint, good as well as evil sometimes resulted. A complete swinging of the pendulum to the quantitative side of interpretation was feared, where the attempt was made to substitute for individual experience and judgment pseudo-quantitative measures of doubtful significance. Some of these efforts, in which statistical laws frequently were ignored, will be discussed later in this paper. In general, however, a realization is gradually coming over the sanitarian that statistics as a means, rather than as an end, has much to offer in the clarification of his problems. If the succeeding pages seem somewhat bare, in their statistical implication, the professional statistician should remember that the concepts there discussed mark the advance of a new light in sanitary engineering, which, though feeble in its flicker, gives promise of a greater brilliance in the not distant future.

Attempts to formulate water supply standards of composite character represented one of the earliest applications of semi-statistical method. Most of these were based upon the erroneous conclusion that methods of evaluating units had been standardized throughout the country. Attention has been called to this fallacy of endeavoring to establish limiting values of units attained by varying methods by Hinman,[20] Norton,[21] and Morse and Wolman.[23] Fundamental training in statistical interpretation no doubt would prevent the adoption of water supply quality standards before the principles of unit evaluation have been rigidly enforced.

It is not amiss, perhaps, to call attention at this point to the close analogy between the so-called scoring of a water supply, or the quantitative allocation of the quality upon the scale of sanitary safety, and the statistician's concept of index numbers. Wolman[14] has shown recently that the operations involved in making a price index number are similar to those followed, to a greater or less extent, by investigators of water supply scores. In the case of price index numbers, the object of weighing is to give each commodity included in the index number an influence upon the results corresponding to its commercial importance. In water supply index numbers, the object of weighing likewise is to give each factor making up the score an influence upon the results corresponding to its sanitary importance. Although the problems in the two fields are the same, their solutions are necessarily different, since, in the case of water supply scores, the conversion to a common base of such units as bacterial results, sanitary surveys, operating efficiencies, etc., cannot be carried out because of the presence of varying personal opinion or judgment. It has been noted,[14] however, that it still remains possible to make use nationally of simplified index numbers of water supply quality restricted in their range of significance and composed of similar units or, better still, of individual units, provided the method of evaluation of such units has been definitely and completely fixed.

Interpretations of the quality of a water include frequently more than a summary of the structural and environmental features of the supply. The possibilities of the intelligent and fruitful application of statistical devices, such as the coefficients of correlation and of variation, to other phases of water supply are mentioned only briefly here, since their complete discussion would involve a paper of a far too great length. Whipple,* for instance, has suggested the use of the coefficient of correlation in analyzing the vital statistics of cities which have made changes from poor to good quality water supplies, in order to demonstrate quantitatively the existence of the Mills-Reincke phenomenon. Hazen[15] has made excellent use of statistical method in his analysis of the storage provided in an impounding reservoir on any stream and the quantity of water which can be supplied continuously by it. He introduces the coefficient of variation as a measure of the degree of variation in flows of different streams, and by its further use has found it possible to get an approximate expression for the storage required to carry the surplus water of wet years over to dry years, which expression, in general terms, applied equally well to streams in different localities. In addition, he describes methods of estimating the probable errors in the results obtained and makes the important comment that "frank recognition of the large probable errors in many of the results cannot fail to be advantageous."[15]

The opportunities for further application of similar methods have appeared in the present writer's studies of the correlation of bacterial contents in water supplies with rainfalls upon stream watersheds and with hygienic results of inferior quality such as typhoid fever and diarrhoeal diseases. In these particular studies, the statistician could contribute excellent aid, since the writer is not aware of an effective method of comparing correlated phenomena in which one series of characteristics is continuous, while another is discontinuous. In addition, quantitative variations in magnitude of the values in both series are not of

* Personal communication.

paramount importance, but the direction of such variations is the interesting event. The coefficient of concurrent deviations in this instance, does not appear to supply all the desiderata. An example may make our problem clearer. In the study of the daily tap water analyses of a city water supply, we find, by inspection, that the B. coli contents rise after rains on the watershed of the stream supplying the town. It is also found that such rises are masked, to varying degrees, by purification processes and by the efficiency of operation of such processes. If changes in method and efficiency of purification are brought about and the qualitative reflection of rainfalls in resultant B. coli density in tap waters is modified, how can we measure quantitatively the change in sensitiveness of tap water quality to rainfall from month to month? The data at hand for this purpose, reduced to simplest terms, are in each month B. coli values for each day (continuous series), which differ in density from day to day, and rainfall records (discontinuous series) which may give a zero value for all the days but three or four during the month. If, during the month of July, the B. coli per 100 c.c. rose from 2 to 2,000 from July 7 to July 8, following a rain of 0.8 inch on the stream on July 7, and during August the B. coli per 100 c.c. showed no jumps above 5 in spite of a number of days of rainfall of about 0.8 inch, what should be the statistical relation between the months of July and August for these particular considerations?

This paper should not be concluded without some reference to the part that the study of purification processes has played in modifying and determining the quality of water supplies and the importance therein of the mathematician's tools. It is frequently the sanitarian's problem to include in his valuation of a water's safety some definite estimate, among other things, of the efficiency of operating features involved in the treatment of such a supply. This problem has given rise to various measures of treatment efficiencies, which only recently have been subjected to rigid statistical study. As an illustration of this type of measure the percentage removal of bacteria from untreated to treated waters has persisted. Statistical objections to this measure are well known to the reader and substitutes for this measure of performance, and indirectly of quality, have been much sought after. It was long recognized that the real measure of performance should include data regarding the distribution of the efficiencies over long periods and recommendations suggesting the classification of bacterial results according to frequency distributions have done much to clarify the interpretation of treatment figures.

Further development of the same problem of plant performance along statistical lines has been made by Wolman,[23] in the study of the nature of bacterial removal in filtration plants. In this discusion, it was suggested that "the normal performance of a water filtration plant may be represented by a curve having the equation: $y = x^c$, where y and x

are respectively the raw water and final effluents counts, and c is a constant for the particular plant under discussion." In other words, the tentative hypothesis was brought forth that the final effluent count, on the average, is an exponential function of the raw water count. The evaluation of "c" replaces also the unsatisfactory percentage efficiency as a more adequate measure, by using the ratio of the logarithms of the counts instead of the ratio of the actual bacterial values.

It is apparent that a measure of performance to be effective for adaptation to quality interpretation should include more than an array of its daily values, since it is the *consistency* of bacterial removal which predetermines the position of a form of treatment in the scale of the safety of a supply. Heretofore, no single unit of measure of this degree of consistency of removal has been available, although the fitting of normal performance data to the logarithmic curve of filtration supplied at least a graphic method of testing consistency.[23] If bacterial data are arranged and plotted on the probability paper already referred to in the discussion, it becomes extremely easy to obtain the values of the semi-interquartile ranges of the figures in successive steps of purification. The ratio of such values of the ranges for any two steps appears to the writer to present some promise of a real measure of the "levelling" effect of purification processes, since it measures the change produced in the frequency distribution of bacteria in passing through the treatment. The demonstration of its value may be more apparent to the reader by reference to material given elsewhere.[24]

REFERENCES

1. Yule, G. U., An Introduction to the Theory of Statistics.

2. Levine, Max, A Statistical Classification of the Colon-Cloacae Group, *Journal of Bacteriology*, Vol. 3, No. 3, May, 1918.

3. McCrady, M. H., The Numerical Interpretation of Fermentation-Tube Results, *Journal of Infectious Diseases*, Vol. 17, No. 1, July, 1915.

4. Wolman, Abel, and Weaver, H. L., A Modification of the McCrady Method of the Numerical Interpretation of Fermentation-Tube Results, *Journal of Infectious Diseases*, Vol. 21, No. 3, September, 1917.

5. McCrady, M. H., Tables for Rapid Interpretation of Fermentation-Tube Results, *The Public Health Journal* (Canada), Vol. 9, No. 5, May, 1918.

6. Stein, Milton F., Making the B. Coli Test Tell More, *Engineering News-Record*, Vol. 78, No. 8, May 24, 1917.

7. Stein, Milton F., On Numerical Interpretation of Bacteriological Tests, *Engineering News-Record*, Vol. 82, No. 23, June 5, 1919.

8. Stein, Milton F., The Interpretation of B. Coli Test Results on a Numerical and Comparative Basis, *Journal of Bacteriology*, Vol. 4, No. 3, May, 1919.

9. Greenwood, J., Jr., and Yule, G. Udny, On The Statistical Interpretation of Some Bacteriological Methods Employed in Water Analysis, *Journal of Hygiene*, Vol. 16, No. 1, July, 1917.

10. Wells, Wm. F., The Geometrical Mean as a B. Coli Index, *Science*, N. S., Vol. 47, No. 1202, January 11, 1918.

11. Wells, Wm. F., The Bacteriological Dilution Scale and the Dilution as a Bacteriological Unit, *American Journal of Public Health*, Vol. 9, No. 9, September, 1919.

12. Wells, Wm. F., On a Standard System of Bacteriological Dilutions, *American Journal of Public Health*, Vol. 9, No. 12, December, 1919.

13. Whipple, G. C., The Element of Chance in Sanitation, *Journal of the Franklin Institute*, Vol. 182, No. 1, No. 2, July and August, 1916.

14. Wolman, Abel, Index Numbers and Scoring of Water Supplies, *Journal of the American Water Works Association*, Vol. 6, No. 3, September, 1919.

15. Hazen, Allen, Storage to be Provided in Impounding Reservoirs for Municipal Water Supply, *Trans. American Society of Civil Engineers*, Vol. 77, p. 1,539.

16. Stein, Milton F., A Critical Study of the Bacterial Count in Water and Sewage, *American Journal of Public Health*, Vol. 8, No. 11, November, 1918.

17. McEwen, George F., and Michael, Ellis L., The Functional Relation of One Variable to Each of a Number of Correlated Variables Determined by a Method of Successive Approximation to Group Averages: A Contribution to Statistical Methods, *Proc. American Academy Arts and Sciences*, Vol. 55, No. 2, December, 1919.

18. Michael, Ellis L., Concerning Application of the Probable Error in Cases of Extremely Asymmetrical Frequency Curves, *Science*, N. S., Vol. 51, No. 1308, January 23, 1920.

19. Johnstone, James, The Probable Error of a Bacteriological Analysis, *Rept. Lanc. Sea-Fish, Lab.*, 1919, No. 27. (Not read.)

20. Hinman, J. J., Jr., American Water Works Laboratories, *Journal of the American Water Works Association*, Vol. 5, No. 2, June, 1918.

21. Norton, J. F., Comparison of Methods for the Examination of Water at Filtration Plants, *Journal of Infectious Diseases*, Vol. 23, 1918, pp. 344–50.

22. Morse, Robert B., and Wolman, Abel, The Practicability of Adopting Standards of Quality for Water Supplies, *Journal of the American Water Works Association*, Vol. 5, No. 3, September, 1918.

23. Wolman, Abel, A Preliminary Analysis of the Degree and Nature of Bacterial Removal in Filtration Plants, *Journal of the American Water Works Association*, Vol. 5, No. 3, September, 1918.

24. Wolman, Abel, and Powell, S. T., Sanitary Effect of Water Storage in Open Reservoirs, *Engineering News-Record*, Vol. 83, No. 18, October 30–November 6, 1919.

Fluorine and the
Public Water Supply*

Epidemiological studies have progressed sufficiently far to indicate that the fluorides have certain protective actions against dental caries in certain age groups. In general, it is assumed that an inverse relationship exists between the prevalence rate of dental caries and the fluoride concentration of municipal water supplies. Where domestic waters show fluoride concentrations of 1.0 or more parts per million the incidence of caries is low. The incidence is high where such concentrations in turn are 0.5 ppm and less.

To complicate the situation, however, an excess of fluoride frequently produces chronic dental fluorosis, commonly known as mottled enamel. The water control officer, therefore, is at once confronted with the necessity of determining the minimum effective concentration of fluorides which will produce satisfactory results without at the same time causing deleterious effects on the teeth.

So far over 20 cities have been studied in this country. In view of these studies, the question naturally arises as to why water supplies deficient in fluorine should not be promptly supplemented to such an extent as to prevent the objectionable caries effects in children of the 12–14-year age group. The findings covering now some 7,257 children continue to emphasize the marked differences in the amount of dental caries between

* Reprinted from *Dental Caries and Fluorine*, AAAS Pub. No. 25, pp. 108–111. Copyright 1946 by the American Association for the Advancement of Science.

the 8 cities whose public water supplies contained less than 0.5 ppm of fluoride and the 5 cities whose water supplies contained 0.5 ppm or more. When these comparisons are extended from the incidence of proximal dental caries to the basis of affected tooth surfaces, the rate in the cities with the lower fluoride water supplies was about 19 times as high as in the cities with the higher fluoride content.

To the water purveyor in communities with water supplies of fluoride concentrations of less than 0.5 ppm, the problem is now posed of deciding upon the validity of using the public water supply as a medium for the introduction of an element in such amounts as to produce beneficent results, without at the same time running the risk of causing other effects of less favorable character.

In exploring this challenge to which he is being increasingly subjected by the dental hygienist, the officer responsible for water supply treatment and distribution is confronted with a series of opposing considerations, some of which it is desirable to review at this point.

Epidemiological Status

The water supply engineer obviously is in no position to evaluate the epidemiological status of the protective action of fluoride against dental caries. As a citizen he is fully aware of the over-all importance of the disease, of the subjective criteria which must necessarily be applied to its diagnosis as well as to its treatment, and of the many problems attached to the determination of cause and effect. He can only assume at the present writing that the studies, although impressive, are still limited in numbers and in extent; that they are circumscribed by inherent difficulties in all forms of physiological research; that there are differences of opinion on the professional level of the validity of some of the conclusions to be drawn from the studies; and that, furthermore, extended controlled experimentation in the field of correctives has not yet been fully accomplished.

These judgments, however, are bound to be preliminary in nature and even temporary in conviction. The water supply officer, therefore, must remain receptive to increasing evidence and responsive to evaluation of such evidence on the part of the professional health officer, physician, and dentist. Until the epidemiological background is fortified, additional issues require examination.

The Public Water Supply as a Vehicle for Medication

In principle, the water supply engineer resists the use of this liquid for the delivery of substances extraneous to the normal water supply business. This principle sounds more convincing that it really is. Chemicals have been added to water supply for many centuries. Their list is long and their physiological effects, at least in earlier days, were debated at length. Many will recall the long professional battles that antedated the application of aluminum sulfate to water. Similar struggles attended the introduction of chlorine for disinfection purposes. Not only were the professional journals filled with arguments for and against this chemical, but considerable court action took place in order to prevent the widespread use of this material. Expert opinion was strong on both sides, and profound, though erroneous, professional judgments were freely expressed under oath.

Objective review of the past 50 years will disclose, however, that the advantageous results of the use of many of these chemicals far outweigh the disabilities which it was charged that they would produce on the physiological activity of the body.

It is true that in the earlier days of water treatment, chemicals were applied largely to eliminate objectionable inert or living constituents of the water. This dominant consideration has slowly given way, however, to the addition of other chemicals which are intended so to adjust the character of the water as to meet considerations other than those of clarity or of freedom from pathogenic organisms. Today the water engineer takes some pride in the partial truth that he is able to produce a water on a "tailor-made" specification. To accomplish this purpose, either for domestic or for commercial purposes, demands a balancing of constituents by the addition or subtraction of various chemical elements and compounds.

This transition in principle of water treatment has been slow and subtle, which accounts for the fact that it is so frequently assumed that the function of the application of chemicals to water is almost entirely to eliminate objectionable materials rather than to supplement the water for the advantage of the consumer. Both principles in fact now control the general field of water treatment.

The addition of calcium and sodium salts, of sulfuric acid, of Calgon and of other active and inert materials are all for the purpose of stabilizing and improving water supply quality. They are, however, not all removed in the process and some are even intentionally designed to accompany the water to the consumer, if not actually to the point of ingestion, at least to within a few inches thereof. Realistically, it cannot be supposed that some of the added materials or their by-products are not regularly ingested.

In view of these practices, the resistance of the water purveyor to the addition of materials, sometimes even naturally present in a supply, cannot be sustained too long, at least in theory, if other considerations of public health significance warrant such a practice.

It is well to record the fact, however, that objectors to such additions have other important practical reasons for objection. The addition of fluoride, for example, to the public water supply is relatively wasteful in that a large proportion of the public supply is not used for drinking purposes. This means that more than 90% of a volume of water is treated in order to make effective 10% or less for direct human ingestion. So much of 'the public water supply of a community goes into consumption for purposes other than ingestion that the water supply officer dislikes a treatment which wastes so much of what is applied. Treating a water with fluorides which would be used for fire fighting purposes, for industrial water, for bath room use, etc., appears wasteful in original application. On the other hand, the same criticism may be directed toward more orthodox and familiar chemical applications which have long been part of our practice.

Problems of control of dosage, particularly in view of the sensitive range between upper and lower limits under which fluoride application must operate, add another disability from the standpoint of the water supply officer.

He will not knowingly or willingly accept the responsibility for such medication unless the evidence is overwhelmingly in favor of such application. He would require from the health officer an assurance that the evidence favoring the use of the water supply as a carrier for fluorides is comprehensive and rests upon strong epidemiological grounds. He would insist upon the assurance that such additions, even though helpful to certain age groups, might not be deleterious to other age groups or to individuals in the same age group having other physiological susceptibilities or idiosyncrasies.

In addition, in order to avoid the use of the water supply as a medium for therapeutic activity he will naturally inquire as to whether some other medium of food or drink might not serve the same purpose equally well and at much less cost. He naturally thinks in terms of the analogies of iodized salts and "enriched flours."

If we were to summarize, therefore, the present probable state of mind of the officer responsible for water supply control with respect to the problems posed at this symposium, it would be one of "watchful waiting." He would probably confess under duress that there are no inherently theoretical difficulties to be met in the addition of fluorides. Given sufficient epidemiological basis to warrant balancing of equities and conveniences in such application, the technical proficiency is available by which to guarantee a reasonably continuous and relatively undeviating dosage.

In broad policy it could be anticipated that any decision to supplement the water with fluoride would have to rest upon strong certification as to the necessity of so doing by the municipal and state health officers. Such certification naturally would presuppose more extended field studies and more confirmatory data than are at present available. The full scale experiments in Kingston and Newburgh, in New York State, and in Brantford, Ontario, Canada, after some years should produce important values helpful toward any ultimate general adoption of supplementation of water for the prevention of dental caries.

At this stage of available information the present writer maintains the position already well stated by Dr. Dean at the Cleveland, 1943, meeting of the American Water Works Association. There is still no reason to modify these dicta, although there are many reasons in this, as in every other, scientific endeavor to keep the mind of the water works official open to the possibilities in this field of public health endeavor. Dr. Dean's words are as follows: "Much investigative work, however, is necessary before serious thought can be given to a recommendation for its general application . . . it is well to emphasize again that the conversion of this observed natural phenomenon into one of general usefulness necessarily requires that specifically planned epidemiological studies clearly demonstrate the safety of low fluorination as it might relate to other aspects of the community's general health."

BIBLIOGRAPHY

Arnold, F. A., Jr., Dean, H. T. and Elvove, E. 1942. Domestic water and dental caries. IV. Effect of increasing the fluoride content of a common water supply on the *Lactobacillus Acidophilus* counts of the saliva. *Pub. Health Reports*, 57: 773.

Ast, D. B. 1943. A program of treatment of public water supply to correct fluoride deficiency. *Amer. Waterworks Assoc. Jour.*, 35: No. 9, p. 1191.

Dean, H. T. 1938. Endemic fluorosis and its relation to dental caries. *Pub. Health Reports*, 53: 1443.

——————. 1942. Domestic water and dental caries. *Pub. Health Reports*, 57: 1155.

——————. 1943. Domestic water and dental caries. *Amer. Waterworks Assoc. Jour.*, 35: No. 9, p. 1161.

——————, Jay, P., Arnold, F. A., Jr. and Elvove, E. 1941. Domestic water and dental caries study, including *L. Acidophilus* estimations, of a population severely affected by mottled enamel and which for the past 12 years has used a fluoride-free water. *Pub. Health Reports*, 56: 365.

——————. 1941a. Domestic water and dental caries. II. A study of 2,832 white children, aged 12 to 14 years, of 8 suburban Chicago communities, including *Lactobacillus Acidophilus* studies of 1,761 children. *Pub. Health Reports*, 56: 761.

Dean, H. T. and Others. *Pub. Health Reports*, 52: 1249 (Sept. 10) 1937; 53: 1443 (Aug. 19) 1938; 54: 862 (May 26) 1939; 56: 761 (April 11) 1941.

Knapp, H. J. 1943. The public health significance of dental deficiencies. *Amer. Waterworks Assoc. Jour.*, 35: No. 9, p. 1187.

McClure, F. J. 1941. Domestic water and dental caries. III. Fluorine in human saliva. *Amer. Jour. Dis. Children*, 62: 512.

Wolman, A. 1943. What are the responsibilities of public water supply officials in the correction of dental deficiencies. *Amer. Waterworks Assoc. Jour.*, 35: No. 9, p. 1198.

Industrial Water Supply from Processed
Sewage Treatment Plant Effluent
at Baltimore, Maryland*

The Bethlehem Steel Company of Sparrows Point, Md., is a subsidiary of the Bethlehem Steel Company, which operates plants in several localities on the Atlantic Seaboard. It has been engaged in the manufacture of steel and its products, and in the construction of ships, for well over half a century, in Baltimore County not far beyond the boundary line of the city of Baltimore.

The Sparrows Point plant manufactures rod and wire, tin plate, rails, pig iron, nails, pipe, ships and miscellaneous steel products. It employs approximately 25,000 and will probably reach a figure of 30,000 people in the course of the next few years.

For its various industrial and domestic purposes the company uses over 185 m.g. of water per day. Of this amount, some 35 to 50 m.g.d. are of fresh water origin essential for various industrial purposes, for boiler feed water and for potable supply in the town of Sparrows Point. Large amounts of sea water are used for cooling and condenser purposes.

Underground sources for almost half a century have adequately sup-

* Reprinted with permission from the *Journal Water Pollution Control Federation*, Vol. XX, No. 1, pp. 15–21 (January, 1948), Washington, D.C. 20016. Presented in symposium "Reclamation of Sewage Effluents" at 20th Annual Meeting of the Federation of Sewage Works Associations, in Joint session with the American Water Works Association; San Francisco, Calif.; July 23, 1947.

plied the domestic and industrial fresh water needs of the company. With plant expansion, however, and with increase in the use of the same underground reservoirs by the entire industrial area of Baltimore City, the demands upon these underground resources have grown so large and so continuous that dangerous depletions have occurred.

The static levels of water have fallen in virtually all of the wells in use and at practically all of the water bearing strata. Pumping levels have increased and the water has become increasingly contaminated by salt in varying degrees at different water bearing levels. The water bearing strata now in use extend to depths of 650 to 700 ft. below the ground level. At this depth the underlying beds of granite are encountered. In earlier underground water development, various horizons were tapped and are still used. These include depths of 150, 200, 300, 400 and 500 ft., respectively.

Owing to these circumstances the company has been confronted with the necessity of finding new sources of water supply or the expansion of existing well systems. A search was, therefore, made in 1941 by the writer for new sources of water supply with a minimum safe yield of approximately 50 m.g.d. Although the company at that time had not yet reached this fresh water demand, it was considered wise to develop a supply which could ultimately be exploited economically to such an amount.

Quality of Water Required

The quality of water desirable for the various industrial purposes was not easily definable, since the exact specifications of water quality for these uses were not known in detail. No unanimity of agreement existed apparently in the steel trade on the characteristics of water harmful or harmless in the individual industrial process.

These waters for the most part are used for cooling of blast furnaces and open hearths, of rolls in all the rolling mills, of gas washers, of wire machines and for the quenching and granulating of blast furnace slag and for cleaning of gases. For this reason a number of plant scale experiments were carried out in the various processes and over extended periods, in order to shed some light upon the desirable or objectionable characteristics.

These local studies, and field observations made elsewhere throughout the country, indicated that the following characteristics determine a desirable quality of water for steel manufacture. They are:

1. Temperature preferably below 75° F.
2. Chlorides preferably below 175 p.p.m.
3. pH between 6.8 and 7.0.

4. Hardness below 50 p.p.m.
5. Suspended matter below 25 p.p.m.
6. Organic content as low as possible.
7. Corrosion potential at the lowest possible level.

Possible Sources

A thorough canvass was made of the following possible future sources of water supply. The conclusions regarding each are briefly noted below.

1. *Underground Sources, Local and Distant:* These were ruled out because of possible interference with existing supplies, excessive costs and because additional yields appeared to be improbable upon further study of the available underground reservoir capacity.

2. *Baltimore City Potable Water Supply:* This was found to be inadequate in quantity and far too expensive in cost. In addition, the city was already confronted with the necessity of developing new sources of supply for its own use. Since the fresh water requirements of the company represented almost a third of the entire water consumption of the city of Baltimore, it was deemed impracticable to obtain water permanently from this source, except ultimately for potable purposes.

3. *Baltimore City Raw Water:* Studies were made on obtaining water before treatment in Baltimore City. This was ruled out on approximately the same bases as already listed immediately above.

4. *Treated Effluent of the Back River Sewage Treatment Works of Baltimore City:* This plant offered in 1941 a continuing yield of between 90 and 100 m.g.d. It was selected after careful review as the most satisfactory source of supply, sufficiently economical to be processed and delivered for industrial purposes. The features of this particular program will be given later.

5. *Various other sources* were explored and all were discarded as inadequate in safe yield or excessive in cost. Among these sources were the use of other surface waters in the vicinity of Sparrows Point; the treatment of the local wells for demineralization; mixing various sources to produce a controllable quality of delivered water; the use of evaporators for either underground or surface local sources, or both; and the development of more distant sources such as the Patapsco River, Gwynns Falls or the Little Gunpowder River.

Use of Processed Sewage Treatment Plant Effluent

The decision to develop a water supply with the treated effluent of the Back River Sewage Treatment Works of Baltimore City as the source rested upon the following major considerations:

1. Continuous undisturbed and probably permanent flow of not less than 85 m.g.d. For intervals of only a few hours a day this flow drops to 45 m.g.d. and rises to a maximum of approximately 165 m.g.d.

2. It is a liquid which now serves no useful purposes and produces no revenue.

3. It is within economical distance of transmission to the company plant.

4. It reflects reasonably well the desirable characteristics of water supply quality, after processing, which are necessary for company use.

5. It can be purchased at a reasonable cost which, together with the capital and operating cost to the company, will result in a reasonable total cost for industrial water supply.

Baltimore City operates two sewage treatment plants at Back River, both of conventional design. The trickling filter installation, comprising detritus tanks, primary settling, trickling filters and secondary settling, can handle well over 125 m.g.d. The activated sludge plant, of a design capacity of 20 m.g.d., normally handles not much over 15 m.g.d. The average flow in 1946 was approximately 113 m.g.d. The anticipated flow in 1960 is 120 m.g.d.

The raw sewage is a relatively strong typical municipal sewage of mixed domestic and industrial wastes, running about 250 p.p.m. of suspended matter and of B.O.D.

The Bethlehem Steel Company therefore developed an agreement, at the writer's recommendation, with the Mayor and City Council of Baltimore, which was ratified by both parties on June 20, 1941. At that time, the city of Baltimore permitted the company to take at the sewage treatment works, a maximum of 50 m.g.d. of the treated effluent from either the activated sludge or the trickling filter plant, or both.

The company uses the activated sludge plant effluent without additional processing, but with continuous chlorination at a dosage of approximately 5 p.p.m. This effluent has produced between 10 and 15 m.g.d.

The effluent of the trickling filter plant has been further processed, however, by chemical precipitation, on the grounds of the Back River Works. The treatment determined upon was the result of a long series of field and laboratory experiments with virtually all of the available coagulating chemicals.

The treatment practiced has been consistently with alum at a dose of 4 to 5 grains per gallon. An effluent is generally produced with a turbidity between 5 and 10 p.p.m. The chemicals are flash-mixed with the trickling filter plant effluent, followed by 42 min. of flocculation and 1.5 hours of settling at rated capacity.

Two settling units with continuous removal of sludge and operating in parallel were installed in 1942. Each has a capacity of 15 m.g.d., with the design permitting a flow of 20 m.g.d. through each if desired. Screening devices are provided at the outlets of each. The overflow rate is 1,140 gal. per sq. ft. per day.

Alum feed equipment was installed in duplicate, with each unit of sufficient capacity to take care of requirements at maximum flow. Provisions were made for lime feeding equipment, although experiments to date have not indicated continuous use of this chemical.

When the activated sludge effluent is inferior in quality for any reason, it is sometimes passed through the chemical processing plant for joint treatment with the trickling filter effluent.

All of the liquid is intermittently chlorinated at Back River to prevent slime accumulation in the transmission line to Sparrows Point. The chlorinating equipment is in duplicate with each machine capable of dosing the full flow of 50 m.g.d., using a maximum of 10 p.p.m.

The chlorine piping is so arranged as to permit prechlorination, postchlorination, or both, of sewage leaving the chemical processing plant. Prechlorination has not proven itself to be particularly helpful, even during the summer months.

The effluent after processing at Back River is delivered to the steel company plant through approximately 24,300 ft. of 60-in. reinforced concrete transmission pipe, to the north of Humphreys Creek. This cove is dammed off and a surface storage reservoir was created with approximately 70 m.g. storage. The bulk of the flow (up to some 48 m.g.d.) from Back River to Humphreys Creek is by gravity. A booster pump will be installed at Back River or on the line for increased demands at a later date.

The water from the Humphreys Creek reservoir flows into a suction well of a high head pumping station, from which it is pumped into a new industrial water supply distribution system throughout the plant. The high head pumps operate at a head of 140 ft., with an installed capacity of 55,000 g.p.m. About 30,000 ft. of cast iron distribution mains, varying in size from 12 to 42 in. were installed. This water is continuously chlorinated with a dosage of approximately 5 p.p.m.

The industrial water system is completely independent of and is not used for any sanitary purpose. It has no physical connections with the town supply or any system used for washing, flushing or drinking purposes. The pipe lines and valves are all painted a distinctive and distinguishing color and are lettered in accordance with an agreement with the State Department of Health of Maryland.

Elevated storage on the industrial water distribution system is provided by a tank of 750,000 gal. capacity.

During the past four years, the plant has performed consistently with no extraordinary difficulties other than those normally experienced with a water treatment plant. The turbidities have been under 10 p.p.m. and frequently under 5 p.p.m. The chloride content has averaged under

100 p.p.m. When short periods of excessive chlorides occur the water is bypassed and the open storage reservoir is used. The pH has varied between 6.6 and 6.8. Sulfates are less than 75 p.p.m. Methyl orange alkalinity shows wide fluctuations and at high figures requires doses of alum as high as 6 or 7 grains per gallon.

The bacteriological quality of the industrial water distributed in the plant has been consistently negative for coliform organisms in 1-ml. portions, and often negative in five 10-ml. portions.

Recurrent difficulties have been experienced with algae growths in the Humphreys Creek reservoir. These have been kept in check reasonably well by combined chlorine and copper sulfate treatment at frequent intervals.

The quality of water produced and the experience with its use has been so good since the construction of the plant in 1942 that the company decided to construct in 1947 an additional plant for the same purposes and at the same site with a capacity of 20 m.g.d. This plant is now under construction and on its completion by the end of 1947 the company will be in a position to produce a total of 65 m.g.d. This will be composed of 50 m.g.d. of chemically processed water of trickling filter plant origin and of approximately 15 m.g.d. of unprocessed activated sludge plant effluent, when the latter is available.

At the same time the company has negotiated a modification of its existing 50 m.g.d. contract with Baltimore City, raising the amount which the company can withdraw from the Back River Sewage Treatment Works to a maximum of 100 m.g.d., based on monthly averages. Approximately 100 m.g.d. will probably be used by the company, barring an economic recession, within the next three to five years. When this demand is reached a booster pumping station will be required on the main transmission line from the Back River Sewage Works to the Bethlehem Steel Company plant at Sparrows Point.

A summary of the industrial water use during 1946 is presented in Table 1. The findings are typical of the usual results during the past five years of operation.

During 1946 the cost of this industrial water has been 1.73 cents per thousand gallons, exclusive of interest and amortization on the investment.

Agreement with Baltimore City

The Bethlehem Steel Company is responsible for financing all of the costs attendant upon processing, pumping, delivering and distributing the effluents from the Back River plant.

Baltimore City agrees to make available these effluents at the Back River Sewage Treatment Works. It will not expend any money in con-

Table 1
1946 Data on Reclamation of Sewage Effluents for Industrial Water Supply, Bethlehem Steel Co., Sparrows Point, Md.

| | Volume (1,000 gal.) | | | | Chemicals Applied | | | |
| | Trickling Filter Effluent | Activated Sludge Effluent | Plant Flow (1,000 g.p.d.) | Chlor-ide (p.p.m.) | Alum | | Chlorine | |
Month					Pounds	G.p.g.	Pounds	P.p.m.
January	161,343	371,360	17,756	75	109,492	4.78	16.500	3.75
February	247,266	67,213	11,220	75	49,587	5.2	11,000	3.84
March	273,778	432,116	22,770	75	200,037	5.15	36,500	6.25
April	260,203	454,176	23,812	80	188,415	5.1	58,500	7.5
May	41,375	434,075	15,400	90	40,017	6.7	30,000	7.6
June	192,972	441,915	21,200	85	137,200	5.1	40,000	7.6
July	208,448	465,837	22,500	85	158,711	5.34	43,000	7.7
August	299,621	389,426	22,200	85	228,872	5.4	50,000	8.75
September	428,024	231,452	21,200	90	318,981	5.2	51,000	9.35
October	325,776	305,094	21,000	100	250,000	5.4	40,000	7.25
November	388,481	382,519	24,860	95	270,638	4.9	53,000	8.3
December	270,721	342,654	20,455	80	192,980	5.0	31,000	6.1

nection with this enterprise. The steel company built, maintains and operates all of the works necessary for the use of this supply. Its capital expenditures will be somewhat over $2,000,000.

Under the terms of the agreement between the city and the company,

The City will make every practicable effort to operate and maintain the Treatment Works and any additions thereto so that the effluent at the point of delivery to the Company shall have the following characteristics (to be tested from time to time in accordance with the most recent standard methods of water and sewage analysis prescribed by the American Public Health Association):

(a) The hydrogen ion content shall not exceed 7.8 or fall below 6.5, calculated on the basis of monthly averages.

(b) The total suspended solids shall not at any time exceed an instantaneous maximum of fifty parts per million and the monthly average of such solids shall not exceed twenty-five parts per million. This requirement shall not apply to effluent discharged from the secondary settling tanks connected with the trickling filter unit, which effluent shall not at any time contain total suspended solids in excess of an instantaneous maximum of eighty parts per million and not exceeding, in monthly average, fifty parts per million.

(c) The five-day twenty-degree Centigrade biochemical oxygen demand shall not exceed an instantaneous maximum of forty-five parts per million, and its monthly average shall not exceed twenty-five parts per million. This requirement shall not apply to effluent discharged from the secondary settling tank connected with the trickling filter unit, the five-day twenty-degree Centigrade biochemical oxygen demand of which effluent shall not exceed an instantaneous maximum of eighty parts per million and the monthly average of which shall not exceed forty parts per million.

(d) The chloride content shall not exceed one hundred seventy-five parts per million calculated upon the basis of monthly averages.

The company pays to the city the following sums of money for the use of the effluents, upon a graduated basis:

(a) Fifteen days after the end of any month during which an average of less than twenty-five million gallons of effluent per day have been delivered to the Company, the sum of one thousand dollars ($1,000).

(b) Fifteen days after the end of any month during which an average of twenty-five million gallons or more, but less than thirty-seven and one-half million gallons, per day have been delivered to the Company, the sum of fifteen hundred dollars ($1,500).

(c) Fifteen days after the end of any month during which an average of thirty-seven and one-half million gallons or more, but less than fifty million gallons, per day have been delivered to the Company, the sum of two thousand dollars ($2,000).

(d) Fifteen days after the end of any month during which an average of fifty million gallons or more, but less than sixty-two and a half million gallons, per day have been delivered to the Company, the sum of twenty-five hundred dollars ($2,500).

(e) Fifteen days after the end of any month during which an average of sixty-two and a half million gallons or more, but less than seventy-five million gallons, per day have been delivered to the Company, the sum of three thousand dollars ($3,000).

(f) Fifteen days after the end of any month during which an average of seventy-five million gallons or more, but less than eighty-seven and a half million gallons, per day have been delivered to the Company, the sum of thirty-five hundred dollars ($3,500).

(g) Fifteen days after the end of any month during which an average of eighty-seven and a half million gallons or more, but less than one hundred million gallons, per day have been delivered to the Company, the sum of four thousand dollars ($4,000).

The agreement further provides that a minimum payment, however, shall always be made by the company, whether it uses the effluent or not, of the sum of five hundred dollars ($500) per month.

The city handles the sludge produced by the company processing plant on a monthly graded payment by the company.

Studies of the Baltimore Sewer System

One of the major difficulties encountered with the use of these effluents was in the chloride content of the sewage. It is surprising how meager the information on this score is in the Baltimore City sewage analyses as well as in most of the important plants of the United States.

Detailed studies of this particular characteristic had been carried out by the company over a period of almost 12 months on both influent and effluent liquids of the Baltimore City plant. These have been made continuously during stated intervals each day and for every day in the month for a period of almost 12 months.

The average chloride concentration of the final sewage works effluent was between 125 and 150 p.p.m. It frequently dropped to below 100 and on occasions rose to 600 p.p.m., although for a very short period.

Since it is important for the company to have processed water in which the chloride content is kept at a minimum, a detailed survey by the company was undertaken for many months, of the entire sewage collection system of the city. As might have been anticipated, it was found that that part of the sewer system of the city which collects sewage from domestic areas showed chloride concentrations of less than 40 p.p.m.

The high concentrations almost invariably occurred in the low-level collection and interception system, providing service for the industrial and commercial areas of the city. In parts of this system chloride concentrations as high as 3,500 p.p.m. were encountered.

These are intermittent and difficult to detect, but they have been gradually isolated. Some of them are due to industrial processes, such as meat pickling and packing, the salt pickling of hides, the salt water discharges from zeolite water-softening plants, and to harbor water infiltration in breaks in low-lying sewers.

Some of these sources have been eliminated. Some continue to discharge into the sewers. Peak concentrations in excess of 175 p.p.m. have been sufficiently reduced so that the concentration of chlorides has been kept below the level of danger at the steel plant.

As far as the author is aware, this is the first known comprehensive survey of a large municipal sewer system with the intent of disclosing the sources of high chloride concentrations as a preliminary to the gradual elimination of the more important of them. The effort may inspire other communities to gather and make available information on chlorides and other ingredients of sewage, which are more important in industrial water use than for the current control of sewage effluent discharge into receiving bodies of water.

Acknowledgments

Mr. S. J. Cort is General Manager and Mr. Thomas Wilson is Chief Engineer of the Bethlehem Steel Company Plant at Sparrows Point, Maryland. The Chief Engineers of Baltimore City during the period of negotiations were respectively the late Mr. George Cobb and

Mr. Nathan L. Smith. Mr. George E. Finck is Sewerage Engineer of the city of Baltimore.

Messrs. L. F. Coffin and William P. Hill, with their associates William A. Hazlett and John L. Hellman, of the operating staffs of the Bethlehem Steel Company, shared in all of the details of the development of this industrial water program.

The detailed drawings and specifications for the system as outlined were prepared by Whitman, Requardt and Associates, Consulting Engineers.

The author has been consulting engineer to the Bethlehem Steel Company in the selection of the industrial water project, in its design and construction, during operation of the completed system, in the development of additions to the project in 1947 and in the detailed negotiations on contractual arrangements with the city of Baltimore. Messrs John C. Geyer and Herbert L. Weaver have at various times participated in the studies under the direction of the author.

The State Department of Health of Maryland, through the sympathetic cooperation of its Chief Engineer, George L. Hall, and his staff, did much to smooth out many steps which might otherwise have retarded the installation.

The Nature and Extent of Radioactive
Waste Disposal Problems*

In a period of less than 15 years a new industry has developed in the world. It represents in the United States a capital investment now in excess of $6,000,000,000. This atomic energy industry, through the control exercised by the Atomic Energy Commission, has kept the hazards in the disposal of its industrial radioactive wastes well below any appreciable effect upon the industrial worker or the population at large.

As in every other industry, the disposal of its wastes has posed hazards and problems. In significant instances many of these problems so far have been unresolved, if we hope for actual disposal (in the familiar meaning) of the materials producing radioactivity.

Wide variation in the nature and characteristics of radioactive waste are to be considered. Great differences in concentration and kind of radioactive materials are to be found in the gaseous, liquid, or solid state. The volumes to be managed and their physical and chemical characteristics increase the complexity of the problems and the solutions.

The management of radioactive waste materials, under the continuing and careful scrutiny of the Atomic Energy Commission, has followed two general precepts for the protection of man and his environment. The safe application of these precepts still remains the central

* Presented before the Joint Congressional Committee on Atomic Energy, January 1959.

theme of the Atomic Energy Commission policy. These precepts are: with high level radioactive wastes, concentrate and contain; with low and intermediate level radioactive wastes, dilute and disperse to nature.

The utilization of fissionable material in the controlled production of thermal energy or in sudden explosion results in highly radioactive products. The industry produces wastes, at various steps from the mining of the ore to the development of power, with great variations in quantity, level of activity, toxicity, and chemical and physical form. The levels of activity range from hundreds of curies per liter in high level wastes to fractions of microcuries per milliliter in low level wastes.

A characteristic distinguishing these wastes from any other industrial waste, and which makes them perhaps more dangerous as they may be released to the air, the soil, or to surface waterways, is that they are not detected by the human senses. With appropriate instrumentation and radiometric analysis, however, their nature and concentration may be determined with accuracy. The toxicity of these wastes to humans is in addition much greater than that of any hitherto familiar industrial poison.

Additional significant differences from more orthodox industrial wastes are the long half-lives and the damaging properties to human tissues of certain of the materials produced. The supervision and control of some of these wastes, therefore, must be viewed, not from the standpoint of temporary expediency, but from the necessity of guaranteed supervision and control, in some instances for hundreds of years. Such a contingency places a major responsibility upon and challenge to all the public and private agencies dealing with the problem.

The protection of the public health and of the natural resources of this and of every country, entails a greater depth of continuing responsibility than for any other industrial waste hitherto confronting society. The total environment of man, therefore, becomes the area of responsible public interest. Since the creation of these wastes is related to the nature of the industrial process, to the environment, to the permanent maintenance of equilibrium conditions for the protection of biological life, every problem of plant location in relation to its environment must be considered. Once the industry comes into operation, the continued and rigid supervision and monitoring cannot be relaxed. Solutions to the problems residing in these wastes and the objectives to be met, demand the participation of the disciplines of health physics, radiation hygiene, sanitary, chemical, electrical, mechanical and civil engineering, biology, chemistry, and physics.

The levels of activity of radioactive wastes from the various industrial processes involved are generally quite low until the fission reaction takes place in nuclear reactors. These hearings will disclose the origin, the nature, and the amount of these wastes from the processing of radioactive ores of uranium to the ultimate preparation of enriched feed material. These procedures are chemical and metallurgical in nature, involving in many instances machining of final products. In each instance, wastes result as the ultimate fuel is produced.

When the fuel is irradiated by neutrons in the reactors, tremendous amounts of heat are produced. Since such reactors are cooled by air, water, liquid chemicals, or other media and since these are in turn exposed to neutrons in the reactors, they become irradiated. These irradiated media must then be ultimately disposed of or managed in a safe manner.

When reactors are disassembled their irradiated parts are removed. A major problem of disposal then ensues. This particular operation requires extraordinary care and the time and amount of exposure of the workers is rigidly controlled. Highly active material is stored in designated areas or is buried. A rigid inventory of such buried radioactive material is maintained. The potentialities of an accident are carefully reviewed, and the resulting wastes therefrom are provided for in design and in operation.

The high level wastes originate principally, but not entirely, from the chemical processing of fuel from nuclear reactors. Since the burn-up in most reactors represents a very small percentage of the fuel installed, it is economically essential in present practice to recover unburned portions. Associated with these irradiated fuels which are to be recaptured for further use are the fission products which have resulted from the processes. These have radioactive half-lives varying from seconds to millions of years.

These high level wastes at the same time contain almost the entire spectrum of fission products when the uranium atoms are split. To make the recovery of fuel and hence the disposal of wastes even more difficult, a variety of salts and acids must be used for the dissolution of the fuel materials. The characteristics of typical reactor fuel processing wastes are therefore complex and pose one of the great problems of the atomic energy industry.

Other problems arise in the production of selected radioisotopes for beneficent uses in medicine, in biological laboratories, in industry, and in general research. These uses have grown tremendously in the last 10 years. As they find their way into almost every form of activity, problems of supervision, inventory, and disposal arise. The transport of these materials across the country, the continuing control over their distribution, the insistence upon adequate means of disposal for the protection of the worker and the public have created a vast governmental obligation. The exercise of this obligation has been surprisingly good, even though minor lapses have occurred which merely point to the necessity for continuing intensity of supervision. This degree of governmental responsibility is unlikely to decrease. Although the levels of activity with which the country is concerned in radioisotope use is relatively low in comparison with those already commented upon, the radioisotope for universal application must not be ignored in public responsibility.

Present Quantities of Wastes

In 1958, the industry has somewhat over $23,000,000 invested in treatment and release facilities for low level liquid wastes. Approximately 1.5^9 gallons of low level wastes have been discharged during the year on a rigidly controlled, quantitatively monitored basis, after various forms of treatment ranging from orthodox waste treatment processes, such as coagulation and settling, to evaporation. The total curies discharged in low level wastes to date is somewhat over 2,600,000 curies. A summary of the low level liquid waste situation is shown in Table 1 as of the year 1957.

Table 1
Low and Intermediate Level Liquid Waste Data

(a) Investment ($1,000)	23,000
(b) Volume discharged per year (10^6 gals)	1,530
*(c) Total curies discharged (10^3) (to date)	2,600
(d) Annual operating and monitoring costs ($1,000)	2,000

* Approximately 95 percent of total activity (c) is associated with Hanford operations.

For the most part, solid radioactive wastes, such as machine turnings, contaminated equipment and contaminated trash have not constituted a serious technical problem. They have either been buried in the ground under controlled conditions or have been disposed of at sea. The materials so disposed of at sea have been small in radioactive contribution. The problem now confronting the industry with respect to solid wastes is the location of additional centralized handling, disposal, and burial areas. Costs are not excessive, but they are high.

Gaseous radioactive wastes result from many operations, such as air-cooled reactors, chemical processing plants, and fissionable material fabrication facilities. In these instances the levels of activity and the concentrations of pollutants vary widely with the type of operation. Facilities for the treatment and handling of gaseous wastes so far represent a total investment of some $45,000,000.

The treatment and disposal of fuel processing wastes represent perhaps the most difficult, expensive, and so far, unsatisfactory features of the entire problem. Up to the present time, approximately 65×10^6 gallons of high level liquid wastes have been placed in tank storage. The investment in tank storage now represents something over $126,000,000. A brief summary of the high level waste situation is given in Table 2.

Table 2
High Level Liquid Waste Data

(a) Wastes in storage (10^6 gals)	65
(b) Total tank capacity (10^6 gals)	110
(c) Cost—tanks and appurtenances ($\$10^6$)	126

Various estimates have been made of high level wastes which will result from future nuclear power generation, based on estimates of the extent of such future nuclear power production, fuel irradiation levels, and unit volumes of waste per unit of fuel processed. Without attempting the role of a prophet, and on the assumption that nuclear power generating capacity may attain in 1980 something of the order of 1.1×10^5 megawatts of, heat, the accumulated wastes volume in gallons will be of the order of 10^8. The total fission product activity in curies will then be approximately 10^{11}. These assumptions are shown in Table 3. Supplemen-

Table 3
Estimates of Future Wastes
(Summarized from Wash—742, Lieberman, August 1957)

	1965	1980
(a) Nuclear Generating Capacity (MW heat)	2×10^4	1.1×10^5
(b) Fission Products (curies)	2×10^{10}	10^{11}
(c) Processing Capacity (tons per day)	5	25–80
(d) Accumulated Waste (gallons)	5×10^6	$1–3 \times 10^8$

(Based on irradiation of 4,000 MWD per ton U and 1,000 gallons high activity waste per ton U)

tary data of pertinent interest are shown in Table 4. The future situation will be discussed specifically in the course of these hearings.

Table 4
Example of Status of Shipment of Irradiated
Fuel and High Level Wastes in 1980
(After Wash–742, Lieberman, August 1957)

(a) Megawatts of heat-stationary reactors	1.1×10^5
(b) Fission products, curies per ton U	
after 100 days cooling	5.2×10^6
after 2,000 days cooling	8.0×10^5
(c) Megawatt days per ton, burn up	4,000
(d) Tons U per day processed	27
(e) Gallons liquid waste per ton U processed	1,200
(g) Fission products, curies in transit (fuel)	189
(h) Gallons of waste in transit	9.8×10^8
(i) Fission products, curies in transit (wastes)	227,000
(j) Fission products, curies per gallon of waste	660

Note: Fuel shipped after 100 days cooling.
     Wastes shipped after 2,000 days cooling.

Source: A. Gabaldon

All of these figures simply demonstrate that the industry will be confronted increasingly with a waste disposal and management problem, which one is unlikely to escape in the present state of the art. Although a great deal of attention is now being paid to this problem, to many industrialists the problem of waste disposal appears to be non-existent. The reason for this happy state of mind lies in the fact that under present procedures the Atomic Energy Commission holds itself responsible for the handling of these most difficult materials.

The total investment in waste handling and disposal facilities within atomic energy operations already approaches $200,000,000, of which almost two-thirds represents capital investment in tanks and appurtenances for long term retention of high level radioactive wastes.

Prospects for the Future

Any evaluation of the prospect in waste disposal in the atomic energy industry must be predicated upon foreseeable technological advances. The hearings of this Joint Congressional Committee should disclose, however, whether procedures described are in the category of hypotheses, are in the laboratory stage, with reasonable prospect of being translated into effective use, or are expositions of actual current practice. Since most informed people are concerned about this problem, some tendency is exhibited to announce treatment processes, by-products recovery possibilities, and forms of disposals which have high imaginative content but low ingredients of reality. The distinction among these should be sharply delineated in these hearings.

A large amount of effort is being expended in research and development toward waste treatment. Very little, however, is yet available in large scale practical ultimate disposal systems. The findings to be presented may lead to more optimistic conclusions. At this writing, however, the safe dispersal of large quantities of radioactivity in the environment is not only remote but improbable. It is undoubtedly the part of wisdom to contain and to control the more hazardous and perhaps the potentially useful materials.

The technical feasibility of direct disposal of high level wastes into specific geologic formations is sufficiently clear to drive one toward at least limited application of such a procedure, either in salt domes or salt beds, in deep, isolated basins, in shale formations or even in porous formations. It would certainly be inadvisable to move to these presumed solutions to the problem, without far more extensive exploration and pilot plant application than are yet at hand. The engineering and economic issues involved are still in the very preliminary stages.

The artificial fixation of radioactive materials into stable, solid media has now been experimentally studied for some 4 to 5 years. The objectives in each instance are to fix materials of high hazard in media of non-soluble, non-leachable character, so that these materials might then be placed or stored in manageable size and character so that their hazard to surrounding environments would be almost nil. Here, too, these efforts may not yet be adjudged to have demonstrated either engineering or economic feasibility. The findings to be presented at these hearings may modify these conclusions in a more favorable direction.

The recovery of valuable by-product materials, such as particularly Cesium[137] and Strontium[90], would have two important assets. The selective high efficiency removal of such specific nuclides from high level wastes would reduce somewhat the high level waste disposal problem. It would not eliminate it, but it would make the holding of such materials less difficult in time and in risk. Such separation might produce materials of value to society. Unless the separation or recovery, however, was very high, the waste disposal problem would not be much relieved. One must distinguish between *recovery* and *removal;* for example, 95 per cent Cs[137] recovery might be fine for fission product utilization but does not do much good for waste disposal directly. The search for valuable by-products of industrial wastes is interminable in this and in other industries. Historically, it is unfortunately true that promises of great financial returns from waste recovery by-products or solutions to waste problems through by-product use have fallen far short of fulfillment in most industries.

Even if these hopes of by-product recovery and use should be fulfilled in the case of radioactive materials, the problem of management and of governmental supervision not only will not be reduced by such procedures, but in fact may be greatly increased because of the wider use and dissemination of highly toxic materials.

A general recapitulation of the directions of effort in the treatment of high level wastes is given in Table 5.

Table 5
Possible Methods of Treatment of Fuel Re-Processing
Wastes Prior to Ultimate Disposal on Land

(a) Decay storage
(b) Precipitation
(c) Neutralization
(d) Evaporation
(e) Ion exchange
(f) Solvent extraction
(g) Crystallization
(h) Solid fixation
(i) Recovery of by-products

The disposal of high level wastes in the ocean has had much discussion. It is not unfair to conclude in the present state of understanding of the ocean that such a procedure is unlikely to be sanctioned for some years to come. So many unknowns and unpredictables with respect to oceanic behavior still remain that management and government will be driven to the safer practice of keeping high level radioactive materials under more obvious scrutiny and control than would be provided by most ocean disposal procedures.

Sufficient has already been said in this presentation to make clear that the rapid development of the atomic energy industry is in no small measure contingent upon more prompt and more complete answers to the waste disposal problem. If the situation is somewhat pessimistic, it is only because sufficient energies have not yet been expended in developing economic and safe improvements in waste handling and disposal processes. Progress in this field is unlikely to occur if the problems are not realistically confronted. It is a tribute to the Atomic Energy Commission operations that so many ad hoc solutions have been provided which have safeguarded the public during the last 10 to 15 years. It is, however, equally clear that approaches to the management and disposal of these materials will require increased attention, expenditure of large amounts of money for research and development and the integration of multi-disciplines for accomplishing a more satisfactory long-term answer than is now at hand.

Simultaneously with such emphasis, increased attention will necessarily be devoted to the location and type of reactors and chemical reprocessing facilities, the location of suitable ultimate disposal sites, the shipment of highly radioactive materials and associated hazards, and equating economic validities with all of the less tangible, but equally important, considerations herein discussed.

Much thought will be required in the foreseeable future as to the best way of continuing long term responsibility for disposal of radioactive materials. It is not inevitable that in this responsibility government will always have to play a dominant role, except in a supervisory capacity. Industry must increasingly assume responsibility for the physical operation of waste disposal plants under the criteria to be established promptly by government. The selection of sites for nuclear energy facilities is closely related to waste handling and disposal operations. The recognition of this close relationship is not yet dramatically obvious to many individuals concerned with the development of this industry.

No student of this field can escape the additional conclusion that waste handling and disposal has international as well as national aspects. Technological solutions made in this and in other countries will make a major contribution to these international answers. This is peculiarly an area where political boundaries have little or no relation to the waste disposal problem. This is particularly true in the dispersal of materials to the environment via the atmosphere and the surface waters. From both the national and international standpoint, one cannot ignore the increasing problem which will result from the rapidly extending use of mobile reactors, such as submarines, surface ships, and aircraft. The problems resulting from these operations are rapidly appearing on the horizon and are not specifically developed in oral presentations although they will be noted to some extent in the record of the hearings. This does not mean that they will not emerge rapidly in the not too distant future and should not be overlooked.

75 Years of Improvement in
Water Supply Quality*

In 1798, readers of the *Philadelphia Monthly Magazine*[1] were advised:

> Pure water . . . is the best drink for persons of all ages and temperaments. By its fluidity and mildness it promotes a free and equable circulation of the blood and humours through all the vessels of the body, upon which the due performance of every animal function depends, and hence water-drinkers are not only the most active and nimble, but also the most chearful and springly of all people. . . . But to delicate and cold constitutions, and to persons unaccustomed to it, water without wine is a very unproper drink.

Centuries before this, even, water drinkers may have been complimented in much the same fashion, and water purveyors placed on their mettle to provide this commodity in such a manner as to make it of the maximum usefulness and satisfaction to man. Conscious technological and scientific effort toward these objectives is more than 75 years old. With the creation of the American Water Works Association in St. Louis, Mo., 75 years ago, however, action toward these age-old objectives was given new stimulus and a new and continuing forum.

* Reprinted from the *Journal American Water Works Association*, Vol. 48, No. 8 (August, 1956). Copyright 1956 by the American Water Works Association, Inc. Presented May 10, 1956, at the Diamond Jubilee Conference, St. Louis, Mo.

The increasing importance of water supply quality since that time may be traced in any of the several excellent summaries now available. The exciting and detailed expositions by M. N. Baker,[2] Harry E. Jordan[3] and perhaps a dozen others, have placed in the record the significant advances in water supply quality and treatment in this three-quarters of a century of important progress.

When confronted, therefore, with the task of reviewing this progress once more, the simple repetition of these accomplishments, numerous and exciting as they are, would have little appeal to the reader and even less to the writer. We might repeat with Jordan[3] that "The history of water supply in the United States is an epic of constant progress and achievement." And, bringing his figures up to date, we might point out that in 1850 there were only 68 cities with planned water supplies, while today, in 1956, there are over 17,000 urban supplies in operation. The recapitulation of the changes in water treatment from slow sand filtration through rapid sand filtration and of the struggles concerning coagulation and chlorination would still stir up reminiscences and inspiration. References to current texts, far more elaborate than the present contribution, would better supply the student in this field, however, with myriads of detail concerning processes, issues in debate, scientific progress, and personalities.

These texts would likewise recall that in this period the improved sanitary quality of the public supplies has brought about one of the most dramatic improvements in public health that the world has ever known. Typhoid fever alone declined from 75–100 deaths annually per 100,000 persons to less than 0.1 in 1955. Today the average water practitioner accepts and operates standard water treatment processes of effective coagulation, sedimentation, filtration, and disinfection as if they had always existed. Sometimes he is even unaware of the public battles, the court procedures, the contesting scientific judgments, the extensive laboratory studies, and the resistant public opinion upon which these milestones rest.

Great Investigators

Throughout all of these accomplishments, the great giants of the water works industry moved forward with clarity and speed. It is not amiss to recall today the significance of James P. Kirkwood, the Hyatts, Allen Hazen, George W. Fuller, Paul Hansen, G. C. Whipple, Robert Spurr Weston, and George A. Johnson. This is an appropriate place also to point out that this galaxy of stars owed their inspiration to the great leader of environmental sanitation of the period, William T. Sedgwick. It is with no little pride that the author observes that Sedgwick emigrated from Johns Hopkins University to the Massachusetts Institute of Technology, which now claims him exclusively as its own.*

The history of chlorination, since 1908, has likewise been marked by a succession of dramas. Here, too, detailed summaries of this progress have fortunately been preserved in the literature through excellent monographs by Faber and others. The work of E. B. Phelps, Joseph W. Ellms, S. J. Hauser, Linn H. Enslow, the author himself, and others, placed chlorination practice upon a national basis and hastened its almost universal adoption. This evolution was not without its conspicuous opponents, particularly in Massachusetts, where it was claimed that the water supply sources in that state had not been polluted and that chlorination was therefore not needed. Even today there remain certain nostalgic practitioners in that region who still pursue the will o' the wisp of the "virginal innocence" of surface sources of water supply, which contra-indicates any urgent necessity for treatment.

Struggle for Quality

Of greater interest in some respects than the rehearsal of these accomplishments is the review of the changes, both in quality and in treatment, through which public water supplies have moved over the last 75 years. Blake[4] has recently done a great service to the water works industry by reviewing the history of the urban water supply problem in the cities of Philadelphia, New York, Boston, and Baltimore. This volume provides entertaining and convincing illustrations of the changes which have taken place in both ownership and quality of the supplies of these great cities. In the city of Baltimore, for example, after years of struggle, the consumer was still using the Jones Falls supply, which was described by one of its opponents as being introduced "not to water the city, but to whitewash the Know-Nothing party." It was described as a water furnished "from manured and impure watersheds" in which "the organic matters thus derived, undergoing decomposition, breed myriads of vegetable and animal germs, or infusoria, which, drying, and in their turn decomposing, give rise to the putrescent odor and tastes so noticeable in hydrant water during the first weeks of the heated term."[4]

Chemical analyses of waters shed little light upon such problems as these, even though strenuous and sometimes successful efforts were made to glean from the standard chemical analysis of the day indications of water supply quality and means of correction.

In 1896, for example, the Baltimore city chemist reported 88 complete analyses of water from house taps in all parts of the city. Forty of

---

* To set the record straight, Sherman Chase of Boston, the next speaker on the program, pointed out that Sedgwick went to Johns Hopkins from Yale.

these were analyzed in detail, with the following results (in parts per million): volatile solids, 36.2; mineral solids, 38.0; total solids, 84.2; chlorides, 6.28; free ammonia, 0.043; albuminoid ammonia, 0.08; nitrogen from nitrates, 0.129; nitrogen from nitrites, none. The chemist judged (from what constituted at that time the standard for good potable water) that the water supply of the city of Baltimore had been chemically good throughout the year and "satisfactory and considerably above the normal in quality." He goes on to declare that "the unpleasant (fishy) taste, which had been a source of annoyance to the public during the months of November and December, whilst no doubt very disagreeable, was in itself perfectly harmless from a sanitary standpoint."

The use of such data, necessary in the absence of significant biological, physical, or other chemical information, led of course to tortuous techniques and explanations for objectionable water quality. The water served to Baltimore at that time was physically objectionable, was obviously bacterially contaminated, and, from a standpoint of taste and odor, was at regular intervals unpleasant to the consumer. On the basis of the chemical analyses already presented, however, it would compare very favorably with a totally different commodity furnished in 1955 in the same city. In 1955 the finished filtered water showed the following comparable constituents (in parts per million): volatile solids, 27.6; total solids, 90.8; nitrates, 0.4; chlorides, 8.0. These comparisons merely confirm the conclusion that the use of chemical analyses alone left much to be desired as a means of assessing comparative water quality. Their hold on the water diagnostician, however, persisted in some areas in this country; in these areas they remained almost the *sole* basis of assessing water quality until the late 1920's.

This is further exemplified by the report submitted in 1881 to the Joint Standing Committee on Water for Boston, Mass.[5] by perhaps the most distinguished chemist of his time, Ira Remsen, later president of Johns Hopkins University. The following quotations from Remsen's report are worth recording for permanent reference.

> As there is a great deal of misconception in regard to the value to be attached to chemical analyses of drinking waters, a few words of explanation may not be considered out of place. The [type of contamination] most frequently to be feared . . . is sewage. This cannot be detected directly by means of chemical analysis, nor by any other means; but, nevertheless, a fairly accurate judgment may be formed in the case of a suspected water by taking into consideration the results of the analyses, as well as the conditions surrounding the water. If we find a considerable quantity of solid matter in the water, together with an abnormal quantity of chlorine, of nitrates, and of nitrogenous organic matter, the presence of sewage would be suspected. If, then, on examining the surrounding conditions, we should

find good reasons for believing that sewage might find its way into the water, the conclusion would be justified that the water is contaminated with sewage matter. Such water should be condemned at once, and no one should be allowed to drink of it under any consideration. . . . Water may, however, become contaminated in other ways, and might easily become contaminated in such a way that chemical analysis would be powerless to detect the foreign material, or, if it should be detected, to determine its nature. The whole subject is, in short, in an unsatisfactory state, and should any one, in the examination of some waters, confine himself to cut-and-dried rules, he would be very apt to come to false conclusions. Common sense is a very essential condition of success in the examination of waters, as well as in most other difficult processes.

Remsen proceeds to make comparisons between the water supplies of Boston and Baltimore. Disconcerting as these comparisons may be, they are repeated here for purely historical purposes.

It may be instructive to compare the water as it is at present in Farm-Pond with that which I examined last spring in Baltimore. As far as I am able to judge, the taste and odor of the two waters are identical, only I do not remember that the Baltimore water ever had these as strongly developed as they are in the pond. In every respect the two waters conducted themselves in the same way. When heated, the odor of both was intensified, and the taste of the water on cooling was much improved. On standing for some time, the Farm-Pond water loses its odor and taste, as did the Baltimore water. The only difference which I have observed is this: the Baltimore water when passed through a good large filter of animal charcoal and gravel lost its taste completely, and analysis showed it to be perfectly pure. The Farm-Pond water, however, does not, at least with those filters which I have been able to procure here, lose its taste entirely when filtered, though it is much improved by the process. I should judge that this difference is only one of degree. The Farm-Pond water [was] certainly much worse than the Baltimore water at the time I made my examination.

It is not with malice aforethought that this paper includes Remsen's invidious distinction between the quality of the Boston city water and that of Baltimore. The distinction, apparently so disadvantageous to Boston, might not have been borne out by more modern techniques of examination.

The Boston report of 1881 also makes clear that these problems of water supply quality were handled on a very high level, since not only did the later president of Johns Hopkins University participate, but he extends special thanks to the president of Harvard College, to Desmond Fitzgerald, and to C. W. Andrews—Bostonians all—who assisted him in his activities and provided laboratory facilities.

Tastes and Odors

It was during these early periods that much of the progress was made in the identification of sources and causes of taste and odor, particularly through the highly significant field and laboratory observations made by the distinguished George C. Whipple in his studies of the water supplies of New York City and Boston. Several of the earliest, if not in fact the first, photographs of the now familiar algae forms were made in 1892 in the Boston water works at the Chestnut Hill reservoir. They were made almost exactly 65 years ago. There was no electricity available in Whipple's laboratory, so the photographs had to be taken by gaslight. Considering the difficulties which accompanied the making of these photographs, they are remarkably clear in reproduction and played a highly significant part in subsequent efforts to prevent and to control taste and odor in public water supplies. This phase of water quality probably has greater impact upon consumer reaction that almost any other with which the water producer deals.

Taste and odor problems 75 years ago were very serious because there were no known corrective measures other than aeration, which too often was relatively ineffective.

The first record of discussions concerning odor problems in an AWWA publication was in the report of the third annual meeting held in Buffalo, N.Y., in 1883. Based on discussions at that time, the troublemakers were undoubtedly algae. Whipple's work demonstrated that algae were responsible for the taste and odor conditions. It was not until 1904 that copper sulfate was announced as an algicide; although copper sulfate was a considerable aid in the control of algal growths, it was only a partial solution to the associated odor problem.

World War I resulted in a tremendous expansion of this country's chemical industry, whose wastes added still further to the growing odor problems. The advent of the automobile resulted in construction of hard-surfaced roads, and rain water washing the macadam roads added phenol and related compounds to the already perplexing odor problems.

In 1924, John R. Baylis, then principal sanitary chemist for the Baltimore Water Department, declared:

> There are objectionable tastes in many of the waters of our country that will always remain objectionable, unless removed. It is the removal or prevention of these that should receive more consideration from our water works officials than heretofore. Changes in our modes of living and this vast amount expended for things that add comfort and pleasure to our lives justify the assumption that we are now ready for more rapid progress in improving the palatableness of our drinking water.

Possessed of such strong beliefs, it was natural that Baylis should turn to activated carbon, because of its potential for removing these objectional tastes. His work on granular activated carbon at the Chicago Experimental Filter Plant in 1927, coupled with his emphasis on producing palatable water, was the flux necessary to develop a countrywide interest. His early work on granular activated carbon, coupled with his later work on powdered carbon, has resulted in his being affectionately dubbed "Mr. Activated Carbon."

In 1929 George R. Spalding and Paul Tamer, of the Hackensack Water Company, New Milford, N.J., conducted laboratory tests with powdered activated carbon. Results were so encouraging that the first plant test was conducted in March 1930. Within a year, many water plants throughout the country were trying powdered activated carbon, because it could be used without the costly expenditures for additional filters necessary to accommodate the use of granular types. Powdered activated carbon was so successful that today well over 1,200 water treatment plants in this country alone use it for taste and odor control.

Since the advent of powdered activated carbon, many other methods of odor control have been tried. Surviving methods, however, are limited almost entirely to ozone, free-residual chlorination, and chlorine dioxide. Activated carbon still has a major position as a positive method for producing palatable water even under severe conditions. The road to universally palatable water, however, has been only partially traversed, even though suitable control methods are available. Some operators refuse to admit their responsibility to their consumers, while others laugh off complaints, and still others honestly do not know that the water they are delivering is unpalatable. John Baylis' statement in 1924 is still applicable in many communities today and is worthy of repetition. "The removal or prevention of [objectional tastes] should receive more consideration from our water works officials."

Standard Methods of Analysis

One of the most effective stimulants to the development of improved water quality obviously was in the evolution of standard methods of water analysis. No record of the improvement of water quality in this country would be complete without emphasizing the great contribution which the leaders in the water supply field provided in the period from 1890 to approximately 1898. This is an appropriate place to pay tribute to that great group of investigators who foresaw the tremendous significance of providing a standard technique of examination, which would become a universal language for all water works investigators to learn and to use.

The development of filtration and disinfection methods owes much to the researches of water bacteriologists, who early recognized the essentiality of a standard analytical procedure. Wyatt Johnston of Montreal was the first to call the attention of the American Public Health Association to the necessity of more uniform and efficient methods of analysis. At the Montreal meeting of the APHA, in 1894, the committee on the pollution of water supplies suggested a broad cooperative investigation. A subcommittee to determine methods of laboratory procedure, under the chairmanship of W. H. Welch of Johns Hopkins University, extended the discussion at a convention at the Academy of Medicine in New York City, June 21 and 22, 1895. This convention created another committee to report at the APHA Buffalo meeting in 1896 and its report, in revised and amended form, finally was submitted for publication at the meeting in Philadelphia in 1897. Thus was initiated the long series of official procedures in water analysis known throughout the world.

In these early deliberations, the following were active participants: J. G. Adami of McGill University, George W. Fuller, T. M. Cheesman of New York, William T. Sedgwick, Theobald Smith, W. H. Welch, George M. Sternberg, C. A. Smart, and T. M. Prudden. In the initial preparation of these proposals many cooperative laboratory workers participated. The listing of these is not possible in this limited review. They include some of the distinguished medical and bacteriological investigators in this country and in England. The accomplishments of the late 1890's cannot be overestimated.

George W. Fuller, who was one of the prime movers in establishing the acceptance of the principle of standardization of method, continued to pursue this activity for the rest of his life.

The author's own diary of his trip to Europe with George W. Fuller discloses that, in the early part of January 1926, extensive conversations were held with Z. R. Spitta of the Public Health Department of Berlin, with Selskar Gunn of the International Health Bureau of the Rockefeller Foundation in Paris, and with H. T. Calvert of the Ministry of Health in London. All of these gentlemen were in agreement with Fuller's proposal that standard methods for the analysis of water and sewage should be developed on an international basis. Most AWWA members know, of course, that this effort, so strongly emphasized on the author's trip to Europe in 1926, has not yet reached fruition.

The World Health Organization has now undertaken, however, to explore this task. It has already created a small working group under the chairmanship of F. Wellington Gilcreas, to move toward the development of international standards of drinking-water quality and of approved methods for the examination of water. This working group has already had one session in Geneva, Switzerland, in 1955, and will have a regional session, with many other countries participating, in Manila, Philippine Islands, early in the summer of 1956.

Gilcreas has already prepared for the World Health Organization elaborate data from 71 countries. For the major part the data are scanty in nature, but highly informative as to deficiencies. In brief summary, the findings indicate that no official standards of water quality are generally in use. Methods for the examination of water are almost as lacking in uniformity as are standards for quality. It may be predicted, however, that this operation initiated by the World Health Organization will undoubtedly result in an accomplishment visualized in European negotiations three decades ago by the late George W. Fuller.

He exhibited in this field, as in so many others, an imagination and a courage in undertaking new tasks, the accomplishments of which are as numerous and as significant as those of almost any other contributor. The Louisville and Cincinnati experiments, curiously enough, anticipated a great deal of knowledge of today. The corps of workers engaged in these enterprises showed remarkable scientific acumen and advanced the science and the art of water purification by more than a century. Only the keenness of their laboratory observations could account for the superb diagnostic values which came from these elaborate studies.

Commercial Equipment

Most of these studies were carried out at a time and with equipment which was dominated by commercial patents and patent-holders. It speaks well for this group of scientific investigators that they were not deterred from undertaking their important tasks by the fact that in many instances they were struggling with proprietary devices already in contest in court and in technological forums.

So strong was this underlying feeling that William T. Sedgwick, one of the supreme public health investigators of his day, felt impelled to write to George W. Fuller, on Sept. 22, 1895, a letter as follows:

My dear Fuller,

As I understand it, the paper on Typhoid Fever in Lawrence is to be by Copeland and myself jointly, but in any case it seems to me that courtesy, if nothing else, should have led you to consult with me about the matter. However, as you have resigned [from the Lawrence Experiment Station—*Author*] we need not discuss the matter, but I may rather hasten to say that while I congratulate you warmly on the one hand and feel anxious for you (as being more or less in the hands of those money-makers) on the other, I am really *very* sorry to have you resign from Lawrence. Your going will be a real loss to us all and to the work. You have done exceedingly good work at Lawrence and have kept the Station at a high state of efficiency. I feel that you have done honor both to yourself and to the Institute from which you came; and our warmest good wishes will go with you into your novel and difficult undertaking. I hope you will get Weston and take him with you for he seems to be a fine fellow, and will not easily be hood-winked.

As to the work I trust that whatever you do or do not do you will remember the Institute and the S.B.H. [State Board of Health] to both of which you owe so much. Especially, I hope you will, if it be-comes necessary to make comparisons of any kind with the Lawrence work, do everything in a friendly spirit. It is Massachusetts and its S.B.H. which has made all these other things possible and desirable.

I hardly need to urge you to be not only harmless as a dove with the mechanical filter men but also as wise as a serpent. You know all that. If I am not overcome by the heat before morning I shall go up to see you tomorrow, early.

With best of good wishes and kindest regards, I am,

Sincerely yours,

Wm. T. Sedgwick

Most members of the profession are aware of the fact that these fatherly pieces of advice were followed. It is well to remember the debt we owe to the omniscient and kindly Sedgwick, and to the rugged, real-istic, and acute Fuller. Today one may heartily acknowledge the great contributions to the art of water treatment by the skillful manufacturer, without ignoring the injunctions of Sedgwick that the judicial investi-gator must forever preserve scientific objectivity and accuracy in the evaluation of any commercial process or equipment.

Future Prospects

M. N. Baker, in his scholarly volume[2] on the quality of water, epit-omizes the situation in the past in the following terms:

> In the earliest days of the human race, water was taken as found. It might be pure and abundant, plentiful but muddy, scarce but good, or both scarce and bad. . . . Man's earliest standards of quality were few: freedom from mud, taste, and odor.

The fragments presented in this paper illustrate the long road tra-versed, the great progress made, the ever-tightening criteria of chemical, physical, and biological characteristics, and the rapid trend toward the literal tailoring of water for the domestic, industrial, or farming customer. The requirements become more numerous and more complex.

Simultaneously with these demands, investigators move forward as in the past toward new solutions, new experiments, and the adjustment of old concepts to new challenges. The refining of water proceeds apace with the work of the Geyers, the Hudsons, the Renns, the Thomases, and other unsung heroes in the water purification field.

With the intensification of work on desalting, on the application of fluorides to water, on the re-exploration of the silver salts, and on the studies of the viruses, we find ourselves once more on the threshold of a new era. What the future holds, the crystal ball does not disclose, but that it will be an exciting one to review at the hundredth anniversary of the AWWA may be predicted with assurance.

REFERENCES

1. On the Means of Preserving Health. *Philadelphia Monthly Mag.*, 2:83 (Aug. 1798).

2. Baker, M. N. *The Quest for Pure Water*. Am. Wtr. Wks. Assn., New York (1948).

3. Jordan, Harry E. Water Supply and Treatment. *Centennial Trans. ASCE Papers*, No. 2609 (1953).

4. Blake, Nelson M. *Water for the Cities*. Syracuse Univ. Press, Syracuse, N.Y. (1956).

5. Remsen, Ira. Report to the Joint Standing Committee on Water. *Boston City Documents*, No. 143 (Nov. 19, 1881).

THE SEARCH
FOR
STANDARDS

An Inquiry into Standards Proposed for Stream Cleanliness*

The first national meeting of the Federation of Sewage Works Associations is a natural occasion upon which to discuss the basic criteria of virtually all of the activities of its membership. The determination of the extent of sewage treatment necessary to provide adequacy and safety of use of receiving bodies of water has always been a subject of engaging scientific character.

The answers to these fundamental questions of the profession and of the public have naturally taken on new importance as population densities have increased and as the uses of receiving bodies of water have multiplied. The natural scientific understanding of the issues involved has likewise advanced, although the empirical criteria used a half a century ago are today surprisingly unchanged as the result of more detailed technical knowledge.

The central question regarding standards proposed for stream cleanliness is revived today for two reasons. First, the entrance of the Federation of Sewage Works Associations into the national scene as a conscious forum for future discussion brings with it an added responsibility. Such a national body must now take stock of the bases of its activities. No

* Reprinted with permission from *Journal Water Pollution Federation,* Vol XII, No. 6, pp. 1,116–20 (November, 1940), Washington, D.C. 20016. Presented at the First Annual Convention of the Sewage Works Federation, Chicago Ill., Oct. 5, 1940.

more important one exists than this particular field which dominates the design, construction and operation of the facilities with which the Federation membership is concerned.

The second reason is that we are now entering an era of even stronger competition for the public dollar than has hitherto been the case. Public services in competition with vast defense enterprises must depend for their construction and operation dollar upon clear and convincing validities. Stock taking, therefore, in this instance implies rigid scrutiny of the purposes for which sewage treatment plants are to be constructed and operated. Criteria for these decisions cannot and must not be determined in a vacuum. They must rest upon the realities of the changing American scene and fiscal situation.

Standards for stream cleanliness have undergone extensive evolution within the last half a century. They have developed from the purely qualitative, aesthetic determinations of John Ruskin, the British poet and artist, to the detailed quantitative statements of M. M. Ellis of the Bureau of Fisheries. The poet bemoaned the disappearance of the sparkling, crystal clear brooks of England through the ravages of industrial and domestic wastes. His standard for cleanliness of streams was a simple one, a stream wholly undisturbed and completely free of everything but the natural wash of virgin soils of agricultural and forest use. Strangely enough the quantitative standards of Ellis essentially define such bodies of water as Ruskin longed for. The standards proposed by Ellis are descriptions of natural bodies of water quite undisturbed by any of the deleterious influences of modern civilization. The complex which he defines is the "ideal aquatic environment." Deviations from it, by the additions of other substances, are to be avoided.

Between these two chronological periods all gradations of approach to the problem are available, beginning with the estimates of Hering, Stearns, Hazen and Goodnough just preceding the Twentieth Century. The observations of this group, largely based upon the actual conditions created by sewage discharges, resulted in dilution values which are still remarkably helpful and simple for modern practice.

These observations of 50 years ago were followed by theoretical studies initiated and largely directed by Phelps. The studies at the Cincinnati station of the United States Public Health Service have further elaborated the technical bases of the newer standards.

In addition, the studies by Wolman in 1918, later confirmed and extended by Streeter, established the bacterial bases for many of the standards for raw water for water treatment plants.

All of these gave emphasis to the need for additional studies with particular reference to fish life, finally resulting in the extensive field and laboratory studies of the United States Bureau of Fisheries, and of many State fisheries groups.

The resultant increases in knowledge regarding the effects of discharges into receiving bodies of water have produced a literal flood of standards of cleanliness during the past 10 years. It is toward the control or the regulation of this flood that the present remarks are primarily directed. Are the standards now being promulgated with increasing velocity and perhaps decreasing validity adequate scientific and practical bases upon which the case for sewage treatment is to rest? Can the standards be met? Should they be met? Does the expenditure of the sewage treatment dollar rest upon a reasonable balancing of convenience and of public service?

This is not the place, of course, to review or to repeat the various standards proposed for water quality. It is sufficient to point out, however, that their number is great and that in many instances they are approaching the asymptote of the Ellis standards for the natural habitat of fish life. All gradations of standards, of course, are now available. Some define, as Ellis does, the characteristics of the receiving body of water, some define the quality of the discharges, while others range happily on both sides.

The trend, furthermore, is toward the adoption of standards on a wide geographical base by repeating the standards promulgated elsewhere, not always with the local conditions of use and necessity dominant. This is not at all an unusual procedure in the making of standards. The fallacies as well as the validities of an existing standard tend to be perpetuated in succeeding ones.

In other areas of stream quality, particularly in the case of open bathing beach standards, the situation borders on the chaotic. This distressing state of affairs is being met by and large by classifications of areas, a frank concession, but a necessary one, to the balancing of practical necessities against epidemiological ignorance. In most standards, however, the philosophy predominates that, in the absence of knowledge, the more rigid the standard, the safer the engineer. How else can one account for the fact that one administrative agency suggests that the *Coli* density in open bathing beach waters should not exceed 5 per 100 c.c., while another, equally competent and diligent, stands firm for a maximum of several thousand per 100 c.c.? How long this state of tightrope walking may continue with safety from attack by the public it is difficult to predict.

Unfortunately many of these definitions have crept into law and only now are they beginning to demonstrate their danger.

Proposals for Federation Activity

What should all of this mean with respect to the Federation? The writer proposes a series of activities by which the Federation may produce values important to the public and to its membership. These proposals are briefly discussed below:

1. *Testing the Results of Corrective Measures by Sewage Treatment*

For many years the advocates of sewage treatment have pointed out the values to be received by the adjustment of stream quality through the forces of sewage treatment. A limited number of followup reviews have been made of streams on which corrective measures have been established. Examples of such checks on reduction in pollution are the studies on the Raritan, the Niagara, the Scioto, the Illinois and the Potomac Rivers. The Federation should stimulate additional studies of this character in order to build up substantiating data for the promises made and for the development of practicable criteria for future enterprises. How far has promise been met by fulfillment and at what cost? The development of such reviews will gradually result in the establishment of a body of facts which should be rich in their availability for increasing diagnosis and treatment.

2. *The Economics of Standards and Correctives*

Almost all workers in the sewage treatment field are by this time familiar with the current unit—B.O.D. No discussion, no paper, no argument in this field proceeds far without the introduction and use of this unit of measure. May a plea be made for the introduction of a parallel unit of measure of equal importance, but hitherto unduly neglected in discussions of stream cleanliness? The unit proposed is C.O.D., or cash on delivery. The engineer should be educated to exhibit an equal concern with respect to C.O.D. as he does with B.O.D. The Federation should enforce its obligations to bring back into focus the balancing of costs vs. benefits or C.O.D. vs. B.O.D.

In some instances, this balance of B.O.D. against the limitations of C.O.D. appears to be increasingly ignored. What is the warrant, for example, of a State Board of Health requiring a complete sewage treatment plant, including sand filtration, for a population on a highly polluted stream, where the effluent discharged has a quality infinitely superior to the probable quality of the receiving body of water below it for the next 25 years? Is it sufficient justification to say that the fixed and operating costs of such installations are sacrifices to the laudable desire to make a beginning in the cleaning up of the stream? How much should the first conscientious municipality be penalized for the delayed consciences of the remaining offenders?

Are per capita sewage treatment expenditures for capita investment as high as $50 to $100 warranted by the exigencies of such a case? Those members of the profession who are mathematically inclined should be persuaded to develop an "expediency index" which should be compared with the "sludge index" and other indices which now hold the stage in sewage treatment. An "expediency index" which is a function of per capita debt and of per capita B.O.D. reduction required for reasonable stream uses should appear in forthcoming sewage treatment plant tabulations.

May we further intrude with the suggestion that the Federation might begin to give consideration to what place in the list of priorities sewage treatment plants should take with respect to the increasing public services now exceeding a hundred functional types in the average large municipality. Where does and should sewage treatment appear in this list? Must it always have priority No. 1? Must the standards of stream cleanliness be at such a level as to require sewage treatment to supersede any other public service? Is the desire of some to raise the criteria of stream cleanliness to a level approaching that available in the time of De Soto, a sensible desire, even though it may be conceded that it is a praiseworthy one?

In the consideration of these questions should we not give serious thought to the anomalous situation which is created by the enforcement of some of the standards? Many of them, if put into effect, will produce a water environment of the vintage of 1500 A.D. with an adjacent land environment of the chronology of 1940 A.D. The waters bordering on certain municipalities or just below them will permit trout fishing by the people living on the adjacent land, who continue to be deprived of necessary services for the maintenance of health, welfare and safety. This imbalance of land and water environment seems to have been wholly lost sight of in the desire to raise to the highest point the levels of stream cleanliness. The results of encroachments of civilization make necessary the adjustments of not only the water but of the land environment.

Given a limited tax dollar, does governmental discretion demand that it must be spent to permit a maximum of fish life in a receiving body of water at the sacrifice of houses, hospitals, food, water supply, smoke prevention, etc., on land? If the cost of preserving the amenities in the land and in the water environment were so low that all could be accomplished with satisfaction, none of the issues need to be raised. In present operations, however, this condition of adequate funds for all purposes has not prevailed, does not exist and is not likely to appear in the near future.

Summary

The observations noted above, necessarily brief in character and deliberately antagonistic in form, are intended to indicate some of the basic problems with which the Federation might confront itself in the immediate future, through committee action or otherwise. These fundamental questions of sewage treatment and stream cleanliness may be summarized as follows:

(*a*) What are the quantitative bases for the standards so far promulgated in the United States?

(*b*) What are the controlling principles which should dominate the policy with respect to such standards?

(*c*) Are universal quantitative standards for stream cleanliness desirable?

(*d*) Are universal quantitative standards for effluents desirable?

(*e*) Is it possible to develop reasonable criteria of the economics of sewage treatment?

(*f*) What are the results of the installation of sewage treatment devices on stream cleanliness?

(*g*) What are the epidemiological aspects of sewage treatment programs?

These questions, of course, do not exhaust all of the aspects of the standards proposed for stream cleanliness. There are probably a dozen others. The objectives of this paper will, however, have been served if the standards now available and those being proposed from day to day are subjected to conscious objective scrutiny by a national body, not only in the light of the observations made above, but with respect to other realistic problems which now confront the engineer and the public administrator.

Virtually every city in the United States will be concerned in the next two decades either with increasing the degree of treatment for its sewage or with providing treatment facilities now wholly lacking. Expenditures for this purpose will probably exceed a billion dollars. No more important problem confronts the profession than how to steer a reasonable course between the perfectionists and the opportunists in this difficult field. "Sanitas sanitatum" is a good and militant slogan, but it should not transcend the cautions of common sense in the use and abuse of our streams.

Bacterial Standards
for Natural Waters*

It is difficult, if not impossible, to discuss any standards for engineering application or to formulate quantitative requirements therefor, without giving serious consideration to the whole philosophy of standardization in the sanitary engineering field. The questions which must be posed are:

1. Is quality an area in which standardization is either indicated or desirable?

2. If such standards are worthy of formulation and of application, what should they be?

A sharp distinction should be made between the standardization of methods for diagnostic application and the standardization of practices or concepts. In the first category, tools are required which possess both uniformity and interchangeability of technical language. In the second, the criterion of judgment is introduced and it must loom large in final decisions. When one attempts to standardize judgment, by developing convenient and often illogical devices as substitutes for reasoning, nothing but confusion is likely to result. It is recognized, of course, that for many workers in any field "handbook criteria" are invariably sought and equally invariably applied injudiciously. In the subject matter which this

* Reprinted with permission from *Journal Water Pollution Control Federation,* Vol. XXII, No. 3, pp. 346–52 (March, 1950), Washington, D.C. 20016. Presented at 22nd Annual Meeting, Federation of Sewage Works Associations; Boston, Mass.; Oct. 17–20, 1949.

paper covers the desire for easy and convenient substitutes for thought and judgment, in the form of standards of quality, has reached a new high. Standardization for all features of natural waters has become one of the major sanitary engineering indoor sports.

Historically, ample support may be summoned for the thesis that standards of judgment are dangerous, fallacious, and inappropriate to scientific workers. These warnings range all the way from the sharp but cogent comment of the late Professor Sedgwick, in describing standards of sanitation as "devices to save lazy minds the trouble of thinking,"[1] to equally significant but more refined warnings by Phelps, Whipple, Schroepfer,[1] Velz,[2] and Hedgepeth,[3] to mention only a few through the last half century. Even the writer,[4] at the annual convention of the Federation in October, 1940, reflected on the absence of any sound basis for universal standardization of desirable or desired characteristics of stream quality. Sedgwick's criticism is still valid that "standards are often the guess of one worker, easily seized upon, quoted and requoted, until they assume the semblance of authority."

Reasons for Growth of Stream Standards

In the intervening decade, however, the search for and the introduction into law and regulation of stream criteria has proceeded at a fast pace. Part of the process has been engendered by the literal intimidation of many workers in the field by the imaginative demands of certain militant organizations. In other instances, the appeal of the convenient handbook has been overwhelming. In still others, the subtle attractiveness of "zoning" has given the necessary fillip to this standardization technique. In this pursuit toward the quantitative millennium for qualitative matters of judgment a number of underlying philosophies have found their full play. At the one end of the spectrum are found the criteria established to preserve original quality and concomitantly, therefore, to avoid original sin. In this particular philosophy the studied and judicial comment of the late Professor Whipple that a regulatory edict, both in law and in philosophy, should establish the minimum for safety rather than the maximum of hope, is being ignored. The re-emphasis on this dictum was equally cogently and intelligently set forth by Frost and others, in sharpening the distinction between standard methods and so-called standards of judgments.

In the other extreme the philosophy has predominated that standards of quality of streams should be descriptive of the actualities and the realities of the local scene, a more justifiable basis of description than that already suggested.

In his paper some 10 years ago, the author[4] proposed certain tasks for the Federation. His arguments at that time, persuasive as they seemed to him, did not fall on fertile ground. The suggestions for Federation consideration, which revolved around the central problem of undue standardization of judgments, have yet to be fulfilled. In the interval new adherents to the cult of standards have entered the field. Some point with pride to the fact that virtually every state, either by statute or by administrative rule, has formulated criteria of quality. Many of them have given substantial scientific clothing to the criteria by introducing the concepts of zoning, to add additional difficulties to the administrator who is confronted with moving situations within a framework of restraint.

Paralleling these steps has come the unprecedented rise in the costs of sewage and industrial waste treatment. In 1942, reasonable per capita construction costs for sewage disposal were listed as from $3.00 to $12.00. Now that these costs have climbed 4- and 5-fold, it is again timely to remind the Federation and its members that stocktaking, both as to philosophy and as to quantitative translations of philosophy into action, is past due. At a recent Florida meeting of a professional group in the public health engineering field one of the speakers[5] warned that the public may get fed up before long with excessive costs for capital, maintenance, and operation investments in sewage treatment. His plea was, of course, for the introduction of imagination into this popular field of development rather than to the continuing adherence either to forms or to standards of applicability, which cannot be and in many instances should not be supported by corrective structures.

The hold which stream criteria have on both professional and lay workers in this field is sometimes astonishing. The slide rule and mathematical devices have begun to force out of consideration critical appraisals of stream pollution abatement decisions.

Ohio River Report

When the Ohio River study was under way, the Supervisory Board, of which the writer was a member, went to extraordinary pains to avoid setting up criteria of stream quality in its major report tabulations. It spent hours in selecting language that would warn the reader that the tabulations were intended to be simple descriptions of characteristics of various sectors of the river. They were not intended to zone, to delimit, or to restrict the stream in any or all of its portions by a special set of criteria. In spite of all this care and what was thought to be a relatively happy choice of phrases, wherever one turns one is confronted with these descriptions of a stream adopted in law or regulation throughout the country as stream quality standards. The language in the Ohio River report is worth repeating here:

In view of the variety, distribution, and extent of surface water uses, it is undesirable to establish rigid stream quality standards for general application in the Ohio River Basin, and the data in table 7 are not to be applied in that matter. The public interest can be served only by adapting standards to conditions existing in individual stream reaches, and by giving consideration to the most valuable stream use.[6]

These Ohio River characteristics, designed entirely for purposes of study, have found their way into law and into regulations with sufficient modification to add both to their complexity and to the general confusion in their applicability. The revisions are often mere reflections of a desire for originality on the part of the person responsible for them.

Standards vs. Judgment

What can one say about criteria of stream quality, solely from the standpoint of bacterial content, when one state alone offers five ways of avoiding original sin, depending on the economic status of the bather? And what can one say, furthermore, of the state of affairs in which, as was pointed out 10 years ago, one state insists that it is unsafe to swim in a body of fresh water which exceeds 5 coli per 100 ml. and an adjacent state insists with equal fervor that equal safety is afforded to the swimmer by a bacterial density of 500 times that amount? What can be said about a regulatory agency's desire when it establishes a standard of bacterial density that virtually rules out of use 95 per cent of the available surface streams within its territorial limits, provided, of course, it rains on occasions and the agricultural terrain is in part washed into the surface streams?

The most sedulous search of current literature discloses only one carefully controlled epidemiological survey[7] of this problem, yet the criteria which resulted from that study have been ignored in many of the states.

How valid is the reason frequently given for this drive that every municipality and every industry must know in black and white how a stream is zoned before its problem may be intelligently reviewed with a state regulatory agency? To the writer, at least, the validity of this argument for confounding judgment with precept holds very little water. Almost every situation on almost every body of water in this country is a problem in itself. As a rule, the solution to such problems is not assisted materially by referring to a convenient handbook. The solution lies in most instances in the considered balancing of technical and financial conveniences and equities, out of which the perennial compromises of judgments ensue. In more instances than one, any criterion, in law or in rule, which stands in the way of these compromises is unfortunate. They lead either to unwise and unwarranted expenditures or to acrimonious debate and delay in correctives. Administrative judgment and decision are the results of intelligent diagnostic techniques, bargaining, availability of the dollar, and adaptability to the local scene. They are not and never have been the result of legislative fiat, even when this is re-enforced by formulas of pseudo-mathematical character.

Members of the Federation have their major interest in the underlying philosophy, perhaps rather than in the quantitative explorations thereunder. At first sight the latter dominates most of the literature. Beneath the surface, however, in administrative practice the qualitative applications as a rule will determine the success or failure of the pollution abatement programs. Where this is not the case and the rule is both formalized and applied, there is a reasonable expectancy, based on past experience, that the public is being forced to pay more than it should for the desired result. This practice is doomed to failure when the public begins to understand the way in which the criteria were born and how they are being applied.

Ultraconservative Safety Factors

One is pushed to discover or to enunciate even a general principle in stream quality which can be guaranteed to be applicable without modifications to every scene in the United States. Someone has said that "no generalization is true," even including that one.

This problem of safety as applied to bacterial standards in waters is not peculiar to sanitary engineering practice and discussion. Its epidemiological bases are unfortunately extremely limited. They are so limited that Stevenson and Woolsey, of the Public Health Service, have undertaken a thoroughgoing study, long overdue, of the relationship between natural bathing water quality and the occurrence of illness attributable to bathing in natural waters. Even when the results of their study are available the very nature of the case would predispose the careful student to adopt rigid criteria with a maximum of caution in the administrative field.

The search for objective criteria of safety in fields much more susceptible to answers has gone on for many years, as in the problems of structural design. Freudenthal has recently said: "The concept of safety is probably the most important—and certainly the most controversial and vaguely defined concept in structural design. Safety factors varying between 1.25 and 10 are found in current design specifications for different materials and structural parts. These values were chosen arbitrarily on the basis of subjective judgment."[8] If this is true in structural design, in which the evidence for behavior is greater in amount and in laboratory and field experience, how much truer is it in the field of bacterial stan-

dards where the peculiar history and characteristics of the phenomena
are extremely limited and complex?

Wide Range of Permissible Limits

This paper might elaborate on the assumptions now underlying the
various standards established for fresh and sea water over the last few
years. To this author at least, that type of record is quite pointless, particularly in view of the fact that in 1942 such a review was carefully and
elaborately made by Schroepfer[1] and in 1948 equally carefully and elaborately canvassed and extended by the Joint Committee of the Conference of State Sanitary Engineers and of the Engineering Section of
the American Public Health Association. Both documents disclose a wide
variation in the different states in the range of permissible limits, virtually
all of them relatively unsupported by anything but precedent, imagination, ingenuity, enthusiasm, and nostalgia. The author finds himself in the
same predicament as the aforesaid Committee in attempting to cull from
this spectrum of criteria a conclusion which would stand the scrutiny
of an objective judge.

The Joint Committee makes the best of a confused situation in the
following judicious language in several of its conclusions:

> There is still a wide divergence of opinion as to the standards of
> acceptable bacteriological quality for outdoor bathing places in
> streams, rivers, lakes, and tidal waters, although there is apparently
> some crystallization of thought on the subject.
>
> Early attempts to set a limiting bacteriological standard equiva-
> lent to 120 coliform organisms per 100 ml. (50 coliform organisms
> per 100 ml. according to Phelps' index) have been largely discarded.
> Such values are usually attainable only in lakes and excellent quality
> tidal waters. Streams subject to no pollution other than animal con-
> tamination may often show a coliform index of 240 to 1,000 per 100
> ml., with occasional samples showing still higher indices. In West
> Virginia, the State Water Commission describes a Class A water as a
> food source of recreational water where the average coliform index
> of samples each month does not exceed 1,000 per 100 ml.
>
> In the summer of 1948 the New York City Board of Health
> adopted a declaration of policy for the guidance of the Department
> of Health in classifying bathing beaches. The action of the Board
> does not affect that section of the Sanitary Code which prohibits the
> operation of bathing establishments in certain specified areas. The
> classification adopted is as follows:
>
> *Class A: Approved Beach Waters*
>   Group 1. Safe Waters
>   (a) Epidemiological experience satisfactory, and
>   (b) Sanitary survey satisfactory, and

(c) Coliform average not in excess of 1,000

Group 2. Approved, but subject to reclassification in light of continuing observation.

(a) Epidemiological experience satisfactory;

(b) Sanitary survey satisfactory, but beach waters exposed to increasing pollution; or

(c) Coliform average above 1,000, but not in excess of 2,400.

Class B: Polluted Beach Waters Not Recommended for Bathing

(a) Epidemiological experience satisfactory;

(b) Sanitary survey discloses sewage material on beach or in water immediately adjacent to beach; and

(c) Coliform average above 2,400, with 50 per cent of samples in average above 2,400

Class C: Unsafe Beach Waters

(a) Epidemiological experience discloses evidence of infection incident to beach bathing;

(b) and (c) Not necessarily relevant in light of (a) above.

In connection with this system of classification, the Commissioner of Health will issue warning to the public and the proprietor of the beach that the waters of that bathing beach are polluted and not recommended for bathing when a beach falls in the Class B designation; when a beach falls in the Class C designation, warning to the public and the proprietor will be given by the Commissioner of Health and he shall, within 24 hours, call a special meeting of the Board of Health for the consideration of such other measures as appear necessary for the protection of the public health. This classification is reported to be based on epidemiological experience, bacteriological findings and sanitary surveys, and is influenced by the unique conditions found in the harbor waters of New York City.

The Joint Committee went on to say:

It is emphasized that final classification of bathing waters should depend largely upon sanitary survey information. Bacteriological analysis findings should be used as a guide. Some areas of the country are reported to be able to meet bacterial standards for natural surface waters with minimum limits of coliform indices (as used herein) of not more than 240 to 500 per 100 ml. Such excellent quality is, of course, greatly to be desired. However, experience indicates that other sections of the country, especially those located in more densely populated areas and among cultivated lands, cannot maintain such conditions.

Waters showing a concentration of most probable numbers of coliform organisms of less than 1,000 per 100 ml. are considered in most such areas to be fairly acceptable for bathing unless the sanitary survey discloses immediate dangers from human sewage pollution; however, it must be admitted that bathing beaches where the content of coliform organisms runs as high as 2,400 per 100 ml. on the basis of most probable numbers, or sometimes even higher, have been used with reported evidence of illness, and this limit of 2,400 per 100 ml. is still employed as a criterion of acceptability in some states. The trend is, of course, to reduce bacteria counts where possible by sewage treatment if human sewage is a threat, and the attainment of reasonable progress in this direction is to be hoped for. While bathing areas should always be free of visible forms of sewage matter that might contain pathogenic organisms, serious pollution may be present in many waters where treatment of sewage removes visible evidence of sewage solids but does not eliminate dangerous concentrations of bacteria.[6]

Validity of Limits Questionable

These statements selected from the Joint Committee's report offer about as reasonable a description of the present state of affairs as the author has been able to find, leaving the central question open for further discussion as to whether the final suggested limits have any validity. The Federation should stimulate discussion by its members as to whether or not standards should be developed which are acknowledged to be without scientific foundation, even though as in these cases, the weight of authority is heavily placed on the continuation of their use.

Little or nothing has been said about the bacterial standards, particularly in fresh waters, where such waters are to be used as sources of potable water. This omission has been deliberate, simply because the issues are not as controversial or of such practical significance as they are in respect to standards of quality for recreation. One of the primary reasons for this view lies in the fact that wide areas of operating possibility are provided in the raw water bacterial standards, as applied to water works intakes. Until very high concentrations are reached (in excess of 10,000 per 100 ml.) the well designed modern water treatment plant handles normal and shock loads of bacteria with both economy and practicability. In other words, regulatory agencies have found it unnecessary to establish rigid limits for these purposes at the same time that they have been constrained to develop far more rigid limitations in bathing waters, where the evidence for such action is much less convincing. It is only in special instances that some administrators have moved toward heavy expenditures in sewage treatment to relieve the bacterial load on water plants, even though the costs of accomplishing the same purpose via water treatment are generally materially lower than by sewage treatment.

Application to Salt Waters

A word should also be added with respect to the situation in sea water of various salinities. The evidence is accumulating that in salt water, varying from as low as 4,000 to as high as 40,000 p.p.m. of chlorides, coliform organisms tend to decline more rapidly than would be accounted for by strictly dilution calculations. Whether these effects are primarily due to saline content or not still remains to be demonstrated. The findings by Zobell, Anderson, and Smith[9] in the Great Salt Lake in Northern Utah, by Ketchum *et al.*[10] in the salt water areas of New England, by Wolman[11] in Puget Sound and by Tyler and Seabrook[12] in Commencement Bay (Puget Sound in the vicinity of Tacoma) all disclose, however, that the mortality of the coliforms and associated bacterial groups is undoubtedly greater than dilution alone would provide. These reductions are reflections of the whole unfavorable environment to be found in such saline waters. By and large, the index organism does not appear to survive under the conditions provided by many salt water areas, in spite of the fact that some limited studies disclose that some pathogens, as in fresh water, may survive for extended periods in small numbers.

All of the restraints in the application of standards to fresh water should, therefore, be critically observed when they are applied in salt water areas. The same absence of epidemiological warrant and the same consideration of economic balances must control any judgment decision on the permissible bacterial concentrations in salt waters. It is extremely doubtful whether efforts to restrict the uses of these waters for recreational purposes, where concentrations of coli are in excess of hundreds per 100 ml., with resultant unwarranted expenditures of public monies, will bring any measurable parallel return in public health or safety.

Conclusions

All of these discussions lead to the suggestion that the Federation should pursue the following important objectives:

1. To participate officially with other voluntary associations in discussions of the general validity of judgment standards.

2. To participate with both voluntary and official agencies in the discussions of judgment standards which such agencies perpetuate.

3. To evaluate in selected areas of the United States the results of sewage treatment plant installations, with particular respect to the bacterial accomplishments originally anticipated.

4. To appraise realistically the practicability of actually using the wide variety of stream bacterial standards which have already been translated either into law or into administrative rule.

These proposals are made under the assumption that the Federation, interested as it must be in sewage and industrial waste treatment, should begin to shed light officially on the validity of the criteria which should guide the designer, the operator, and the regulatory agency. The late Max Planck[13] succinctly establishes the basis for such hopes in the following terms: "But even the keenest logic and the most exact mathematical calculation cannot produce a single fruitful result in the absence of a premise of unerring accuracy."

REFERENCES

1. Schroepfer, G. J., "An Analysis of Stream Pollution and Stream Standards," THIS JOURNAL, 14, 5, 1030 (Sept., 1942).

2. Velz, C. J., "Factors Influencing Self-Purification and Their Relation to Pollution Abatement." THIS JOURNAL, 21, 2, 309 (Mar., 1949).

3. Hedgepeth, L. L., "Stream Standards, A Critical Discussion." Lecture at In-service Training Course in Sewage and Industrial Waste Disposal, School of Public Health, University of Michigan (Mar. 14, 1949).

4. Wolman, Abel, "An Inquiry into Standards Proposed for Stream Cleanliness." THIS JOURNAL, 12, 6, 1116 (Nov., 1940).

5. Williamson, J., Jr., "Other Economic Aspects of Stream Sanitation." *Proc.* 1st Annual Public Health Engr. Conf., Bulletin Series No. 26, University of Florida (April, 1949).

6. "Report of the Ohio River Committee." Part I, p. 27, House Document No. 266, 78th Congress, 1st Session, 1948.

7. Winslow and Moxon, "Bacterial Pollution of Bathing Beach Waters in New Haven Harbor." *Amer. Jour. of Hygiene*, 8, 3, 299 (May, 1928).

8. Freudenthal, A. M., "Let's Stop Overdesigning Structures," *Engineering News-Record*, 143, 9, 206 (Sept. 1, 1949).

9. Zobell, Anderson, and Smith, "The Bacteriostatic and Bactericidal Action of Great Salt Lake Water." *Jour. of Bact.* (1937).

10. Ketchum, Carey, and Briggs, "Preliminary Studies on the Viability and Dispersal of Coliform Bacteria in the Sea, Limnological Aspects of Water Supply and Waste Disposal." A.A.A.S., p. 64 (1949).

11. Wolman, Abel, "City of Seattle, Report on Sewage Disposal." (1948).

12. Unpublished reports.

13. Planck, Max, "Scientific Autobiography." The Philosophical Library (Oct., 1949).

Concepts of Policy in the Formulation of
So-Called Standards of Health and Safety*

The staff of the Joint Congressional Committee on Atomic Energy has posed two primary questions for this discussion. They deal with the exploration of the evolution of standards in the fields of health and safety, other than standards pertaining to radiation control. Such an exploration should reveal precedents, similarities, differences, and difficulties that may make the task of guiding public policy in radiation control more rational or more universally acceptable and intelligible. The questions are paraphrased as follows:

1. For hazards other than radiation, what have been typical practices in public health in developing protection criteria, with particular reference to benefits, risks, and costs in the broadest social and economic sense?

2. How do common arguments applied to radiation hazard appear if applied to historically more familiar hazards?

Fortunately, detailed elaborations of answers to these highly important questions are now available in the superb articles by Parker, Weber, Taylor, Williams, and others in the invaluable joint committee publica-

* Reprinted from the *Journal American Water Works Association*, Vol. 52, No. 11 (November 1960). Copyright 1960 by the American Water Works Association, Inc. Presented May 24, 1960, before the Joint Congressional Committee on Atomic Energy, Washington, D.C.

tion of May 1960.[1] This document of approximately 1,250 pages provides
for the diligent reader a comprehensive review of the assigned subject.
It is too much to expect, however, that the millions of citizens concerned
will choose the document for extended perusal. Therefore, brief generalizations will be made here from the wealth of data already in print, with
the hope of delineating some historical peaks and troughs for guidance in
the effort to establish standards.

Need for Standards

From its beginning, society by one means or another, has surrounded
itself with restraints. These have had, for the most part, empiric origins—
moral, ethical, economic, or spiritual. All the restraints have had the
common basis of an assumed benefit to the particular society establishing
them. As societies became more complex and more sophisticated, efforts
toward both standardization and restraint became more frequent, more
necessary, and presumably less empiric, although examples of the last
are not as numerous as one might expect.

There are all kinds of standards. Rigid definitions should preclude
the loose application of the term "standards" in discussions of standards
for radiation control. The procedures often used to establish standards
may roughly be classified as:

1. Regularization of techniques of measurement
2. Establishment of limits of concentration or density of biologic
   life and physical and chemical constituents
3. Regularization of administrative practice
4. Regularization of legislative fiat
5. Specification of materials.

As one reads from No. 1 to No. 5, the procedures become not only
more complex but also more nebulous. The hope that authoritative rule
will be substituted for thought and judgment is ever present in the minds
of some administrators, quantitative-minded precisionists, lawyers, and
distressed citizens who are beleaguered by the multiplicity of problems.
To resolve these by formula has always been the will-of-the-wisp hope
of workers in every field of human endeavor. It is not surprising that the
search for mathematical certainty persists so diligently in the field of radiation, paralled as it is by the vast uncertainty in the underlying scientific principles that have generated the radiation problem.

Previous Standards and Revisions

The history of the general field of public health practice should
disclose precedents, philosophy, implications, and examples of the de-

velopment of standards. Fortunately, Parker, Weber, and Taylor have discussed many of these aspects.[1] What do they teach us?

The development of criteria for the protection of health has invariably preceded full scientific understanding and acceptance. These criteria have always been subject to reinterpretation, adjustment, and reframing as newer knowledge and experience were forthcoming. Sometimes such revisions have been overdue, even though the machinery for revaluation, both voluntary and official, was at hand. Experience has disclosed that where criteria have been made rigid by law, revision becomes a heroic effort. Administrative rule is far more flexible.

A familiar example of the revision process is in the changing criteria for drinking water quality. In the last 40 years, several adjustments have been made, with one in the offing for 1960 or 1961. A more striking example of the difficulties confronting the criteria maker is in regard to food additives. With the rapidly increasing number of food additives and the tremendous gap between an understanding of their effects and their hazard to public health, years will undoubtedly elapse before empiricism is separated from scientific accuracy. Even in the assumed understanding of the behavior of toxic chemicals, much remains to be learned by the toxicologist, physiologist, and hygienist. The responsible health officer, however, cannot wait for perfect knowledge before interposing barriers between man and industrial poisons. He utilizes the best knowledge at hand, always paying a price for overestimating or underestimating hazard. He is perhaps the prime exponent of those who must act prayerfully in the absence of complete data.

The development of standard techniques of measurement has continued, even though standardization has had a tendency to stultify scientific advance. When the advantages of standardization are weighed against the chaos of dissimilar techniques of measurement, which preceded standard methods, the balance is undoubtedly on the side of a common language.

In the standardization of methods for water and milk analyses, it should not be forgotten that much scientific work, but not all, was at hand. One of the significant provisions in the activity was for continuing revision by carefully established machinery—a frank recognition of progressive science and art. The resulting revisions span half a century and yield valuable lessons for the radiation field, for the voluntary professional societies in the United States had a dominant hand in revising standard methods of water and milk analyses.

Criteria to guide administrative practice have been used with caution in the public health field. Appraisal sheets, coupled with assessments of current practice, have had variable results even when issued by voluntary groups. The fear of making a practice rigid and, at the same time, the desire to facilitate its administration are characteristic of at-

tempts to assess current practice. The appraisal sheets have provided aids
to improved coverage in public health and have not proved too resistant
to new knowledge. Again, relative success with standardization practice
is the result, in great part, of the concomitant provision of machinery for
the continuing revision of the bases for appraisal.

Calculated Risks

How has the health worker balanced criteria against risk to life?
The past record of accomplishment in the field of public health, of
which one has reason to be eminently proud, is singularly devoid of such
quantitative evaluations. The fact that the American public lives in one
of the most protected public health environments in the world is not
contested. That this is the result of the composite of public health measures, standard of living, genetic influence, and other factors is likewise
true.

But the saving of lives and the extension of life have been the result
of public health practice to a significant degree. It must be recognized,
however, that the guiding principle that "public health is purchasable"
was a qualitative philosophic precept, rarely a quantitative equating of
protective criteria against loss of men or dollars. Efforts to apply the
latter equation have not been rare, but they have been quite unimpres-
sive in general impact either on the people or on their legislators.
Persistent efforts have been made to measure the economic value of the
newborn babe, but the western acceptance of the general obligation of
society to prevent disease and death is the prevailing one. It is only in
the search for criteria for radiation limits that one finds suggestions that
it should be permissible to kill X people to attain Y benefits to society.
This has undoubtedly been in the minds of all criteria makers, but
rarely has it reached the frank and stark pronouncements of recent years.

Safety Factors for the Public

Has there been a discernible factor of safety in public health criteria
invariably in favor of the public? The answer is unquestionably "yes,"
and the factor of safety has always been large. This principle is well
illustrated in drinking water quality standards to protect man against
typhoid fever, the dysenteries, infectious hepatitis, and cholera. Obviously the best criteria for detecting a dangerous public water supply
are the doctor's certificates showing that the man is dead and the epidemiologic evidence showing that the water he drank killed him. The
health official does not wait for such criteria, specific and quantitative as
they are. They cannot be applied promptly enough, and they do not provide a wide area of protection. The health official chooses to widen this

area immensely by moving to far less specific criteria with broad empiric relationships to disease.

The index preferred for half a century for detecting an unsafe water supply was the coliform organism group—nonspecific, even generally nonpathogenic, and only a qualitative indication of a climate of unsafe quality. But it has served its purpose effectively and is a striking example of intelligent empiricism preceding more refined measures of risk. Fortunately, no easy method of detection of the specific typhoid bacillus was available 30 years ago, because its adoption as a universal indicator would have narrowed measurably the area of safety for the consumer. It is not an unmixed blessing that already the radiation industry is plagued in fixing criteria by a startling multiplicity of specific nuclides and their effects. Another look at the value of gross criteria may be warranted.

The factor of safety was even more enlarged by the essential application of administrative judgment. Water quality appraisal was a composite of an understanding of heredity or origin of source, environmental adjustment or treatment, and of final product. The equilibration of these three factors was a *sine qua non* of assessment and depended on professional proficiency. There were always those, of course, who looked to a single quantitative unit for appraisal. They, in fact, did damage to administrative justice by attempting to oversimplify the complexity of interpretation of many criteria.

Higher Standards

Scientific understanding pressed toward ever more dramatic hopes in public health. Shifts in objective toward ever lower death rates became marked as the means for accomplishment became more evident or were created. For example, in the 1920's a residual typhoid fever death rate of 10 per 100,000 was assumed to be inevitable. To attempt to lower the death rate was considered "impracticable." Yet public health measures were persistently enforced, so that the typhoid death rate last year in the United States was one-hundredth of this figure. Was this desire to save lives foolish? It is to be doubted.

Were the results of continually higher standards for health protection unduly costly in dollars? It is rare to have encountered public or private agencies in the past which did not plead poverty or maintain that costs of correction were excessive. History shows that the public health demand for pasteurized milk was consistently opposed with the argument that capital and maintenance costs would price milk off the market. It is a credit to industry that it meets such challenges while it fights them.

Improvements in water quality have come about rapidly at remarkably low costs, because the technologist has been able to design, construct, and operate plants to meet ever increasing and more rigid criteria. Fear has been expressed that the establishment of too rigid criteria in the field of radiation may stifle progress because of excessive costs of attainment. One may view this fear with some cynicism in the light of the whole history of health and safety endeavor. This fear has always been expressed, but history consistently belies it. Criteria must be based on public health protection and not cost. No one, of course, should advocate excessive and unnecessary restraints. Those restraints most logically suggested, however, within the framework of current scientific understanding should not be resisted solely because resulting costs may threaten to throttle their application.

Standards for Radiation

The lessons of the past in general health and safety practices are easy to read. They are characterized by moving empiric decisions, by persistent reappraisals, by consistently giving the public the benefit of the doubt, by an ever narrowing gap between knowledge and application, by qualitative rather than quantitative slide-rule assessments of hazard, and by objectives calling for the elimination of fatalities due to disease. The kind of reasoning that proposes as a goal a reduction in the number of deaths due to coronary thrombosis to the level of violent highway deaths that seem to be taken for granted has never been accepted. Such subtleties of philosophic irony, if invoked, would cost many a health officer his job.

The radiation field today is confronted with problems and decisions similar to those in general public health practice, but radiation problems are greatly complicated by the very nature of the biologic effects to be considered. The somatic and genetic resultants are unclear and not fully predictable; perhaps they will not be predictable for many years. Yet one cannot bide one's time in placing restraints on the public and private producer. The latter do not have an unblemished record of self-policing. Hence, society must look to scientific groups and public officials for providing criteria and guides, which are, at times, admittedly uncertain or admittedly tentative. As knowledge increases, reappraisals ensue, either for relaxation or for tightening of criteria. These supposedly fumbling steps have much historical validity and precedent in public health practice. They are unpalatable to the precisionist and to many others seeking to find formulas in place of evolving judgment and declining ignorance.

The day of handbook rule for measuring the hazard of radiation is a long way off. In the meantime, one must act with limited knowledge. In such action, the guiding principle must be the maximum protection of people, not because of sentiment, but because society demands it. An agreed acceptance of a number of consequent disabilities is not an appealing basis for the development, say, of nuclear power. Industry will do better than rest upon such an affront to man.

Whether the costs of protection will prove to be exorbitant, it is too early to predict. All radiation effort is in evolution; consequently costs are still high. It is not unreasonable to anticipate that all such costs will decline. With this decline, costs of built-in health and safety measures will also be reduced. The past record amply justifies such a prophecy. In the interval during technologic advance, one might profitably follow the wise conclusion of Lauriston Taylor:

> We have a deep moral responsibility to make certain that the problem does not become a critical one for those that follow us. We are thus inescapably compelled to consider, and consider carefully, the question of the long-range uses of all radiation sources whatever, to be certain, first, that any level we set is not seriously exceeded and, secondly, to be certain that no one source causes us to use up our exposure allowance at the expense of other uses, which may in fact be essential to our overall health and well-being.[1]

REFERENCE

1. Selected Materials on Radiation Protection Criteria and Standards: Their Basis and Use. Report of Joint Congressional Committee on Atomic Energy, Washington, D.C. (May 1960).

WATER PLANNING

AND

POLICY

Providing Reasonable Water Service*

The water works industry in the United States has had an enviable record of accomplishment and service. Water utilities, largely publicly owned and operated, have invested more than 7.5 billion dollars in essential facilities to provide adequate service for 100,000,000 urban consumers. In recent years the water works industry has expended in excess of $400,000,000 a year on new construction. This expenditure, relatively large though it is, has not been sufficient to keep pace with the requirements of the growing population.

In the United States, a sharp rise in the use of water since the end of World War II has not been accompanied promptly by increases in facilities to meet the demands upon them. These deficiencies in sources and in distribution are naturally accentuated when droughts occur during the same periods as increased demand. This was the situation in the summer of 1953, a somewhat dry year, which was followed, in most parts of the United States, by an even drier summer in 1954.

The inadequacies of service encountered in 1953 have been broadly described and diagnosed by the US Geological Survey.[1] More than 1,000

* Reprinted from *Journal American Water Works Association*, Vol. 47, No. 1 (January, 1955). Copyright 1955 by the American Water Works Association, Inc. Presented Oct. 21, 1954, before the Pennsylvania Water Works Association, Atlantic City, N.J.

systems reported a shortage, defined by the USGS as a situation in which the system was unable to supply the peak demands of customers and restrictions in the use of water were instituted. These difficulties were not confined to systems supplying small populations. Of the 93 systems serving more than 100,000 people, 35, or 38 per cent, experienced a shortage.

The USGS survey disclosed that 51 per cent of those systems reporting had shortages because of population growth and increased use; about 34 per cent, because of supply failure; and 14 per cent, because of a combination of these reasons. In the shortages experienced, 20 per cent were attributable to inadequate distribution facilities. A parallel survey conducted by AWWA in 1953 covered approximately 500 systems serving populations of 10,000 or more. Sixty-eight per cent of these needed additional treatment and distribution facilities, and 27 per cent needed additional sources. During that same year about 24,000,000 consumers were restricted in the use of water. Again, these restrictions were common to small and large communities.

In 1954 inadequate service was perhaps more extensively experienced than in 1953. Inadequacies prevailed in the Midwest, the Southeast, and the Southwest. Difficulties were faced by communities of all sizes, and restrictions in use were common.

Generally, the consumer was militantly unhappy with what he considered to be bad planning on the part of the water works. In the June 25, 1954, issue of the New York *World Telegram*, for example, George Montgomery, a staff writer, opened his discussion of the water supply problem with these words:

> The shortsighted planning and the pinchpenny policies of many Greater New York water systems have handed the suburban home owner an annual lawn-browning headache that will cost him many millions to wash away. . . . The utilities apparently failed to realize the great interest in gardening—and, hence, the need for water—that would be generated by the move to the country; [and] the fact that the modern home is loaded with water consuming appliances like dishwashers and washing machines.

In Baltimore, writers in the newspaper letter columns were equally uncomplimentary and expressed vehement dissatisfaction with a municipal service that can supply more water than is needed in the winter but insufficient water in the summer. Bad tempers characterized the deficiency situations in every other part of the United States. Technical explanations for the objectionable nature of water service did not impress the general public, because they were not too well understood and, in some instances, were obviously not persuasive. Bans on sprinkling of lawns and gardens prevailed in many parts of the United States until the end of September 1954. In some water systems, these bans have been in force for 7 of the last 10 summers.

It is pertinent to point out that the average consumption of water, based on a sample of 548 water supply systems in this country, is now about 150 gcd. In 1910 it was 100 gcd. This rise should be borne in mind when the difficulties to be overcome are under discussion. Great as this increase has been, it is not nearly so great as the increased requirements of the individual for a variety of other, less important services.

The situation will not be improved without heroic measures in the immediate future. There is no hope of setting the clock back in regard to population to be serviced, water to be used, or peak requirements for normal demands. By 1960 the people to be served by public water systems will undoubtedly exceed 120,000,000. Legitimate per capita water use will slowly increase, even with the best water conservation measures which may be appropriately required.

Foreign Water Problems

As misery loves company, it may hearten the water works official in the United States to know that his headaches are more than matched in most foreign countries with public water supply systems. The London metropolitan area, with its vast population, is confronted by increasing water use, a limited group of economical sources, and a future demand for water for about 10,000,000 thirsty consumers. There, too, population growth and increased installation of water-consuming devices are pressing the water works official for large expansions.

In Manila, inadequate water service is the subject of almost daily newspaper attack. Competent management has found it impossible to keep pace with the tremendous population growth, and there was a long delay in expansion prior to the liberation. Source and distribution problems confront this metropolitan area containing 1,500,000 consumers. Many of the suburban areas are frequently without water, while others receive service only during certain times of the day.

A large population in peripheral sections of Tokyo's municipal area is getting limited or no water service. A new source will probably not be available for another 2 years. Distribution difficulties are great. In Hong Kong, perhaps the most acute water shortage in the Orient resulted in service, even to fashionable hotels, only between the hours of 5 and 9 PM each day. The business of supplying a city of 2,300,000 people with water in the distribution system for only 4 hours a day is an enlightening one. New sources are under construction but probably will not be available until the end of 1956. The summer of 1954 was none too helpful in rainfall.

Inadequate water service, definitely unsatisfactory to the average consumer, is a problem not only in the United States but throughout the world.

Causes of Inadequate Service

1. *Wars, depressions, inflation, and scarcity of materials and of manpower* have operated to intensify the water service problem in this country. The responsibility for interference and delay rests with no single group. The intelligent consumer accepts such explanations as valid, but he looks to the same speeding-up process in the water works field that has been demonstrated to be feasible in many other industrial enterprises.

2. *Increased per capita use* has resulted from the development and widespread installation of many devices and improvements in homes and commercial establishments. Air conditioning, the increase in lawn sprinkling (due undoubtedly to the great overflow into the suburban areas), the washing machine, the dishwasher, multiple bathroom facilities, individual swimming pools, and other known and unpredictable products of American ingenuity are undoubtedly raising the average and peak water demand.

3. *Unprecedented industrial expansion* requires more and more water for old and new processes. This demand is likely to continue to increase, even with the best of conservation measures.

4. *Unexpected and unprecedented increases in population* have taken place in old cities and, to an even greater extent, in the metropolitan rings around them. To the water works man, this population growth, quite unparalleled throughout the nation's history, has supplied one of the major headaches. Although it is said that the population curve is likely to flatten out in the years to come, the water industry should not rest too optimistically on this hope. For example, the population gain from 1950 to 1954 in suburban areas of Connecticut, New Jersey, and New York has been 17.1 per cent. In several of these areas, such as Nassau and Suffolk counties in New York and Middlesex County, N.J., there have been percentage increases, in the same 4 years, of 43.7, 37.4, and 24.6 per cent. These figures offer no great consolation for responsible water utility officials.

The water works industry has tended to assume that it is confronted with an insoluble problem, quite unlike that encountered by any other public service. Although the population of the United States has increased since 1920 by approximately 50 per cent, in the same period the per capital production of energy went up more than 500 per cent. By and large, this increased requirement has been adequately met by most of the public power utilities. The amount of water produced has increased only about 100 per cent in this interval. Water works men need to lift their sights greatly. Ernest T. Weir, Pres., National Steel Corp., has recently stated: "If we did not have today at least 50 years' reserve of coal and ore ahead of us, I would not feel very safe." This comment from a leader in a collateral industry is not intended in any fashion to give a criterion for the water works industry. It does, however, represent the kind of thinking which prevails in a major industry responsible for supplying a commodity as rapidly and as regularly as the consumer desires.

5. *Decentralization and metropolitan growth* have been familiar phenomena in American life since 1910. The area and density of population spilling into the metropolitan fringe have been extended rapidly in the last 10 years. That this is a source of complex water service problems is no surprise, as such areas have not been geared to high standards of water service. It is equally true that no small share of the responsibility for this situation lies in the hands of official and practicing engineers.

6. *The inertia of the public* in arriving at prompt decisions for the expansion of water works facilities is likewise well known. It has been tacitly assumed that the interval between the conception of a program for meeting immediate necessities and the date for actual initiation of construction should be 10–20 years in average municipal practice. Such inertia need not remain undisturbed and unchallenged. By taking for granted that delays in execution are inevitable, the water works industry virtually sanctions the continuance of an undesirable situation.

7. *Restrictions on increases in water rates* have, in some instances, retarded expansions required for the provision of adequate service. It is frequently assumed that such increases in rates would be difficult to obtain. There are many indications that this fear is not borne out by customer attitudes. In Baltimore, for example, an "across-the-board" increase in water rates, approaching 50 per cent, was accepted by the community in 1951 with virtually no dissent. Similar accomplishments are on record in other communities where appropriate public education has been carried out.

8. *Prevailing water works opinion* over the last half century has perhaps had something to do with the situation in which the industry now finds itself. If there was a philosophy on water service, it encompassed high efficiency coupled with a perpetual emphasis on curtailment of use. It is true that this policy was always lightly qualified with footnotes to the effect that the reductions were pointed primarily at illegitimate or wasteful use, but it is difficult to recall a parallel case of systematic insistence upon selling less and less of a product.

The power industry, of course, has had to initiate curtailment of use on many occasions, owing to roughly the same causes as those which have confronted water works. The power industry, however, did not make a virtue of this necessity. It always considered restriction of use as an undesirable commodity-marketing process. It would be interesting to know how the power consumer would respond to an almost continuous onslaught of suggestions that he use no electricity from 8 PM to 10 AM every day during the summer. Or how he might respond if he were deluged with suggestions that one bulb per house would be more desirable than a well-lighted establishment. It must be remembered that coal, hydroelectricity, and even atomic-power fuel are limited and costly. Somehow the practitioners in these and other industries intend to keep service adequate to meet the requirements and desires of the paying, consuming public.

Nature of Reasonable Water Service

In recent years much discussion has filled the technical journals in the search for a definition of reasonable water service. These efforts at definition have ranged from the hope that reasonable water service would mean providing water for all parts of the land for all requirements at all times to definitions which rest rigidly upon a service of limited character, dominated primarily by the inflexibility of existing water rate policies. Neither of these extremes is likely to produce the greatest benefits for the customers.

Reasonable water service cannot ordinarily include the dramatic necessities of areas which simply have little or no water resources. The fact that water shortage is a characteristic of Death Valley need not be of overwhelming concern to the day-to-day purveyor of water in other parts of the country. This phase of the problem of water service is very well expressed in the following quotation from a Rand Corp. study:

> As so frequently happens, facts and sober analysis largely dissipate fears. Water is an economic resource, like any other. It will never be "short" in any absolute sense, since there is always more available—at a price. It is true [that] water stringency may limit growth of an area, but only in the same sense in which the limited availability of any resource may be a check upon growth. If a certain region ceases its expansion relative to the rest of the nation or the world for lack of easily available water, it means only that the natural advantages, of which the availability of water is one example, of that region have been utilized to their economic limit. The situation differs in no essential respect from instances in history in which a period of rapid relative growth of one region or another came to an end as the supply of such resources as land or coal was pressed to its economic limit.[2]

The real problem of reasonable water service occurs, therefore, as the result primarily of artificial restraints, largely manmade. Critchlow has recently summarized these restraints, in brief terms, in a newspaper interview: "There is no shortage. In a great many places, the trouble—lack of water due to low pressure—occurs because the mains are too small to meet the big demands of a dry spell."[3] He goes on to suggest that municipal and private systems did not keep pace with the giant growth of the suburbs but sought cheaper, stopgap solutions with minimum expenditures that were bound to cause increasingly frequent restrictions on use. Almost every public statement of water main extension policy is prefaced by restrictive language. Negative policies rather than realistic, militant, positive programming have too often been the guide.

The water works industry should provide a service which is consistently and continuously available, even at peak demands and in anticipation of the requirements of expanding geographical areas. Such reasonable service must encompass the consumers' requirements for all modern water-using devices, including the growing demand for, and interest in, the use of water for gardening purposes. Such a specification by no means implies that the industry must accept wasteful uses of water, illegitimate diversions, inadequate payment, or unsound development of real estate.

Preparation for Reasonable Service

The translation of the above specification for reasonable water service into reality will require an arduous effort along a number of important professional fronts. The kind of service which most water works men would prefer to offer to the consumer, and which complies with the specification noted above, cannot be accomplished without reference to at least some of the following stages. The speed and skill with which these stages are reached and passed will determine when the consumer will be more satisfied with water service than he is today.

1. *Maintenance of continuing technical review.* The uses of water, the sources required, and the distribution facilities essential for reasonable water service should be under continuing scrutiny. Reviews every 10–20 years are too infrequent to meet the demands of the times. It is essential for the industry to scrutinize its problems and its solutions, if not week by week, at least year by year. Coupled with these reviews, similar assays of the financial aspects of water service will undoubtedly be required. The issue of financial restraints looms large in most discussions but is often used as an alibi rather than to diagnose the problem. It should be remembered, as Howson[4] has recently pointed out, that: (1) all water service is cheap; (2) the difference in cost between mediocre and excellent water service rarely exceeds a fraction of a cent per capita per day; (3) increased water rates simply enable water works to give better service; and (4) the cost of water is now comparatively the lowest ever experienced.

Murdoch[4] has expressed similar views in the following colorful language: "Until water works officials stop thinking and acting like managers of bankrupt bargain basements . . . and begin to adopt the attitudes of successful sellers of quality goods, the public will not understand the worth of water works service."

2. *Development of criteria of adequacy.* Many in the water works industry have been aware for years that there are no quantitative criteria of adequate and reasonable water service. This lack of specifications which might guide both the public and regulatory agencies needs to be given thoughtful consideration by professional societies. The fire underwriters have done yeoman service, over the years, in supplying virtually the only criteria of adequacy but would be the first to admit that their specifications are limited in scope. They have served, however, to upgrade the quality of service almost more than those of any other group. Utility commissioners and practicing engineers have still to meet this challenge, even though they have, in many instances, developed qualitative criteria of reasonable service which still remain to be translated into guiding principles for general acceptance.

3. *Development of public relations programs.* These must be extended and must move from historically negative precepts to future positive development. Properly handled, such programs are of inestimable value to the public. Without them, it is doubtful whether the concepts expressed in this paper and elsewhere will make their way expeditiously with the consumer.

4. *Reconciliation of costs and income.* This aspect of the problem needs no further underscoring, as it has been discussed and elaborated upon for years. It is axiomatic that no service can be provided without appropriate financial return. There should be no misguided conception that a magic wand can dispense with adequacy of income.

5. *Provision of machinery for action in metropolitan areas.* One of the greatest omissions of the water works industry is in the failure to provide early and promptly enough for the machinery for engineering, administering, and financing water works development. The responsibility for this deficiency rests squarely upon all concerned—the consulting engineer, state agencies, the industry itself, and the public. Precedents for the establishment of appropriate means for dealing with the problem are extensive. Their introduction into most of the metropolitan areas of the country has faltered, over the last quarter of a century, primarily because of the absence of an active program for providing such machinery. The situation will not cure itself. The cure still awaits an aroused professional and citizen group.

Without the machinery for prompt action, it is difficult to see how the requirements of great population shifts are to be met. The population of Los Angeles County, for example, has shown a net gain of 738,880 since the federal census of 1950. This net gain in less than 4 years is about equal to the population of Pittsburgh or New Orleans. To service such an area without this machinery and at a leisurely pace would certainly result in chaos.

6. *Reexamination of improvement financing.* In 1921 Morse and Wolman[5] pointed out that capital improvements in water systems involved both public and private benefits. The authors further emphasized the fact that construction which is of value to all the community—and, hence, to all taxable property—included reservoirs, pumping stations, treatment works, supply lines, and large distribution mains. The payment for such capital investment, both in theory and in practice, should not and could not come out of current water rates. If these capital improvements were exclusively financed by water rates, only two results were to be anticipated. Either the rates would be excessively high, if appropriate capital expenditures were pursued, or else the necessary capital expenditures simply would not be made.

Of the major sources of revenue of a water works system—general taxation, special assessments, and water rates—the third has dominated the historical scene. Many reasons may be summoned up to account for the position of the water rate as almost the only source of revenue for water system construction and operation. This reliance upon the water rate alone, or in conjunction with the front-foot assessment, was never sound or equitable. The results of the use of only a single source of revenue are dramatically apparent throughout the country. It should not have taken a quarter of a century to show that necessary capital expenditures could not equitably rest only upon water rates. The community significance of a water system has been completely ignored in most rate structures and water fiscal programs. The mere presence of a water works in a community is of value to all of the taxable property. That property which will benefit now or later should share a reasonable part of the cost of planned expansion.

Expansion in advance of reasonably anticipated service necessities could be materially eased if the areas in which such expansions are required are subject to modest property taxation. Only by such means is it probable that the necessities of the area may be anticipated with maximum speed. Pressure for immediate consumption revenue would be materially reduced. Likewise, the number of consumers immediately available to each foot of main would not be the sole criterion for expansion. The identifiable requirements of society would provide the basis for both design and income.

Most present methods of financing water works are restrictive in nature. They do not permit the most realistic and prompt planning, action, and financing. As stated in 1953:

All of us in public health and public administration have fallen down in two areas of effort. We have failed to develop the administrative and fiscal machinery necessary to provide the public amenities of water supply, sewerage, and sewage disposal in areas outside the political boundaries of individual cities. Efficient planning, with very few exceptions, declines as one moves out of the municipality itself into its metropolitan areas, and in turn from the metropolitan areas into the more rural counties. It virtually disappears on an intercounty basis. Here we encounter the absence of either or both a responsible official agent or a militant public interest and knowledge. The two of course, are inseparable, whether in city, metropolitan area, or county.

The tremendous growth in this country in the past decade will probably continue in the next decade, particularly in the metropolitan areas, and generally there is no organization to assure installation of conventional sanitation features. All down the line our official groups for one reason or another have failed to introduce or develop the planning that would have prevented retrogression in this area.[6]

The magnitude of many of the suburban developments is such that the water department of the central city faces severe problems of financing the extensive water supply installations required. It is likewise undesirable to finance such works by the issuance of general-obligation bonds against the general credit of the city, unless there already exists a routine for doing so. The use of revenue bonds to finance suburban installations is a modern and appropriate method of handling the situation. If new legislative authority is required, it should be provided promptly. These measures, coupled with general taxation where necessary, would simplify the suburban utilities' finance problem in county areas.

REFERENCES

1. MacKichan, K. A. & Graham, J. B. Public Water Supply Shortages, 1953. USGS Supplement 3, Washington, D.C. (1954).

2. De Haven, J. C.; Gore, L. A.; & Hirshleifer, Jack. A Brief Survey of the Technology and Economics of Water Supply. Report R-258-RC., Rand Corp. (Oct. 1953).

3. Critchlow, H. T. New York *World Telegram* (Jun. 25, 1954).

4. Cunningham, M. B., et al. Promoting Better Public Understanding of What Water Works Service Is Worth. *Jour. AWWA*, 45: 997 (Oct. 1953).

5. Morse, R. B. & Wolman, Abel. A Plan for Meeting Water Supply and Sewerage Costs. *Eng. News-Rec.*, 86: 22 (Jun. 21, 1921).

6. Wolman, Abel. Unfinished Business and New Forces in Environmental Health Orthodoxy. *Pub. Health Rpts.*, 68: 962 (1953).

The Water Resources Commission
of Maryland*

The biologists tell us that one of the penalties of growth is competition. This axiom is nowhere better exemplified than in the contest for water supply which has accompanied the development of every civilization. When people roamed this country in the pioneer days the assignment of water supply to various groups of individuals did not demand conscious public regulation.

In Maryland, as in other states in this country, the drought of 1930 emphasized anew the necessity for some coordination of the use of the water supply resources of the State. The rainfall deficiency of 1930 was dramatic. During that year less than 24 inches of rainfall occurred in Maryland in contrast with a normal average of from 40 to 46 inches. Newspapers seized upon this situation with the same fervor as they now discuss the deficiencies of Congress. People became sufficiently "water conscious" to be interested in discussing a water supply problem.

To those of us who have been concerned with water supply in the State of Maryland for a number of decades, the drought was merely a useful device for catching and holding the ear of important lay groups

* Reprinted from the *Journal American Water Works Association*, Vol. 24, No. 8 (August, 1932). Copyright 1932 by the American Water Works Association, Inc. Presented before the Four States Section meeting, June 8, 1932.

long enough to convince them of the fact that without water there is no physiological, industrial, or social life.

Although the results of the drought were for the moment unfortunate, the year 1930 may always be looked upon in Maryland as a significant year, in that immediately following thereon the Water Resources Commission was created to investigate the entire problem. The Legislative Assembly of 1931 defined the duties of this Commission in the following terms:

> To review the underground and surface water resources of the State of Maryland in order to determine upon the most effective plan to preserve and allocate such water supply resources for maximum public benefit and use; to study the problem of regulation of streams by storage reservoirs or other means; to survey the necessity for creating water service districts; to review the present practices and future necessities in the location, design and construction of dams and reservoirs; and to prepare and submit a report to the General Assembly of Maryland of 1933 embodying its findings and recommendations, including a legislative program, if such be found desirable in the light of the commission's investigations.

It may be of some interest to this group to sketch the water supply situation in Maryland and to indicate what it is hoped the Resources Commission may accomplish in placing these resources upon a permanently useful and coordinated basis for the future.

Present and Prospective Uses of Water

By far the greater proportion of water supply used for public purposes in Maryland is taken from surface streams. Forty-one public supplies, serving 42 independent municipalities, state institutions, camps, and water districts in Maryland, as well as the District of Columbia and several smaller supplies in Pennsylvania and West Virginia, furnish the daily water consumption of approximately 1,600,000 people. Of these, 1,100,000 live in the State of Maryland and constitute approximately 67 per cent of the total population. These communities draw from Maryland streams about 225,000,000 gallons in every 24 hours, of which 140,000,000 are used within the boundaries of the State.

More extended use of these surface sources will probably result in the future, so that by 1950, 1,580,000 people within and approximately 800,000 outside of the State, should require surface water supplies for public potable use. These requirements are now estimated by the Commission to approximate in 1950, 350,000,000 gallons per day.

The Commission has estimated further, through data supplied by the State Department of Health, that in 1931 the requirements for industrial and stream power uses of water constituted an additional draft on surface streams within the State which exceeded 322,000,000 gallons. Any estimate of such industrial and steam power station water supplies for 1950 is impracticable, although it is reasonable to suppose that increased industrial development along Maryland streams is probable, if stream flows are adequately regulated so as to supply sufficient quantities of water at all times.

From the above estimates the present demand on surface waters apparently exceeds 550,000,000 gallons of water per day. This total demand will probably be doubled by 1950.

Allocation of Surface Water Resources

One of the first concerns of the Commission is to determine what agency, if any, should be created by the State of Maryland to control the allocation of surface water resources to the best advantage of the people. The Commission has before it the task of setting up some agency which will be in a position to issue a certificate of public convenience and necessity from time to time to interested public or private groups, competitively seeking the permanent use of surface streams. Such a certificate, the Commission believes, will be desirable as a prerequisite to any future problem of water use. Something approaching a city plan, sufficiently moving in character, but stable in principle, is desirable for the adequate regulation of these valuable resources. By such a scheme of state control, the balancing of competitive demands and uses should be accomplished. At the same time unwise development, detrimental to large parts of the population, can be curbed and adjusted by some agency technically equipped and qualified to make the necessary investigations and decisions.

Measurement of Stream Flow

As a necessary preliminary to a policy of allocation some careful, permanent, and continuous stock-taking of stream flow is essential. The elementary bookkeeping of water resources is frequently neglected, but without it no intelligent administration of a plan is possible.

Prior to 1925 there were less than a dozen stream gaging stations in Maryland. On April 30, 1932, there were 28 of such stations operating in the State. The continuation of these and the installation of others are important undertakings for the future.

Consolidation of Water Users

Duplication of water supply facilities is not peculiar to Maryland. Its financial and engineering disadvantages have been apparent for many years. Competition for available sources of supply under conditions of duplication is expensive. Consolidation of users into carefully planned water supply districts avoids duplication of supply, purification, and pumping works, eliminates competition for desirable sources and makes it possible to maintain competent engineering forces for the control of the supply. Many communities, too small individually to provide their own water systems, may secure safe and ample public service by such joint action.

Such regional control of the distribution of water may be suggested by the Commission in the form of permissive State legislation, in order to facilitate more prompt accomplishment of this desirable purpose than has been the case in the past, where the creation of each water supply district required a great many years of propagandizing and of education.

Stream Regimentation

The occurrence of floods with their damaging effects has also given rise to careful consideration of the regulation of stream flow. The wide variations in flow characteristic of Maryland streams make the usefulness of these streams without regimentation very limited. The major streams in the State of Maryland show maximum flows ranging from 20 to 80 times their average flow. As a consequence, destructive floods and damaging droughts follow each other in cycles. The most adequate development of these resources calls for procedures of storage and release which would result in the elimination of flood hazards, in the increase of low flows of the stream and in the stabilizing of the safe yields for our major sources of supply.

Control of Structures on Surface Streams

With the exception of the control which the State Department of Health exercises over the location and the design of water supply dams for public water supply systems, no agency in the State is at present equipped by law or by personnel to pass upon the design, construction, or maintenance of dams for public water supplies or hydroelectric developments.

If a dam is constructed in a state adjacent to Maryland on a stream flowing into Maryland, all of the elements of the development of that project are scrutinized by some state agency, even though the collapse of such a dam would create damage in the State of Maryland. If the same dam were built in Maryland on the same stream, the amount of supervision over its design and construction would be practically nil.

With the history of failures of dams before the Commission, this is another water supply problem to which it intends to give its attention.

Summary

The Water Resources Commission, therefore, finds itself confronted in the State of Maryland with a practically uncontrolled situation in the development of water resources. Elements of quality and safety of supply are, of course, controlled by the State Department of Health. A more elaborate and intelligent policy of State regulation to preserve and allocate these resources for best use, to measure their flow, to provide district grouping for their most convenient and economical development, and to arrange for some form of check upon the structures which are placed upon such streams is the aim of the Commission. In this accomplishment of this task the practice of other states in this country and abroad is being reviewed. Their application to the local conditions in Maryland is being considered. When these have been crystallized, it is the hope of the Commission that they may be formulated into law.

The Commission, appointed by Governor Albert C. Ritchie, consists of the following individuals:

Mr. F. H. Dryden, City Engineer, Salisbury.

Dr. Thomas W. Koon, former Mayor, Cumberland.

Dr. E. B. Mathews, State Geologist, Maryland Geological Survey, Baltimore.

Mr. Richard Mommers, Superintendent, American Sugar Refining Company, Baltimore.

Mr. Robert B. Morse, Chief Engineer, Washington Suburban Sanitary District, Hyattsville.

Mr. Philip B. Perlman, Attorney-at-Law, Baltimore.

Mr. Abel Wolman, Chief Engineer, Maryland State Department of Health, Baltimore, *Chairman*.

Problems in Developing a National Flood-Protection Policy*

Synopsis

After every major catastrophe public demand for preventive action reaches its peak and the solutions proposed are as varied as the interests involved. In this respect the March, 1936, floods were no exception. Demands for immediate action, for Congressional appropriations, for financial programs, filled the lay and technical journals. History teaches that in such periods of stress, judgment and logic are unduly influenced by emotion. It is frequently the most unfavorable time in which to formulate policies for control. When public interest is at its height, on the other hand, is the most fruitful period in which to make real progress in the solution of a difficult national problem.

Most thoughtful students of flood-protection procedure would probably agree on the following facts:

(*a*) Engineering studies of past destructive floods are by and large incomplete.

(*b*) Detailed and carefully prepared programs for immediate flood protection are likewise lacking in many areas, although reconnaissance studies are available.

(*c*) In the development of principles and policies much more than engineering information and conclusions is needed.

* Reprinted with permission from *Proceedings American Society of Civil Engineers*, Vol. 63, No. 3, 1937, 429–39.

(*d*) A kind of statesmanship and creative thinking, not yet fully developed, is required, which will balance local and national needs and costs against assessments of benefits.

(*e*) A new sense of social responsibility on the part of local areas is needed.

(*f*) Protection for a local area should be designed not only to meet the flood-control requirements of the area, but for the social and economic advantages of the nation in respect to all water uses.

A large number of reports by Federal or local agencies have been prepared from time to time. The most important undertakings of this type are those known as the "308 Reports" of the Corps of Engineers, U.S. Army. Because of the limitations under which these documents were prepared, they cannot all be considered as of completely definitive character. In such instances adjustment is needed, and, in general, a continuing review is desirable.

The interval between the preparation of reports, where they have been made, and the actual initiation of construction work, is likely to be long. Almost a quarter of a century elapsed, for example, between the preparation of a document on the Muskingum River floods and the building of the control structures.

An analysis of national shortcomings in flood-protection measures soon discloses that the problem is highly complex and that it cannot be reviewed upon so simple a basis as flood protection *per se*. Although many engineers and most laymen would urge strongly the correction or prevention of flood damages, even a superficial review of the situation makes it clear that few flood-protection programs should proceed without consideration of the relationship of these measures to other possible uses of water. When such reviews are undertaken, simplicity of approach gives way to complexity of use and to conflicts in purpose and in policy.

Because of these difficulties in orientation the writer considers it wise to present a brief analysis of the various aspects of determining upon a national flood-protection policy and to outline what measures are under way, as of 1937, to clarify some of the problems involved. In this attempt, it will be apparent that considerations other than engineering loom large in the final solution. Nevertheless, any generalized program for water use must rest obviously upon detailed and careful engineering analysis. In periods of stress and haste this axiom has not always been observed. It is a prerequisite to all that is written in this paper.

Engineering Aspects

What are the links in the chain of engineering evidence that should be available before a national policy can emerge?

To engineers, of course, the first element of deficiency is in incomplete hydrologic data, not only for floods but for every form of river runoff. The Water Resources Committee of the National Resources Committee, in several of its sub-committee publications, has called attention to these deficiencies in basic hydrologic data. Whether these deficiencies are corrected in the future depends upon such organizations as the Society and upon lay support.

Without such book-keeping of hydrologic data, no policy can be adopted with complete confidence. The program should be nation-wide, continuous, and technically accurate, and the results should be regularly interpreted and reported to the profession. Discontinuous observation, although perhaps better than nothing, does not fully meet the requirements.

Even in 1937, detailed analyses of major floods leave something to be desired, although the "308" reports of the War Department and the publications by the Miami Conservancy District, the United States Geological Survey, and the Bureau of Agricultural Engineering, have added material of incalculable value in recent years. The studies should be extended. Findings are spotty geographically, and methods of analysis and of forecast still need improvement.

In determining the effects of different procedures on the control of floods, in some instances the profession is still divided, and the heat of discussion has so far prevented a calm analysis.

What part detention reservoirs, channel improvements, zoning control of encroachment, forestation, soil conservation, small dams, and so-called "upstream engineering" should play in a general water-resources program, still remains to be demonstrated conclusively. The hiatus between claim and substantiation in fact is wide, and competitive claims are scarcely sufficient basis for a permanent policy. Only detailed field and office analysis of water resources control can disclose the relative merits of the various devices and procedures. In this regard, "newspaper experts" have not been the only delinquents. Members of the Engineering Profession have permitted themselves to be diverted into defensive or offensive controversial fields where their capacities for objective analysis have suffered or disappeared. At times, little or no interest has been exhibited by those individuals who should be most interested, in the multiple-use problem in water-resources development. Not all the present difficulties of approach may be ascribed to misguided enthusiasts among the laymen. After all, engineering guidance for public opinion is more necessary to-day than at any other time in the past. Aloofness, professional provincialism, political partisanship, are all strange bedfellows for engineering judgment. Engineering texts, of course, are filled with principles of caution and logic in the matter of water-resources development; but how frequently are they ignored! For example, the zoning principle suggested by the late Allen Hazen, M. Am. Soc. C. E., many years ago, for application in flood areas, when discussed at all to-day is met with scoffing in some groups and with complete disregard in others. Yet as a flood-protection measure, it may some day have the place in the sun that it undoubtedly deserves.

Financial Aspects

The engineering aspects of water-resources control lend themselves to quantitative determination and decision. This is not the case, however, with the financial aspect of the problem. The simple statement that water-resources development, and flood protection as a unit thereof, should be financed largely by local interests, is sound and clear on paper. No one can take issue with this statement of policy; but its practical application requires discussion.

It is not invariably true that a water-resources program is restricted to the confines of a single State. Often two or more States are involved. Often reservoir sites in one State may be used for the control of flow in three or four down-stream States. In this setting, the concepts of damages, benefits, and allocation of the costs of correction are decidedly confusing.

Any one reviewing the damages presumably caused by destructive floods is at once impressed with the absence of any standard criteria for evaluation. Any two agencies, Federal or local, are likely to arrive at separate estimates of the flood damages in a given area that will differ widely. These deficiencies in approach led the Water Resources Committee to appoint a sub-committee in December, 1936, to study the criteria for the evaluation of flood damages. No one believes that an immediate standardized methodology in this field is desirable, but it should be possible to present certain major criteria of approach that would put such estimates on a more scientific basis. Likewise, no one believes that a methodology must be devised which is a substitute for long experience. An analysis of practical criteria may clarify, however, the concepts even for the experienced observer.

Most people assume that the economic justification for flood protection is simple to evaluate. It is surprising to find how little information is available, not only on specific flood damage, but on the general, special, and intangible benefits that might arise from the initiation of flood-protection measures. Various procedures have been used from place to place, but it is rare that the details of such principles of benefit evaluation are presented so as to be readily subject to check.

Since assessment of local benefit, presumably the base of local participation, is still in a nebulous state, the difficulty of adhering to what appears to be a sound policy becomes more complicated as each flood-protection project comes under review.

The pressing question of how much central responsibility for flood protection the Federal Government should assume, is more difficult to answer when viewed in the light of specific undertakings than when stated as a general principle. One reason for this difficulty is that the mere definition of "Federal" interest is continually undergoing adjustment. This is not solely due, as many believe, to the so-called rise in central bureaucracy. It may be the result and the penalty of increasing national integration. It may be the result and the penalty of growth of population and of the difficulty of separating local from regional hazards and corrective measures.

It is a Jeffersonian principle that government in the United States should result "in the partition of cares, descending in gradation from general to particular, that the mass of human affairs may be best managed for the good and prosperity of all." This precept is valid only until its application under the pressure of such difficulties as those encountered in water-resources development makes deviations therefrom necessary. The question is how far such deviations are wise; how much may be accomplished within the framework of State autonomy; how well drainage-basin enterprises may be developed within that framework; and what re-adjustments in theoretical principles, if any, the pressing problems of water resources may make necessary.

In such a complicated problem it is obvious, at least to the writer, that slow motion is a sound principle of action. Heroic changes in procedures of Federal-local responsibility must be approached with caution. At the same time, it may be questioned whether such approaches should be so congealed by precedent no longer applicable, that no comprehensive treatment of water resources is possible.

In the allocation of financial responsibility, it should also be remembered that a simple formula may be a first necessity. The Flood Control Act of 1936 illustrates, however, that in the desire to adopt a simple formula for local participation, many inequities necessarily arise. The percentage to be paid by local areas in terms of land and rights of way may vary from 10 to the maximum legal limit of 50. The intent of such a Congressional Act may be wise, but its application is likely to be inequitable. A logical substitute for the simple formula type of Congressional approach lies in moving administrative control. This gives rise in turn to the charge of increased bureaucracy, although the nature of the water-resources problem would appear to pre-suppose the necessity of avoiding a rigid formula for evaluating local and central responsibility.

When the problem is extended to the evaluation of benefits and costs in multiple uses of a stream, the difficulty of using a formula on a national basis becomes even more apparent. In this field, there may be no escape from continuing administrative adjustment and evaluation. This will no doubt create a variety of geographic apportionments of costs, and necessarily much argument. Here, again, is a fruitful field for the best technical thought of the country.

The formulation of a national fiscal policy with reference to any important public undertaking has always been beset with the necessity of reconciling logical processes with public sentiment and clamor. Changes, supported by local greed, may soon convert a sane national policy into a general "grab-bag" for distributing Federal funds to local projects, sometimes well conceived and involving important national interests, but too frequently badly conceived and purely local in character.

The cold statement of historical facts in regard to national enterprise may be interpreted as disheartening examples of "increasing feeding of local areas out of the Federal trough," or as examples of "the slow evolutionary assumption of Federal financial responsibility for undertakings of national interest." It is the writer's opinion that the correct interpretation lies somewhere between these two extremes.

Experience certainly teaches that before establishing any permanent national policy for financing public works, one should make certain, on the one hand, that the interests of the country as a whole are being adequately protected and advanced, and, on the other, that opportunities are not created for the complete degradation of local responsibility. The tendency, unfortunately, is generally in the latter direction, and safeguards must be provided in the water-resources development policy to avoid the error of expanding Federal power and financial responsibility without local responsibility.

It should be clear from this brief discussion of some of the financial problems involved that a trial-and-error technique is a pre-requisite to ultimate solution. Experimentation in government to-day arouses violent opposition in some quarters, but, carefully organized and carefully controlled, it appears to be a necessary adjunct to the normal processes of desirable water-resources development. A substitute for experimentation is no more desirable in this, than in any other scientific, field where rationalization has long since given way to trial-and-error technique.

More than fifty years ago, Ambassador Bryce made the discerning observation with reference to American political institutions, strongly applicable to the subject in hand, that: "The longer one studies a vast subject, the more cautious in inference does he become."

Administrative Aspects

If future water development should result only from comprehensive study of possible multiple uses or methods, other problems beyond those of engineering and finance present themselves. Decisions must be reached from time to time as to what governmental or private agency should be permitted to undertake the construction of vast water-resources programs, whether for flood protection alone, or for multiple purposes. Controversy again rages in this field as between central and local public bodies and as between public and private agencies.

There are occasions, of course, when this particular administrative difficulty is absent. The development of flood-protection measures within Los Angeles County, California, alone, for example, may present no particular problems of national policy. The type of organization may be controlled locally. The methods of raising funds and assessments may be controversial, but, at the same time, not of national import. When the problem is extended, however, beyond the confines of a single county, or of a single State, and when the best uses of a stream include its development for power, for navigation, for potable water supply, and for tion is posed wthout prejudice at the moment. It should be brought clearly flood protection, can some form of national control be avoided? The question-into the daylight, and its discussion should not rest wholly upon abstract and emotional concepts of political philosophy.

The administrative difficulties are not all resolved when the responsibility for the initial construction has been agreed upon. Similar difficulties arise in the operation and management of undertakings, where further reconciliation of diverging interests may be continually necessary.

Recent experience with one of the reservoirs in the Far West, is illustrative of a type of problem likely to be multiplied in the future. With a full reservoir, technical experts recommended, on the basis of snow surveys, that the reservoir be emptied so that its capacity would be available for catching spring run-off. If this had not been done the heavy spring run-off, equivalent to the reservoir capacity, would have created damaging floods. Yet compliance with this competent technical advice required extensive negotiations with political parties, private interests, and public agencies, leading ultimately to the Governor of the State for final decision. The engineer cannot ignore the brute facts of public pressure no matter how cloistered he may be.

History has shown that each drop of water may be the source of deadly conflict. The problems cannot be settled in the laboratory, but must be adjusted in terms of public demand. Undoubtedly, the Engineering Profession has the task of educating the public in the field of its operations. It is a task, incidentally, in which so far it has made no great progress; otherwise, the clamor for faulty engineering panaceas would not have reached the heights it has attained in recent years.

Suggested Approaches to the Development of a National Water Resources Policy

No easy road to the promulgation of a national policy for flood protection or for a national policy of broader character is available.

Acceptance of this conclusion has led agencies of all levels of Government, and the Water Resources Committee and its predecessors (the Mississippi Valley Committee and the Water Planning Committee of the National Resources Board), to approach the task experimentally.

The operations of the Miami Conservancy District, the Muskingum Conservancy District, the Corps of Engineers on the Mississippi Valley flood-control work, and of the Tennessee Valley Authority are all indicative of a distinct, although unconscious, desire to direct public action into logical engineering, financial, and administrative channels. The varied experiences of each of these organizations disclose a gradual evolution toward emphasis on multiple uses of streams, on drainage-basin concepts, on Federal-local participations, and on generally broader handling of stream problems than those current in the early years of the century.

Whether for better or worse, people are beginning to view the control of a stream for flood reduction as an integral phase of the use of that stream for power, navigation, irrigation, public water supply, and sanitation. To the writer it is an evolutionary step of merit. It creates complications in all fields of attack, but the objectives appear wise.

To the aforementioned approaches by Federal and local agencies, the Water Resources Committee has added several undertakings, which are briefly presented herein as further examples of multiple-use of streams. In its studies, the Water Resources Committee has kept two basic principles in mind: First, it has included in the deliberations on the uses of a particular stream, the States covered by the drainage basin in question (this was done on the assumption that no real progress in analysis or solution of the problem would be successful without the highest degree of local participation); and, second, it has assumed that no standard method of approach has yet been evolved, which is invariably applicable to the United States as a whole.

The Committee assumed further that different problems would require different structural arrangements for experimental demonstration, and that the cost of carrying out such experimental studies in every instance should be borne by the Federal and local agencies primarily concerned.

The Red River of the North. The investigation of the Red River of the North resulted largely from a meeting called on June 3, 1935, in Fargo, N. Dak., by the Governors of Minnesota and North Dakota to consider the problems of water conservation, stream pollution, and sewage disposal in the Red River Valley. The call was directed particularly to the members of the State Planning Boards of the three States—Minnesota, North Dakota, and South Dakota.

This conference was followed by a second one in St. Paul, Minn., on

November 26, 1935, in which representatives of the National Resources Committee participated. At this meeting, a committee was appointed to develop a co-ordinated plan for the development and protection of water throughout the basin of the Red River of the North. As representatives of the Water Resources Committee, W. W. Horner, M. Am. Soc. C. E., of St. Louis, Mo., and Harlan H. Barrows, of Chicago, Ill., were delegated to act. At the request of the conference, Mr. Horner was designated by the National Resources Committee as Technical Consultant in the preparation of the ultimate water plan.

On July 8, 1936, a report of the Third Inter-State Conference on the Red River of the North Drainage Basin was issued, proposing an adequately developed water plan, on a long-time basis, the primary objective of which is the development of dependable stream flows during the dry periods of the year in quantity ample for urban water supply and for the dilution of wastes. To attain this objective, the plan called for the development of storage in head-water areas, the regulation of stream flow in accordance with a predetermined program, and for improvement of stream channels to minimize water losses.

The report also reviewed the physical characteristics of the basin, its economic conditions and trends, and its water problems, and presented a recommended program of projects to put the co-ordinated plan of water development into action.

This is perhaps the first comprehensive program of river drainage basin improvement carefully developed in the United States, with three State groups participating and with competent engineering control and direction. It offers for the first time a skilfully drawn program for water conservation, susceptible to step-by-step construction in accordance with the financial capacity of the territory to carry the load. It provides for flood control in heavy run-off periods and for low-water supplementation in dry years.

The findings of the report are now (1937) being put into effect by local groups, and where money is being spent by Federal agencies in the territory, it is being spent in accordance with the definitely formulated plan.

The development of such a program implies time and the availability of money. It cannot be accomplished otherwise. The case in point illustrates, however, that it is feasible, with a certain amount of central direction and stimulation, to interest individual States in the preparation of a joint comprehensive program of action. It is hoped that this precedent may be followed with necessary local modification by other groups of States having similar pressing problems of water use. It is not implied, of course, that local pressures may not create deviations from the master plan, but the existence of an agreed master plan generally reduces these hazards to a minimum.

The Rio Grande. Competitive uses of the water of the Rio Grande had reached such an acute stage in 1935 that it became necessary for the President of the United States to issue an order preventing the release of further Federal funds for any projects on this basin north of El Paso, Tex., until the National Resources Committee had approved the undertaking. An interstate compact between the States of Colorado, New Mexico, and Texas had been in operation for some time and was to expire in June, 1937.

In view of the conflicts of interest these three States, together with the Federal agencies concerned, undertook a detailed study of the water resources of the basin. Both Federal and State groups have contributed money and personnel to the undertaking. The studies should disclose non-controversial bases for the development of new agreements. They may be substitutes for Court action and may lead to the evolution of interstate agreements for the use of the Rio Grande water without basic controversy. The method of approach is again one for special purposes which might be adopted in other areas. Again, time and money are prerequisites; it should be emphasized that without these two elements programs and policies cannot be "pulled out of thin air."

Kansas River Flood Studies. The first contribution to the study of the Kansas River flood problem by the Water Resources Committee, or its predecessors, was made on November 1, 1934, when $25,000 was made available for expenditure under the direction of the Chief of Engineers, U. S. Army, for survey and investigation of the Milford Reservoir site on the Lower Republican River and the Tuttle Creek site on the lower part of the Big Blue River. Before investigations were started, it was decided to hold up the work pending agreement with the Flood Protection Planning Committee for Greater Kansas City, in regard to the conduct of the study, and the appointment of a Consultant by the Committee. The agreement was soon reached, and the surveys went forward during the summer of 1935, with F. H. Fowler, M. Am. Soc. C. E., as the Consultant.

It shortly became apparent that a complete plan for reservoir control of the Kansas floods might require the construction of additional storage on tributaries entering the main stream below the Republican and the Big Blue, and that considerable information regarding flood conditions in Kansas City might be secured from a river model. On the recommendation of the Water Resources Committee additional funds were made available to the U. S. Division Engineer on November 27, 1935. These funds consisted of $22,500 for surveys and borings at supplementary storage sites, and $12,000 for a river model, which was later constructed at the U. S. Waterways Experiment Station, at Vicksburg, Miss.

During the spring of 1936, the Bureau of the Budget rescinded $8,000 of the $22,500, thus preventing temporarily the completion of the schedule of boring at the dam sites. However, shortly afterward, Congress authorized a preliminary examination of the Republican and Smoky Hill Rivers with a view to the control of floods, and the Flood Control Committee of the House of Representatives authorized the Corps of Engineers to review the Kansas River report already published.[1] As a result $150,000 was made available to the U. S. Division Engineer for additional studies. Of this amount, $8,000 was used to replace the amount rescinded by the Bureau of the Budget. Two series of tests on the river model were completed at Vicksburg during 1936. The results have gone far toward remolding public opinion.

Study of an alternative arrangement of levees, combined with bridges, was initiated by the U. S. District Engineer Office, in Kansas City, after a joint inspection by the U. S. Engineer and the Flood Control Committee in May, 1936.

The development of the final plan should represent the reconciled viewpoint of all interests. The method of approach illustrates the merit of joint review by the Corps of Engineers and the local Flood Control Committee and its engineer advisers.

Potomac River Conservancy District. The Water Resources Committee in 1934 recommended to the President the establishment of a Potomac River Conservancy District, primarily for the purpose of providing a field laboratory for evolving engineering, administrative and financial principles, and methods of control. In this instance, as in others, the district was to be under the supervision of the interested States, with Federal participation in a minority membership on the commission. Financing of the enterprise was to be largely by local agencies, public and private, with the stimulation of the Federal Government. Its purpose is solely to develop methods of arriving at solutions on major drainage basins. No action had been taken on this proposal, as of March, 1937, but it is presented herein as another device for supplying the nation with additional information on the problem of drainage-basin control and development. It was proposed as a more practical alternative to nation-wide drainage basin authorities, for which the ground is not yet prepared and which only future careful study can demonstrate to be valid or invalid structures for drainage-basin operation.

The National Drainage Basin Study. Most civil engineers are familiar with the drainage-basin study of the Water Resources Committee. Its purpose is to indicate the outstanding water problems in the various drainage areas of the country, to fit them tentatively into integrated patterns of water development and control, and to present, where existing data make it possible, specific construction and investigation projects as elements of an enlarged plan.

This study supplements and extends the work of the Mississippi Valley Committee of the Public Works Administration and the Water

Planning Committee of the National Resources Board, which agencies have been succeeded by the present Water Resources Committee.

The study under the title of "Public Works Planning" was presented to the President by the National Resources Committee in December, 1936. The President forwarded it to the Congress of the United States on February 3, 1937. It is to be followed by the issuance of a volume containing the more detailed findings of the Water Resources Committee. The date of the publication of this latter volume is the early part of March, 1937.

For many basins, the plan contains relatively few construction projects, because of the lack of essential data. In others, fairly complete construction programs are already available. Obviously, none of the plans is either fixed or final. No one supposes that any long-term plan for any drainage area can be formulated, immediately, in detail, even if all requisite hydrologic data were available. The drainage-basin study, however, should result in a significant contribution "to the framework of an enduring, but adjustable national water plan." It should serve to arouse professional and lay interest in water resources integration, in the extension of these preliminary studies under local auspices, in emphasis upon multiple, rather than upon single-use, development of streams, and in relating water development more adequately to the entire economy of a basin.

Summary

In this paper, the writer has attempted to show that the development of a National Flood Protection Policy should not be separated from that of a National Water Resources Policy in general; that the elements of such policy are highly complex; that they run the gamut of engineering, finance, and administration; that they are bound up with the problem of public prejudice and pressure; that the contributions of engineering thought are the key to the ultimate evolution of a national policy; and that such engineering contributions must be made on the field of battle and not in *vacuo*. In order to clarify some of the issues and to evaluate some of the procedures, local and Federal public and private agencies are collaborating in certain studies. As time goes on the results of these studies should disclose certain principles of action and should supply the basis for an ultimate national policy, changing in character, logical in administration, and as free from prejudice and greed as is possible in a world still fortunately consisting of human beings. A perfect syllogism of action is probably not attainable.

REFERENCE
1. H. R. Doc. 195, 73d Cong., 2d Sess.

Basic Principles of a National Water Resources Policy*

Committee Report

A report of AWWA Committee 1130—National Water Policy, submitted on May 15, 1957, at the annual conference at Atlantic City, N.J., by Abel Wolman, Chairman, Cons. Engr., Baltimore, Md. Other members of the committee were A. P. Black, E. S. Chase, L. H. Enslow, C. H. Bechert, G. E. Ferguson, S. B. Morris, N. T. Veatch, and W. V. Weir.

Preamble

I feel that I must almost apologize for talking about national water policy, because, actually, there is no such thing. Thus, before presenting the formal report of the AWWA Committee on National Water Policy, I want to make a few remarks, more or less historical and perhaps philosophical, with respect to the subject of the report. In making these remarks, I am not speaking for the committee, but strictly personally.

It is approximately a quarter of a century since the first formal statement of a proposed national water policy was made in the mid-1930's by the Water Resources Committee for the then National Resources

* Reprinted from *Journal American Water Works Association*, Vol. 49, No. 7 (July, 1957). Copyright 1957 by the American Water Works Association, Inc. Only the Preamble is by Mr. Wolman alone.

Committee of this country.[1] That statement of national policy was predicated upon an assumption which we should now look at hard and critically. *The assumption was that we needed on the national level and, of course, on the state and local level a water policy which was uniform and equitable.* Those who have pursued this subject and read its vast literature will note that throughout all subsequent discussions, throughout all subsequent official and voluntary association reports, this assumption—that we need a more uniform and equitable water policy—has stood its ground for almost a quarter of a century.

Past Policy Statements

In this first document, it was stated in round terms—and in what could almost be called beautiful literary style—what this uniform and equitable water policy ought to be and what should be embodied in it. These basic points were spelled out in the first document of the National Resources Committee of which I had the pleasure of being a chairman for a period of about 8 years. The literary quality was provided by one member of the Committee at that time, Professor Harlan H. Barrows, then head of the geography department at the University of Chicago. I still think it is an explicit and clear statement of what such a policy ought to be—if you accept the basic assumption.

The Water Resources Committee statement was followed by a series of official reports, the first of which was the President's Water Resources Policy Commission report of 1950 and 1951.[2] This has great significance, not only because of the bulk—its three volumes included more than 2,000 pages—but because it represents one of the finest bibliographical contributions to water policy discussion in this country. It should be on the desk of every individual who has even the remotest professional interest in this subject.

This commission was both preceded and followed by the first Hoover Commission, formed in 1949 with a broader assignment than the water resources group. The Hoover Commission's assignment was to cover the reorganization of the national government as a whole, but no small part of its effort and its contribution dealt with the water resources problem.[3]

In 1951 the Materials Policy Commission was created by the President of the United States and struggled for well over a year, on a very broad basis, to deal with our problem of total resources. Again a significant portion of its report[4] dealt with water resources policy.

The second Hoover Commission followed in 1955 and it worked for almost a year and a half with a fine and extensive technical staff, again producing a whole shelf of volumes, any one of which would be worth rereading if anyone were inclined to familiarize himself with the history of water resources.[5]

Sixth in the series of documents followed in 1956, and was presented by the President of the United States to the Congress as a report of the Presidential Advisory Committee on Water Resources Policy.[6] It was filed with President Eisenhower in December 1955 and submitted to Congress in 1956. It had the great advantage of being concise—instead of a shelf, instead of a thousand pages or more, it was a mere 35 pages, highly readable, very much crystallized, and generally following the same pattern of enunciating water policy that was employed in the preceding five reports.

In addition to all of these, many, many national water policy documents have been prepared by voluntary groups—professional engineering associations, semiprofessional organizations, and pressure groups. The libraries are filled with such statements, which carry essentially uniform policies throughout the total period of about 25 years.

The Engineers Joint Council report of 1951[7] has a special significance, because it was the result of almost a year's deliberation by well over 80 professional engineers. It had the further distinction of representing a great deal of engineering work without reimbursal. It is one of the outstanding examples of engineering contribution to this country—the contribution of a great amount of devotion, time, and effort. The 1951 report has since been reviewed and revised, a new document[8] having been approved in April of this year.

The AWWA itself has had a water policy committee for many years, as has the American Public Power Association. The United States Chamber of Commerce through its Natural Resources Committee has made a whole series of reports. The National Water Conservation Association has taken a stab at this problem, and so has the National Reclamation Association. The Rivers and Harbors Congress has met regularly over the years and has deliberated on these policies and issued statements following, in general, the same basic principles as others, deviating therefrom only in the directions that seem helpful to some of the pressure groups involved.

It is well to be aware of all these policy statements, because, with all the work, with all the deliberation, and with all the participation by myriads of professional and lay groups for almost 25 years, the sum total of the accomplishment in the translation of these policies into congressional policy and action, if not exactly zero, is almost zero.

I give this as a preface to the added contribution today of AWWA's own water policy committee. This new policy may at least be considered to have distinction in that it is only three pages long. Perhaps this reflects the fact that we may all be getting relatively tired of reproducing these principles at length. More significantly, however, I preface the presentation of the document by questions which are directed to AWWA's own committee and to all interested in the subject. Why have all of these carefully phrased statements of national policy never been translated into reality?

I am not sure that I have the answers. I would pose questions—perhaps three or four of them—largely for the reflection of those of us who continue to operate in this field.

Was a Policy Needed?

The first question that must arise, of course, as one looks over this great library of exposition is whether a policy was really needed. That seems a disheartening question to ask after a quarter of a century, after the devotion, after the recording of the hearings, after the tremendous unpublished record on file in Washington. Was a policy needed?

It would appear that if it was needed it was not wanted. It was not wanted by the only people in the country who could create such a policy —namely, the Congress of the United States. Up to today, it would be my comment, reading between the lines and having attended congressional hearings, that Congress does not want a carefully framed water policy.

A secondary question, of course, stems from that: Why does it not want a policy? I would guess that it does not want a policy because it would consider it as an interference with its liberty of action. You might say that I have phrased it, if not happily, at least too philosophically. What I mean by it, of course, is that they do not want a policy that might interfere with sectional choices, with pressures, with political favor, with advantages for one area against another. In other words, there appears to be a latent hostility to a uniform policy and there is more than a latent hostility to an equitable fiscal scheme. Anyone who has reviewed such policy as we have exemplified in national practice will find we have every conceivable system of financing that anybody could conjure up.

The most recent, of course, are strange, unless you bear in mind that this strangeness stems from the fact that we are always in search of a fiscal policy which will not require the beneficiary to pay for what he gets, but will give a semblance of doing so. The vagaries of that semblance over the last 100 years are extremely entertaining if one takes time off to look them over. We, of course, now have reached the stage where the beneficiary pays for something at some remote century deferred in some remote and complex formula which, I feel quite sure, ends in his paying not an original 100 per cent, not an original 50 per cent, but, in some major enterprises, closer to 5 or 10 per cent of his appropriate cost.

Now, I hasten to add as an observer, that that may or may not be an objectionable national policy. I make the point that, in all these matters, we must remember that we live in a democracy in which decisions must be democratically made. They may seem at times to be either unintelligent or abstruse or pressure stricken, but they are still made by the only body that can make them—the Congress of the United States. So much for my first question—was a policy needed?

The record would seem to show that if it was needed, it was not needed badly enough by the appropriate democratic representation—by Congress, that is. I think the answer is inevitable. If it had been needed badly, I am sure the need would have been converted into a statement of policy.

Was It Too Early for a Policy?

The second question is: Was it too early? Maybe those who follow us, and I mean chronologically as well as professionally, will find that these enunciations of policy are just due to the temper of the time and that they will have to come into action in greater degree than in the past. Perhaps that may happen because of the acuteness of pressure for a policy, the competition for water, or the better understanding of the increasing necessity for a policy.

In a country such as ours, where even water resources may come under greater pressure in the next quarter of a century, the situation may drive us toward a policy which we have not yet been able to convert into congressional behavior. It may actually be that in most countries, including our own, one will not frame a policy or convert it into action unless there appears to be not only a reason for doing so, but a dramatic reason for doing so. In other words, we must begin to see the penalty of not doing so before we are willing to accept a policy.

Were Our Policies Unrealistic?

The third question is—and this, I would, perhaps, give only in a whisper because it is a reflection on our own professional activity: Were all of our documents truly unrealistic? I think in some instances they were. I would say, for example, that part of the most recent Hoover recommendations—say, on public power—to my mind were unrealistic. The suggestion, for example, that we undo everything that has been done in the United States over the last third of a century seems to me to be unrealistic. You may have, and I may have, many philosophical reasons for feeling it should be done if we lived in a vacuum, but I doubt very much if you could practically consider so turning the clock back and obtaining the acceptance of Congress and its constituents.

We may have been too unrealistic in many of our professional recommendations. The hardheaded, hardbitten congressional representative who goes back not only to mend fences, but also to create them, may have looked at these documents sometimes with a jaundiced eye. He may have written them off as being the kind of theoretical hopes of a group that did not quite know its way around. I could lift out other examples of such principles that, in retrospect, would seem to me to have some degree of lack of reality.

Whether or not we would ever recapture principles which we still consider to be sound within that framework, I am not the one to prophesy; I have some serious doubts as to whether we will ever recapture some of them—for instance, that the navigation work of our federal government should be put on a pay-as-you-go basis. I myself have very, very limited hopes that that will ever happen. I could spell out why I think those hopes are so limited. It does not mean that I would not continue to add my signature to the recommendation.

How Much Organization?

The last question is the fundamental issue in all national policy. Bertrand Russell, many years ago, in the title of one of his books, reflected on this when he captioned it: "Freedom Versus Organization," his point being the question of whether a society can be operated in which those two requirements are continuously embattled with each other. How much organization, which is enunciated in our ordinary policy principles, will a democratic country accept? How much does it want to insist that it improvise as it goes along? How many ad hoc decisions does Congress feel it must insist on reserving to itself?

I do not smile at that conflict, because, in some respects, it may lie at the root of our democratic approach even to water resources development, and there is, of course, again this little whisper underlying the battle between freedom and organization in which we stand for an organized approach to this development. It must be whispered that there are enough evidences in the past that the professional has been wrong, that the professional on occasions has not been as deserving or intuitive perhaps as the best politician or statesman, and that, too, must be remembered.

I recall an incident with respect to Grand Coulee before construction was started, during efforts to determine whether or not the National Resources Planning Board would ratify a recommendation that the Grand Coulee Dam be built. On the train, going up with Frederic A. Delano—board chairman, and a very wise professional engineer and statesman—we discussed the question of whether the dam might be deferred for 20 years or more. In other words, the return did not yet seem to warrant the investment. Mr. Delano made the interesting observation at that time that sometimes you construct a project in order to generate a return when the return is not visible.

He called my attention to the fact that we would have turned down Alexander Hamilton's proposals, as they were turned down by many professionals, when he suggested that the New Jersey area be developed for power. He was scoffed at because the area was strictly agricultural in nature at that time. Everyone wanted to know where the power user was. And, of course, the user was nonexistent. Alexander Hamilton stuck to his guns, as the people in New England did—the Frederick Stearns and others—who said that if we developed power in New England we would generate the customers, which, of course, happened. This is the history of the two most heavily industrialized areas in the United States and, as Mr. Delano reflected, one can go wrong in waiting until the customer is there.

You will remember the city engineer of Los Angeles who had the same breadth of vision when his community had less than 100,000 people. It was he who made the trenchant remark that if you wait to bring the water here until you need it, you won't need it.

AWWA's New Policy Statement

It will be well to keep these four questions in mind in reviewing the following statement on national water policy which stems from the AWWA policy committee. It is an attempt in three pages to bring to your attention once more, and to the attention of Congress and all thoughtful citizens, that there is room for the adoption of a sound water resources policy—moving toward equitable distribution of costs; a far greater uniformity of approach on the federal level; a strengthening of state and local participation; an attempt to stem the tide of having all money come from Washington; and an attempt to spell out the desirability of preserving both local interests and local financing, if for no other reason than to bring the expenditure of money closer to the local pocket. The local taxpayer is generally a little bit more thoughtful and, I would say, generally a little bit more guarded, about the expenditure of his tax money locally than he is about his federal taxes. It is the remoteness that disguises federal tax moneys and identifies them with a kind of Santa Claus in Washington.

In pointing this out, however, I want also to note that in its statement of policy the committee again reinforces its emphasis for supporting those federal agencies, such as the United States Geological Survey, in the extension and the intensification of their collection of basic data and their orderly interpretation of such material. In a vast country such as ours, the future will demand more rather than less of that kind of federal participation—what we call the groundwork of most of our studies—than it has ever done in the past. We need the cooperation of all local, state, county, and federal people in this type of federal activity which we feel must have national perspective and emphasis. Of course, such activity will require a far greater degree of financial support than it has ever had in the past. That kind of federal activity lies at the root of anything with which engineers deal, and must be, as I say, extended geographically and professionally, and interpreted to our major benefit.

This preamble has been lengthy, but insofar as the preamble is a review of our failure to move into reality, it is, perhaps, almost as important as the policy statement itself.

AWWA Statement of Policy

So much has been written in the past 10 years regarding water policy that the committee hesitates to add to the bulky volumes already on the library shelf. The reiteration of principles and policies with extensive expository supporting data no longer appears either appropriate or helpful. The present report, therefore, is restricted to a simple summary of the general principles which, it is believed, offer a reasonable basis for the development of the water resources of the country:

1. A sound water resources policy must look toward an adequate supply of water for our people; prevent waste; reduce pollution to its lowest practicable level; provide means for the best and most effective distribution of water; and take steps to check the destructive forces of water which destroy land, property, and life.

2. First priority should be given to providing water for people— for use in their homes and urban activities. The relative status of industry, agriculture, recreation, and navigation depends upon the contribution which each can make to the economic and social welfare of the area or region concerned.

3. The successful administration of a national water policy is dependent upon adequate basic hydrologic data and increasing emphasis upon the interpretation thereof. These, in turn, are dependent upon a greater understanding of the natural laws governing the occurrence, movement, availability, and conservation of the nation's waters. The US Geological Survey is entitled to full support in its water resources activities.

4. The position of a federal coordinater of water resources should be established in order to provide presidential direction and agency coordination and to establish uniform principles, standards, and procedures for planning and development of water resources projects in which there is a federal interest.

5. A board of review, independent of other federal agencies and under its own chairman, should be created to analyze the engineering and economic feasibility of projects, to determine the federal interest in them, and to report to the President and the Congress. Appointments to the board of review should be made for such terms that a majority of the members are not appointed during a single presidential term of office.

6. Regional or river basin water resources committees should be

formed with a permanent nonvoting chairman appointed by the President, with membership composed of all federal departments and states involved, *provided* that the states paramount control in matters involving intrastate waters is maintained.

7. A permanent federal interagency committee on water resources, advisory in character, composed of principal policy making officials of the agencies concerned, should be established under the chairmanship of the coordinator.

8. Planning for water resources and related developments on interstate streams should be conducted on a cooperative basis with representatives of all federal, state, and local agencies involved. This joint participation should be continuous in order that the plans and projects development assure the best and most effective use and control of water to meet both the current and long-range needs of the people of a region, state, or locality and of the nation as a whole.

9. The federal government in its activities in the water resources field, should:

9.1. Provide for the preparation of plans for the unified development and regulation of the interstate river system of the country upon sound hydrologic, engineering, and economic principles.

9.2. Provide for definite and effective programs for the construction of the projects included in such plans, the programs to be prosecuted as found desirable by Congress to meet current necessities which are in the national interest.

9.3. Limit federal contributions toward projects to amounts warranted by the national interests involved.

9.4. Provide for an equitable distribution of project costs among various functions and various beneficiaries.

9.5. Provide for systematic and effective cooperation among federal agencies—and between these and agencies or individuals in the several states—in formulating water plans and programs.

9.6. Encourage the state and local agencies to assume full responsibility for planning, constructing, and operating their water resources projects and, when working in cooperation with the federal government to assume their appropriate share of all allocated costs.

10. As a general policy, all interests should participate in the cost of water resource development projects in accordance with the measure of their benefits.

10.1. The federal government should assume the cost only of that part of projects where benefits are national and widespread.

10.2. Beneficiaries of federal water resources projects should reimburse the federal government (with interest on any deferred payment) for their equitable share of the cost.

10.3. Where projects are primarily local, and the beneficiaries are clearly identifiable, the federal government's contribution should be limited, with nonfederal beneficiaries bearing equitable portions of the construction costs of the project, as well as the replacement, maintenance, and operation costs.

11. The states should fully exercise their rights and responsibilities in the control and development of water resources.

11.1. State legislation should be enacted in due time to provide a basis for the equitable settlement of the problems inherent in each phase of water development and management. Premature legislation, however, tends to perpetuate past use patterns because of their residual political weight. Therefore, each state should be cautious about adopting features of statutes of other states. A new statute should instead be based on a full knowledge of the water problems to be encountered in the state involved. The hydrologist should be an equal partner with the lawyer and the economist in the design of legislation.

11.2. The state should, by appropriate legislation, encourage, and, when necessary, foster the construction of storage reservoirs for control of flood runoff where need is demonstrated. Any water thus stored should be under the jurisdiction of the state allocation agency and should be made available for such use as will promote the greatest economic benefits.

11.3. The states should enact legislation which will permit and encourage the development of water districts, water authorities, or similar agencies (not limited by municipal or county boundaries) for the development, production, treatment, and distribution of water for domestic, commercial, industrial, municipal, and fire protection uses.

11.4. The initiative and responsibility rests upon local agencies for planning, financing, constructing, and operating works for furnishing domestic, commercial, and industrial water supply. The federal government should not participate in such projects unless they are a part of a multiple purpose water development in which there exists definite and justifiable federal interest and benefits.

REFERENCES

1. Drainage Basin Problems and Programs. A report by the Water Resources Committee of the National Resources Committee. US Government Printing Office, Washington, D.C. (1938).

2. A Water Policy for the American People. A report of the President's Water Resources Policy Commission. US Government Printing Office, Washington, D.C. (1950).

3. Water Resources. Report of a task force of the Commission on Organization of the Executive Branch of the Government. US Government Printing Office, Washington, D.C. (1949).

4. Resources for Freedom. The President's Materials Policy Commission. Vol. 1, 4, and 5. US Government Printing Office, Washington, D.C. (1952).

5. Water Resources and Power. Report of a task force of the Commission on Organization of the Executive Branch of the Government. US Government Printing Office, Washington, D.C. (1955).

6. Water Resources Policy. A report by the Presidential Advisory Committee. US Government Printing Office, Washington, D.C. (1956).

7. Principles of a Sound National Water Policy. Engineers Joint Council, New York (1951).

8. Principles of a Sound National Water Policy, A Restatement. Engineers Joint Council, New York (1957).

Water—Economics and Politics*

The planner of water resources development would find his utopia on earth only when it is free of people and of competitive economic interests. The hope of any planner, universally unfulfilled, is to proceed relatively undisturbed with his task of organized collection and analysis of physical, biological, and socio-economic data. These he would turn toward the efficient use of such waters to enhance the health, safety, and well-being of society. His mechanism is via government and private enterprise in order to develop understanding of human needs and to influence and shape policy to serve these needs most effectively.

The desire for perspective, foresight, and logic in national behavior, paralleled by an equal desire for wholeness of plan and control of execution, are undoubtedly laudatory in any scientific and technologic endeavor. The fulfillment of these desires, however, presupposes a greater frequency of omniscience and a predictability of the actions of people and the behavior of political leaders, friendly and hostile, than this world usually affords.

This paper is directed toward a historical assessment of how well

* Reprinted with permission from *Journal Water Pollution Control Federation*, Vol. 37, No. 2, pp. 145–50 (February, 1965), Washington, D.C. 20016. Presented at the 37th Annual Conference of the Water Pollution Control Federation in Bal Harbour, Fla., Sept. 27–Oct. 1, 1964.

or how poorly the planning objective has been fulfilled. Has planning in the water resources field been panacea or delusion? Has a matured national water policy and a machinery for its implementation emerged over the last half a century? If they have not, and the evidence that they have is not impressive, what is the obligation of the water scientist and technologist in this important function of society?

The Historical Assessment

The search for logic and wholeness of perspective in water development in the United States is long and persistent. The literature is extensive and exciting. It has been summarized over the years by Hoyt,[1] Wolman,[2] Fox,[3] Schiff,[4] Maas,[5] Leopold and Maddock,[6] and others.

Without reviewing these rich sources of experience in detail, our purpose would be fulfilled best by rehearsing the salient conclusions:

1. So-called national plans too often have been "thinly-disguised treatises of political dogma and party exhortation."

2. Between 1930 and 1940 profound changes in federal policy occurred which reflected equally profound changes in political philosophy and in temporary, but great, meteorologic episodes such as droughts and floods.

3. As a consequence, federal activities in the water field increased ten-fold in the same ten-year period. The decade's repercussions prevail to this day in their impact on public policy.

4. During the year 1940 alone something approaching $600 million of federal money was spent on measures and practices directed toward modifying to a major degree the runoff phase of the rainfall-runoff cycle.

5. The basic reasons for the ten-fold increase in activity were described by Hoyt,[1] as follows:

(a) The 1930–1940 decade was characterized by a degree of nationwide abnormality of climatic and hydrologic conditions probably not exceeded during the past century;

(b) The impact of an economic crisis with chronic symptoms that began in 1929, and the associated depression, brought about changes in political leadership as well as modifications in governmental theory; and

(c) There was a belated nationwide recognition that the wastage of soil and water is a genuine menace to the national welfare.

Hoyt goes on to say: "In retrospect it has been made to appear, perhaps, that the water policies outlined were adopted and put into practice in a more orderly sequence and manner than was actually the case."

6. In 1963 federal appropriations for water resources and related activities were $1.5 billion.

7. By 1980 the Corps of Engineers, responsible for about two-thirds of the appropriations, estimates their expenditures will reach about $25 billion.

8. Investments in flood control engineering works over the last quarter of a century aggregate about $5 billion. Despite these expenditures, average annual damages from floods continue to rise. In 1960 the Chief of Engineers stated that the present rate of expenditure for flood protection will "just about keep up with the increase in flood damage . . . anticipated by 1980, as a result of flood-plain development over the next two decades."

Almost from the beginning of our country's development, statesmen have recognized the high significance of water resources programs and have poured money into their implementation. The brief listings above have demonstrated their confidence in such works. When one attempts, however, to isolate the terms of a unified national policy and of a parallel uniform system for investment decision-making, no clearly defined guideposts are yet apparent. Although great progress has been made by the responsible federal agencies in the adoption of more and more sophisticated approaches to plan and to evaluation, neither formal national policy nor uniformity of approach are within sight.

It must be recognized, of course, that the desire for a uniform and equitable policy rested on the assumption that such criteria were essential to sensible governmental action. The author raised some serious questions as far back as 1957 as to whether the assumption was really valid. Congress perhaps has been wiser in formulating programs on an episodic or ad hoc basis, often because of its uncertainty as to total policy commitment and sometimes for less salutary reasons.

The Real World

Alexander Hamilton provides an old clue to the behavior of the Congress. He said: "The science of policy is the knowledge of human nature." In most technologists' statements of water policy Hamilton's ingredients of man and his behavior were omitted. In Congressional action it is always militantly present. All decisions are tempered by public and private pressures, by executive agency hopes and aspirations, and by the "winds of political doctrine" which often blow strongly even in our country.

The "hard sell" has penetrated into Washington, to use the Madison Avenue terminology, to a degree unheard of in previous decades. This capital was not quite barren soil for such activity long before, but today the machinery for propagation of myth, of special interest, and of special pleading probably exceeds by far the scientific-technologic equipment available for sound program and analysis.

No group is unaware of this modern medium for public pressure or averse to using it no matter how moral or socially desirable its purpose may be. One has long been familiar with such methods in the private sector but its wholesale adoption by the public government sector is a recent phenomenon.

To particularize, reference may well be made to the use of mass media to inform, to persuade, and to pressure public opinion, for example, in the fields of flood control, recreation, desalination, and water quality control. The merging of propaganda and scientific truth requires a skill not always sedulously applied to these otherwise sound social purposes.

This situation is further exemplified in the increasing efforts to give the semblance of quantitative accuracy to certain important areas of public interest such as recreation. The attempts tend to become ridiculous in the estimating of economic benefits even though no one derogates the profound social impact and value of recreation and allied pursuits. These observations merely underline how far away we still are from perfected parameters in matters of public policy.

In view of the past experience, it is certainly not surprising that national action appears based on no simple uniform formula. Hence, the process of implementation on the federal level is described as "political," rather than "engineering" or "economics" as if both of the latter were devoid of judgment factors and were calculable only in a mathematical, unchangeable form.

It should be recalled that water development has always had a broader goal than economic efficiency alone. Fox[3] recently has pointed out that in water history the basic objectives were to unify the nation via water transport, to develop the west, to provide a competitive force to private industry, and to uplift the economies of depressed regions. Another human, but less attractive, objective always has been to get oneself re-elected with the help of the local, regional, or state projects paid for by federal money. Fox cannot escape the valid conclusion that, in the future, "public investment in river basin development will be determined by a combination of economic and non-economic considerations."

A recent official reviewer of the technology of a controversial water development on the federal level states the conclusion more vividly, but with equal accuracy, in the following terms: "At what cost level 'this' will come into use is, I am confident, going to turn out to be largely a political question."

The Theoretical Perfect Plan

If we accept the inevitable impact of both economics and politics on water resources development, our attention for the moment should be directed to the problem of providing a sound underpinning for non-engineering deviations from the "perfect" plan. The technology of the past is marked by many significant efforts in this direction, not the least of which is the evolution of cost-benefit procedures generally described in recent form as the "Green Book." This long effort at objective assessment of the validity of projects has moved through decades of modification. In the evolution, improved tools of assessment are continually coming into play. Simultaneously, however, since the 1930's, more and more intangibles have been pressed into the mold and have caused and will cause more and more difficulty in evaluation. Unless an abrupt turn-about occurs in this methodology it is likely to provide less and less validity and more and more pseudo-accuracy. No one is willing to admit that national defense, general welfare, recreation, stream pollution, etc., are not yet convertible into quantitative economic terms of dollars and cents although they are obviously of tremendous importance to society.

It is doubtful, in the present state of the art of planning, that any *single* plan is the perfect one. Every plan is restricted within the availability of base data, within the perspectives and prejudices of the developer, and within the political philosophy of the decision-maker. Alternatives are frequently missed or ignored. As a result, often both the Chief Executive and the Congress, with real but nonmathematical instincts, reach out to improvisations, to short-term programs, and to the gradual evolution of national policies. To the professional worker these processes always fall short of perfection, compounded of patch works, shot full of personal and group pressures, sometimes selfish, perhaps even cynical. In the long run this democratic process of implementation of perfect and imperfect plans undoubtedly is costly and wasteful but reflective of the frailties of human behavior.

The Function of the Professional

Within the framework here presented, does the professional have an honorable and significant role to play? If one were easily disheartened by the realities of political life (ergo, society in general), one might easily withdraw to an ivory tower of research. Even this retreat is increasingly difficult to find in modern political practice.

In the author's view, the professional has and will continue to have a prime function, namely, the illumination of choices for the political decision-maker. The task of illumination is a never-ending one, incorporating in its execution expanding knowledge, advanced equipment and methodology for analysis, and the testing and assessment of past and present program decisions. Such a broad function, if diligently and intelligently pursued, must inevitably make its impress on society and its leaders. The second function of persistent restraint and prevention of the foolish, the wasteful, and the cynical represents a natural consequence of the first objective of illumination of choices. These two responsibilities obviously assume that we do not surrender to the vagaries of political action, but that we do attempt, with the best of technical wisdom, to guide policy in the direction of logic, common sense, and national welfare.

In the accomplishment of these primary professional responsibilities, many specific activities may be isolated.

1. Deeper insight into the ingredients of decision-making, particularly with reference to the allocation of costs among beneficiaries and among functions.

2. A re-appraisal of the whole philosophy and methodology of benefit-cost evaluation practices.

3. A hard look at the whole question of interest rates and the life of water structures built and financed by the federal government in order to recapture some economic realism from the present trend in finance toward unrealistic interest rates and long period of repayment.

4. Intensive study of the bases of and alternatives to present policies and practices in the fields of recreation, municipal and industrial water supply, and water quality improvement.

5. Professional societies may well devote much thought to how best to provide an independent audit of present planning processes by some other than the federal agencies themselves. It is startling to note in the excellent proceedings of the Federation that virtually nothing appears on overall national water policy or the many burning issues of details thereof. Does this mean simple surrender or its equivalent, high-minded devotion only to the details of technology without concern for their translation into fruits of society?

6. An evaluation of the experience with multi-purpose projects. How well have they fulfilled their original stated purpose and how much have they deviated therefrom?

7. Is planning for water development on a river basin basis sound? Does the watershed provide the logical framework for such programming or has this assumption just grown into a familiar and happily phrased slogan?

8. Before the responsibilities and autonomies of state and local governments wither away or are whittled away, their strengths and their capacities for growth should be enhanced, so that they may, in fact, exercise their down-to-earth prerogatives. We talk much about local participation in government and do little about it.

9. The professional can do much to dispel myths in current water resources discussions. Often he hesitates to do so militantly, particularly if they are popular myths sacred to special interest groups. A recent editorial contributor[7] lists a few of these in the field of water pollution: (*a*) the myth that detergents are our most serious pollution problem;

(b) the myth that streams purify themselves; (c) the myth that increased back-filling requirements will eliminate existing mine-drainage pollution; and (d) the myth that the federal government's enforcement powers will by themselves clean up pollution problems throughout the nation [he points out that Pennsylvania alone has 50,000 miles (80,500 km) of streams].

If this paper has a central theme it is that man, a political animal, insists on controlling his destiny. Even with water, he does so at times with violence to the technologist. The latter is "impatient with human organizations and political processes, especially as they may tend to stifle his spontaneity and restrict his independence."[8]

The Chairman of the Joint Congressional Committee on Atomic Energy recently remarked that "every scientist thinks his project is the best" and acidly concluded that "the ambition of the scientists cannot be considered a guiding principle."[8]

Notwithstanding all this, the professional will continue to fulfill his commitment to society by illumination of problem and solution and by extending the horizons of scientific and technologic understanding.

Summary

The planner of water resources development on a national scale always hopes that, on the basis of the organized collection and analysis of physical, biological, and socio-economic data, he can evolve the logical, best plan for the most efficient use of our resources. Since he has faith in the wisdom and wholeness of such plans he naturally looks toward their implementation via governmental and private sectors. In the course of time he reasons they may, in fact, influence and shape a private and public policy.

The historical record, however does not fulfill these hopes. Although major developments have been accomplished, these appear in retrospect to have been episodic in nature, fragmentary in approach, and multiple, and often conflicting, in policies. Political sieving of technologic proposals has been the rule whether for good or bad.

Machinery for diagnosis and evaluation, and hence for decision-making, has become more complex and more sophisticated. Whether it serves our purposes more accurately may be doubted. Beyond question, however, is the fact that technical proficiency has progressed greatly although much still has to be learned.

In such a historical climate the question naturally arises as to the function of the professional scientist-technologist. Shall he surrender to the politician or shall he be the continuing restraint and producer of increasingly convincing plans and programs?

The answer is clear. The professional must continue to provide the evidence for the illumination of choices, for the clarification of alternatives, and for the evolution of more satisfactory criteria for evaluation. Decision-makers, in spite of many supposed lapses, do ultimately succumb to logic and to impressive argument. The search for utopia, however, is likely to be endless.

REFERENCES

1. Hoyt, W. G., "Unusual Events and Their Relation to Federal Water Policies." *Trans. Amer. Soc. Civil Engr.*, Paper No. 2180, 108, 290 (1943).

2. Wolman, A., "The Complexities of a National Water Policy." *Jour. Amer. Water Works Assn.*, 44, 9, 775 (Sept. 1952); and "Basic Principles of a National Water Resources Policy." *Jour. Amer. Water Works Assn.*, 49, 7, 825 (July 1957).

3. Fox, I. K., "Basin Planning: Past Experience and Current Problems." Resources for the Future, Inc., Washington, D.C. (1963).

4. Schiff, A. L., "Fire and Water." Harvard University Press, Cambridge, Mass. (1962).

5. Maas, A., "Muddy Waters, The Army Engineers and the Nation's Rivers." Harvard University Press, Cambridge, Mass. (1951).

6. Leopold, L. B., and Maddock, T., Jr., "The Flood Control Controversy." The Ronald Press Company, New York (1954).

7. Lyon, W. A., "Myths and Truths about Pollution." *Clean Streams*, 1st Quarter, 61, 3, Pennsylvania Department of Health, Harrisburg, Pa. (1964).

8. Cook, E. F., "The Scientist as a Political Animal." Rocky Mountain Section, Geological Society of America, Moscow, Idaho (May 4, 1964).

Formulation of National Water Resources Policy
in Israel*
with Aaron Wiener

Some years ago, one of the authors of this paper discussed the lack of comprehensive water policy in view of many policy studies and statements frequently being made. He concluded[1] that "one will not frame a policy or convert it into action unless there appears to be not only a reason for doing so, but a dramatic reason for doing so." Only a dramatic challenge will produce a dramatic response.

Such a challenge has developed in Israel over the last few years and has been met by an adequate policy response. It will therefore be of interest to study the Israeli situation, and the technical, economic, and legal procedures that have been evolved.

Integrated Approach

The background story is quickly told: Israel, semiarid country in the north and arid in the south, is wholly dependent on irrigation for agriculture. The land and water resources are extremely scarce. Out of a total area of 5,000,000 acres only about one-quarter is arable. The po-

* Reprinted from *Journal American Water Works Association,* Vol. 54, No. 3 (March, 1962). Copyright 1962 by the American Water Works Association, Inc. Presented Oct. 19, 1961, at the Eastern Water Co. Conference, Atlantic City, N.J.

tential water resources (1,500,000 acre-ft/yr) are sufficient to irrigate not more than 40 per cent or so of the arable area.

Israel's economic growth over the last 10 years has been explosive. Its population rose from 1,200,000 to 2,150,000. The gross national product (at 1960 prices) increased from 1,570,000,000 to 4,400,000,000 Israeli pounds (I£). At the current rate of exchange, I£ is equal to $0.56. The use of water went up from about 250,000 acre-ft/yr to more than 1,000,000 acre-ft/yr, and the area of irrigated lands, from about 70,000 to almost 350,000 acres.

Israel's economy will continue to grow at a similar rate, except that water scarcity will limit agricultural development. The annual increase in population, including both the natural increase and immigration, is estimated at about 4–4½ per cent; the gross value of industrial production is scheduled to increase by 10–12 per cent annually and agricultural production by 7 per cent. These developments will provide employment for the larger population and increase the income of the now fully employed labor force.

Against these ambitious economic targets stands the shortage of water. Only about 30 per cent of the potential resources (450,000 acre-ft/yr) remain unutilized. The economic future of Israel therefore largely depends upon the efficient use of the remaining resources, and on the improvements that can be made on those already developed.

It is not surprising that Israel has been one of the first countries to adopt and implement a comprehensive water policy based on a nation-wide master plan. This policy—although severely restricting the freedom of action of the individual water user—has gained the support of the public.

The first draft of the Master Plan was drawn in 1950, barely 2 years after the establishment of the state. It included a preliminary inventory of land and water resources, a list of the high-priority projects, and a program for further data assembly, investigations, research, and pilot-scale experiments necessary for further elaboration of the plan. A revised and more detailed issue was published in 1956. The most recent version, published in 1961, includes a detailed water resources inventory, demand forecast, and basic data for proposed projects listed in order of importance.

The Master Plan not only guides the design of all projects, but also served as a frame of reference for the Water Law in 1959. According to this act, all water resources, including ground and surface waters, naturally and artificially impounded water, perennial and intermittent springs, drainage water, and municipal and industrial wastes, are public property and under government control. The development of new resources and the use of present facilities are subject to licensing. The law recognizes the need for an integrated, comprehensive program, and gives the minister of agriculture the power to carry out the necessary plans.

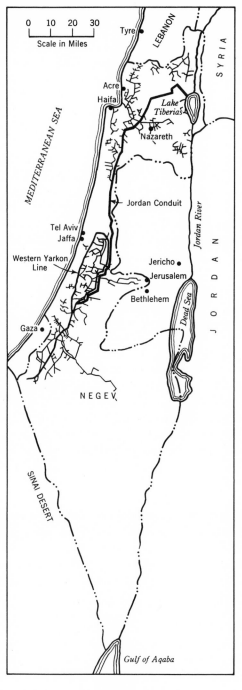

Fig. 1

Israel. The Jordan Project will supply 250,000 acre-ft/yr, or 25 per cent of the total water used in Israel at present.

Water Resources

The point of departure of the plan is the inventory of available resources and the forecast of anticipated demand. It is estimated that potential water resources when fully developed can yield 1,500,000 acre-ft each year.

Ground water and springs are the principal water resources. They account for 58 per cent of the total. The inventory of available ground water is based on a large number of observations which are analyzed every year as more data become available. The wells in two main aquifers of the coastal plain (one shallow, composed mainly of sand and sandstone, and one deep, of limestone) account for 86 per cent of the ground water. The shallow aquifer is now almost fully utilized, with considerable overpumping in the central, densely populated portion of the coastal strip. The limestone aquifer, which often underlies the coastal aquifer at great depth, is fed from outcrops in the Galilean Hills, the Carmel Range, and the Judean Hills. It is almost fully utilized (with some overpumping) in its central and southern portions, but has some untapped water in its northern Galilean extension.

Only one perennial river, the Jordan and its tributaries, is not directly connected to ground water aquifers. Present use within the river basin accounts for 150,000 acre-ft/yr (less than 40 per cent of the river's average annual flow). The rest of the Jordan (about 250,000 acre-ft/yr) is the most important undeveloped water resource of Israel.

Flash floods, occurring after heavy rains, account for about 6 per cent of the potential resources (80,000–100,000 acre-ft-yr). Only 15,000 acre ft/yr on the average has been developed.

The reuse of municipal and industrial wastes is also included in the inventory. Reuse accounts for 11–12 per cent of the potential water available. Present production, however, is negligible.

The total present use is 1,000,000 acre-ft/yr. Out of this total, ground water and springs account for 79 per cent, river water 20 per cent, flash floods and sewage 1 per cent. Of the water produced, 19 per cent is used for municipal and industrial purposes, and 81 per cent for agriculture. Unused resources of 500,000 acre-ft/yr, include 45 per cent Jordan River water, 48 per cent flood water and wastes, and 7 per cent ground water.

Demand Forecast

In regard to household use, a total population increase from 2,150,000 in 1961 to at least 3,000,000 by 1970 is anticipated. This relatively high rate of growth is based on the influx of immigrants and the demographic structure of Israel. The annual increase of per capita consumption has been estimated at 1 per cent for the 1960's and 0.5 per cent for the 1970's.

For future industrial uses prediction is more difficult. Total growth rates seem to be well established, but the type of industries cannot be foreseen beyond the next 5–6 years. Future water requirements were, therefore, correlated to gross product figures. The gross industrial product in 1970 is scheduled to reach 250–300 per cent of the 1960 figures, and the 1980 figure will probably be 100 per cent above the 1970 figure.

Agricultural planners will have to confine farm production to the scope dictated by water limitations, because only the remaining supply will probably be for agriculture. This residual will not be sufficient to grow all the required crops, and economic priorities will have to be established for individual crops.

The quantity which can be allocated to agriculture up to 1970 will probably be 900,000 acre-ft/yr. This is enough to grow the food and fibers for 4,000,000 people. The bulk of grain crops, some sugar, oil crops, tea, and coffee will have to be imported; however, the export of high-value crops (citrus fruits) will be doubled. Any unexpected increase in household or industrial demands will reduce the agricultural output.

Israel has a farm population of 325,000 (about 15 per cent of the total population). Within the limits defined by water supply, the farm population will only increase by 15,000–20,000 in the 1960's. The percentage of the people living and working on farms will drop to 13 per cent by 1970, and then to less than 10 per cent by 1980, unless new water resources can be made available. Irrigated areas will increase from 340,000 acres in 1961 to almost 500,000 acres in 1970, with no increase thereafter. The gross value of the agricultural product is anticipated to rise from I£ 750,000,000 in 1960 to about I£ 1,400,000,000 in 1970, with little increase after 1970.

Resource Allocation

The Master Plan lists water uses in order of importance. Because the total resources that can be ultimately developed is limited and smaller than required, decisions have to be made regarding the allocation of the available supplies. Municipal use is, as a matter of course, given first priority. Nevertheless, every effort is made to keep the rise in per capita consumption as low as possible. Meters and a progressively increasing rate structure have been introduced along with leak inspection, and restrictions on the use of water-washing fixtures. A gradual rise in water consumption is of course inevitable.

On deciding whether to give water to industry or agriculture, the choice rests upon the value of the product per unit of water. It was found that the contribution to the gross national product of a unit of water consumed in industry will, on the average, be 25 times greater than that of a unit consumed in agriculture. A comparative analysis of employment opportunities created by a unit of water used in industry or agriculture shows ratios even more favorable to industrial uses. Therefore, priority is, in general, given to industry. Allocation to agriculture consists of that portion of the available resources which remains after all municipal and industrial requirements have been met.

Within the agricultural sector, priority will be given to high-value export crops such as citrus and those food and fiber crops that are difficult to ship (vegetables, milk) or too expensive to import (some fruits, certain dairy products, cotton). Grain and most industrial crops will be grown with surplus water.

Development Plan

The plan. Within an 8-year period, 1962–1970, the plan includes the development of all reserves of which the location, quality, and economic feasibility are known at present. It covers the production of additional 500,000 acre-ft/yr required to meet demands up to 1970, and consolidates present uses in areas of overdraft. A small reserve is left for the anticipated increased needs of the nonagricultural sector up to 1980. Additional supplies will become available throughout the planning period. The realization of the program will require an investment of I£ 120,000,000 in the first 4-year period and about I£ 70,000,000 in the second 4-year period.

The Jordan conduit, to be completed in 1964, will connect the two existing Yarkon distribution conduits in the south. The major part of Israel's distribution system—including the ground water systems—will actually become one integrated system in which operation can be controlled by a central dispatching schedule which provides maximum yields and storage, and minimum losses.

The Jordan conduit system. This system will connect the Jordan, intercepting it in the Sea of Galilee—to the headworks of the existing Yarkon system which starts near Tel Aviv and goes down to the central part of the Negev desert. The main objectives of the project are to convey the surplus of 250,000 acre-ft available in the Jordan River to the center and south, to pick up en route surpluses from other water projects and convey them south, and to serve as the integrating backbone of the utility's water distribution grid.

Sewage reclamation projects. Because priority has been given to the Jordan Project, major construction on the other portions of the plan had to be postponed. The reclamation of sewage and industrial wastes will follow after the construction of the Jordan Project. Ultimately, all sizable volumes of municipal and industrial wastes will be used. First consideration is given to major urban agglomerations, especially the Greater Tel

Aviv area (1970 population estimated at about 1,000,000), Haifa, and Jerusalem. Waste waters will be reused in some cases (after conventional treatment) for agriculture and industry, as in Haifa. In other cities, such as Tel Aviv, the sewage will be treated, then recharged underground into a sand and sandstone aquifer, and pumped with the ground water of the region for general use.

Intermittent runoff. The intermittent runoff in Israel is extremely irregular and cannot be relied upon exclusively as a water resource. Because suitable storage sites are extremely rare, storage space for seasonal and cyclical storage can normally be found only underground. The usual pattern of an intermittent-runoff recovery project is the construction of a relatively small interception reservoir able to store one major flood, and a conduit (often supplemented by pumping) sufficient to evacuate the water into recharge areas. During the season of peak consumption, the water is repumped from the aquifer and distributed.

Ground waters and coastal interceptor. Some ground water surpluses remain in the north and northwest and in isolated locations in the south. The coastal collector, however, will be perhaps the most interesting feature of the country's ground water development. It will consist of a system of shallow wells and drains near the Mediterranean coast which will closely control the outflow of fresh water to the sea. The otherwise unavoidable loss of fresh water protecting the aquifer, will be reduced from the usual 20–25 per cent of the average annual natural replenishment to a mere 6–8 per cent. This last line of defense will provide large-scale underground storage without the risk of increasing fresh-water leakage into the sea. A pilot project (2.5 mi long) is being constructed.

Seasonal and cyclical storage. Because the Israeli water grid will ultimately be operated as one system, storage requirements to insure a high degree of regulation can be dealt with on a national basis. Deviations of both the demand and the available supply from their averages are great, that is, the demand is usually highest (both seasonally and cyclically) when flow is lowest. Large-scale storage is indispensable if full regulation required to minimize losses is to be reached.

Cyclical variations of the Jordan are relatively low (minimum flow about half the average, maximum flow slightly less than twice the average). Those of ground–fed surface resources vary within still narrower limits. Cyclical variations in the annual totals of intermittent streams are much greater, ranging from no flow to 20 times the average flow.

Demand varies mainly in the agricultural section. It is very low in the rainy season. The winter monthly average in the north then is 10 per cent of the average monthly demand, and in the south, 30 per cent. The summer monthly peak ranges between 170 and 250 per cent of the average monthly demand.

Operation

The project has been designed to minimize losses in conservation, conveyance, storage, and utilization, and to provide maximum yields from the available resources.

This goal could be achieved only by joining the entire system, including surface water–fed and ground water–fed resources into one water distribution grid and centralizing operations according to available storage volumes, their geographical distribution, the distribution of rainfall and anticipated demand. The operation of this water grid would be similar to that of a regional power grid.

The central planning of the operation of Israel's water grid is made possible by a number of built-in features. The principal ones are as follows:

1. The north-south large-diameter conduit system (108 in. from the Jordan to Tel Aviv, 66–70 in. south of Tel Aviv) connects the water resources of the north with arid regions of the south. It links Israel's only large surface reservoir (Lake Tiberias) and the surface resources requiring storage (Jordan, springs, intermittent flood flows) with the great aquifers of central and southern areas.

2. Spare pumping capacity is ready to transfer surpluses to underground storage whenever available.

3. A soundly developed, secondary west-east distribution system crosses the north-south conduit system and connects it to the aquifers.

4. A network of wells—most of which are connected to the distributing system—has a peak pumping capacity high above the safe yield of the aquifers. This spare well capacity makes it possible to use the aquifers in the period beyond the safe yield, to cover immediate needs, and thus incidentally, dewater the top portion of the aquifer, and initiate its cyclical function as storage.

5. The coastal collector prevents excess outflow from underground storage into the sea.

By combining all these projects it will be possible to distribute water from year to year between above-ground and below-ground storage and to allocate needed surface and ground water for different uses.

Outlook

Water resources, when fully used and properly managed, will be sufficient for agriculture planned up to 1970 and for industrial development up to 1980. (This assumes some extra construction beyond that contemplated for the 1962–70 period.) If water resources are properly managed, then water shortage will not jeopardize the development of the economy; no limitations are set for industrial growth, and agriculture will be able to supply necessary food and fibers.

But long-term planning requires projections of water supply and demand even beyond 1980. Therefore, it is part of the Master Plan to investigate possible solutions. An extensive research program has been organized to evaluate ways and means of increasing supplies and raising efficiency. This program will study all approaches that show some promise: intensified use of low-quality water (brackish) mainly for industry and tolerant agricultural crops; watershed management; reduction of evaporation from open water surfaces (Lake Tiberias evaporation losses are almost as high as the yield of the Jordan Project); weather modification (a large-scale cloud-seeding project has entered its second year); and adoption of water saving methods for irrigation, cultivation, and seed selection.

It is hoped that the program will increase the availability of water and the efficiency of its use, and provide water for additional development after 1980, without making it necessary to restrict agriculture.

Summary

1. The future development of Israel's economy is largely dependent on the availability of water. Concurrent with the development of more water for an expanding economy, considerable quantities of water have to be developed to consolidate existing uses in areas of overdraft.

2. The chief undeveloped resources are located in the north of the country, whereas the planned additional consumption will be in the center and south. It will be necessary, therefore, to convey the surpluses of the north (mainly Jordan water) to the south.

3. To cover the needs of the economy, the development and operation of the water resources have to be centralized to insure maximum yields and minimum losses.

4. Such a centralized operation of the water grid is feasible because of the built-in integrating features of the system and the legislation adopted by parliament.

5. Research will be continued over the next decade in an effort to insure the supply required after 1980.

6. The adoption of the centralized operation procedure and the far-reaching water conservation practices will make it possible to provide the water required for agriculture and industry up to 1970.

REFERENCE

1. Committee Report. Basic Principles of a National Water Resources Policy. *Jour. AWWA*, 49:825 (Jul. 1957).

A Report upon a National Policy for the Development and Use of the Water Resources of Ceylon*

The Development and Use of the Water Resources of Ceylon

No natural asset affects life and the development of a country as much as its water resources. This natural resource is rarely considered until stresses arise with its use. When Ceylon takes stock of its future economic development, therefore, it is at once confronted by water problems, the resolution of which poses significant technical, economic and sociological issues. If a country is small and its water needs are simple and easily met, the need for extensive exploration is absent. When the population grows and water demands multiply, deep concern with the problems of water becomes inescapable.

Ceylon has now reached this stage. Thoughtful members of Government are confronted with three major challenges and objectives in the water resources field. They are:

1. To determine the principal water requirements and problems in the various parts of the country.

2. To outline in broad terms an integrated pattern of water development and control for the maximum economic utilization of these resources.

3. To develop specific undertakings which will fit into the integrated

* Ceylon: The Government Press, 1956.

pattern or plan and which may be arranged in priority for the most successful use of the country at large.

In Ceylon, as many years ago in the case of the United States of North America, it may be well stated that:

> The control of a stream subject to destructive floods, the improvement of a river channel for navigation, the procurement of water from a stream for municipal and domestic use, the disposal of sewage and industrial waste in a drainage channel, or other concern in the use and control of water, has been treated as an isolated problem, in disregard both of the inherent relationships between various types of water problems and of the possibilities of multiple purpose development.

Whether the same situation of competitive and haphazard water development is characteristic here is the subject of this particular inquiry. If this should be the case, early correctives are feasible, since the governmental operations in Ceylon have not acquired rigidity and inflexibility. Water resources development in Ceyon, aside from its ancient and remarkable irrigation works, is of recent origin, hence adjustments required in governmental structure, finance and technology may be easier to accomplish.

A number of studies of the water and land problems have already been made. Most of these have been directed toward specific objectives rather than toward general diagnoses and solutions. In each, however, emphasis has been placed upon the fact that an integrated approach to water resources planning and development is an early necessity.

For the best understanding of the problem a brief description of the Island and its physical characteristics is desirable.

I. *Description of Ceylon*

Ceylon is a tropical Island of 25,000 square miles just off the southeastern tip of the Indian subcontinent. It has been described topographically as having somewhat the shape of a hat. The crown of mountains, reaching in some instances over 7,000 feet in height, lies in the south central region. It is surrounded on all sides by a brim of level coastal lands, quite narrow to the east, south and west. In the north, however, the coastal arrangement extends like a visor in a large tapering plane toward India. The rivers, therefore, flow in a radial pattern from the mountains to the sea.

The Island is blessed with extensive rainfall in the southeast corner, reaching at times 250 inches a year. In the remaining three-quarters of the Island, sometimes described as the "dry zone," it varies between 50 and 75 inches annually. The dry zone might at first sight appear to be a misnomer, but it is an appropriate designation, since the heavy rainfall is entirely seasonal in character. At other seasons, the long dry periods per-

sist, when sharp declines in water flow occur in the major rivers and many
of the smaller streams and reservoirs dry up completely. In these areas
evaporation is heavy and as a result the soils dry out and become unproductive.

One hundred and three streams drain into the ocean or into a lagoon.
These basins range over 4,000 to 3.5 square miles in an area. They are
highly variable in runoff, with excessive floods and low flows of considerable economic hazard to the areas through which they move.

Because of these water conditions, about 80 per cent of the people
live in about a third of the area of the Island. The remainder is very thinly
scattered over the dry zone. The rate of growth of the population in recent years is very high. The last census, 1946, showed a population of
6,657,000. By 1951 is was approaching 8,000,000. It may reach 10,000,000
by 1962 and 12,700,000 by 1972.

In virtually all the public documents the distribution of the population is described as predominantly rural and the urban residents are
assumed to account for only about 15 per cent of the total. It is doubtful
whether this description is accurate when considering the problems of
the country in the water resources field. The reverse of the figures given
above is probably more descriptive of the way in which the population
lives. Many of the people are either in large cities or are clustered in
so-called villages or urbanized areas with anywhere from 1,000 to 10,000
people in close proximity.

The issue as to whether the area is rural or urban becomes more than
an academic one, since so many decisions as to water have rested in the
past upon the assumption that the country is predominantly rural. Much
of the economy, it is true, is agricultural, but substantial aggregates of
population account for between 50 and 75 per cent of the people. These
realities need to be thoroughly explored, since technical and fiscal policies
and solutions of the water problems should be geared to these facts.

II. *Present Organization and Functions*

Relatively small as Ceylon is, Government has already developed a
major responsibility for a variety of water resources plans, projects, and
accomplishments. It has engaged in water undertakings for domestic and
municipal use, sewerage and drainage, agriculture and irrigation, electric
power, industrial uses, navigation, forestry, fisheries and reclamation,
flood control and beach erosion. These activities are briefly reviewed
below.

(a) *Domestic and Municipal Uses, Sewerage, and Drainage*

At least four major governmental units have a responsibility for these
particular functions. The more important of these are in the agencies
dealing with health, public works, land development and agricultural

colonization. Of these, the public works unit designs and constructs the greater number of works. All of them are directed toward providing drinking water and water for general municipal purposes, rated throughout the world as the most important use of a water resource. It supersedes every other use. This historical emphasis on first priority is reflected in principle, in policy, in legislation, in expenditure and in court decisions.

In Ceylon unanimity on this first priority on the part of official and lay groups is striking. Enthusiasm for this number one necessity is universal.

Such enthusiasm is completely understandable, since the so-called water and soil borne diseases account for perhaps the largest toll of life and of disability of any of the current diseases. This situation is most succinctly expressed in an excerpt from the recent report (1955) of the Choksy Committee on local Government problems and solutions. The dramatic statement in the above report is as follows:

> In Ceylon, the statistics regarding the endemicity of diseases, due to unsafe water supplied and soil pollution, should shock the country into action. . . . A study of the table will show that 2,845,496 cases, *i.e.* approximately one quarter of the 11,444,206 outpatients and 107,445, *i.e.* one eighth of the 846,001 inpatients, in the Civil Hospitals of Ceylon in 1950, were cases of preventable water-borne disease, due to soil pollution and unsafe water.

The Choksy Report goes on to state that the deaths in Ceylon from dysentery, typhoid fever, diarrhœa and enteritis "present a ghastly picture." The dysentery death rate is some 60 times, the typhoid some 270, and the diarrhœa and enteritis rates some 60 times, those prevailing in 1950 in England.

The situation, though assumed to be somewhat better in 1955, offers no cause for complacency.

The record of accomplishment in the provision of drinking water and of the collateral sewerage and drainage facilities by no means matches the enthusiastic philosophical priority encountered everywhere. One cannot escape the feeling that the tacit acceptance of the priority for potable water development has deteriorated into "lip service," rather than been translated into militant and intelligent programming and expansion of facilities. Less than 10 per cent of the population has public water supply for drinking and general domestic use in the homes. It is doubtful whether as much as 5 per cent is provided with public sewerage facilities, while drainage facilities probably serve less than 1 per cent.

Even the larger cities, such as Colombo, are seriously in arrears in both sewerage and sewage treatment. The requirements for the major cities for a six year plan alone exceed Rupees 100 million.

Of all the municipalities, only Colombo has a reasonably adequate

surface drainage scheme. Three of the seven major cities have none at all.
Of the 36 Urban Councils, 15 have no drainage schemes. Twenty-seven
of the Town Councils have no schemes at all, out of the total of 38. Their
aggregate costs are high, the personnel for designing them all are almost
non-existent and provisions for extending the work are hazy.

The delinquencies in providing public facilities are more than
matched by the inadequacies in providing individual houses with water
and excreta disposal units. Here too actual advance waits upon continuing direction and finance. This task is difficult and time consuming, but
must be accomplished.

The greatest and most immediate returns per unit of energy or per
rupee expended are to be found, however, in the provision of mass or
public facilities. These need not wait upon the understanding or aquies-
cence of each individual to be served.

A diagnosis as to the reason for this small accomplishment, in view
of the general acceptance of the importance of the function, is not simple,
although some of the causes are apparent. It is reasonably clear that considerable confusion in responsibility prevails in this area. A multiplicity
of official agencies are concerned with plan and execution. A less than
adequate influence and leadership has been provided by the Ministry of
Health, partly due to the anomalous position of the Public Health Engineering Division. All of these factors contribute to the absence of
spirited and persistent stimulation of the introduction and expansion of
public water supplies and collateral sewerage and drainage.

(b) Agriculture and Irrigation

The ordered use of water for maintaining and developing agricultural
production is the responsibility of the irrigation division. It plans and exe-
cutes the major water projects. It is perhaps the largest spender of government funds and has a major responsibility in the total agricultural
development.

Until recently no small part of its activities was devoted to the rehabilitation of the ancient works for irrigation. These tasks it accomplished
with high technical competence. Within the last two years the unit has
embarked upon more elaborate new schemes for development, which
may or may not be integrated with the ancient works. This gratifying
escape from the impact of the ancient works upon modern exploitation
is a significant indication of the thoughtfulness and vision of the unit.

In developing these major schemes, the irrigation unit has viewed
the programs on a multiple purpose basis, so as to include the functions
of irrigation, drinking water, power, navigation, flood control and other
significant water features. Schemes for eight major river basins have already been studied and evolved. They provide for the utilization of some
3,735,000 acre feet of water, out of 7,457,000 available annually at pro-

posed project sites. If constructed, the projects would make available 387,000 acres of additional paddy land, 208,000 acres of highland land and some 6,750 K.W. of hydroelectric power.

Other governmental units, with primary concern for collateral water uses, have not been consulted in the planning stage. On the completion of a study, the scheme is made available to other interested agencies. At such a stage their influence is necessarily at a minimum.

In this form of planning by a unit which must have developed a significant bias, decisions on multiple use will frequently be made by viewing most, if not all, of the other uses through myopic eyes.

Since the pressure on the irrigation unit for colonization is very great at this stage of the country's development, schemes for water use may be developed, and probably have been executed, which are neither economical in themselves nor in the best interests of the country as a whole.

The disability of the unit operating as an agent for colonization schemes and as an arbiter for all other water uses, is already apparent not only to the unit, but to most of the thoughtful individuals engaged in general water development.

It is even beginning to appear that emphasis on rice paddy development may be in some instances illogical and unsound. Such fundamental decisions may drive the agency to preparing for the wrong crop in the wrong location and for the wrong use of water. This situation is well and succinctly summarized in the Report on the Six Year Programme (p. 237) in the following words: "The Ceylon economy is said to be eminently suitable for agricultural rather than industrial development. Be that as it may, Ceylon cannot hope to seek her salvation in agricultural development alone."

In spite of the disabilities discussed, however, the Irrigation Department has brought under irrigation for rice cultivation some 765,000 acres of land, out of the 16,000,000 acres of the Island. In addition to these irrigated lands another 135,000 acres are in rice cultivation by direct natural rainfall.

(c) Hydroelectric Power

Activities with respect to this function are carried out in the Department of Electrical Undertakings. Extensive hydroelectric projects have already been developed or are under further contemplation and design. The Norton Bridge Project (Stage I) provides some 25,000 K.W. Stage IIA, now under construction, will add another 25,000 K.W. At the Gal Oya Reservoir, the Irrigation Department has installed a capacity of 5,000 K.W., with provision for a future expansion to 10,000 K.W. At the proposed Walawe Reservoir, also a multi-purpose project now under review, some 6,000 K.W. are proposed.

Ceylon, as with most other developing countries, is power-hungry and must necessarily search for power production, either from its abundant rivers in the southeast and southwest or by the development of thermal power in the strategic areas where the pressure for such use is already great. The world's use of energy is expanding at a tremendous rate, with an increase in the last 10 years of well over 35 per cent over the uses in the 1940's. These uses will expand with great rapidity in Ceylon, even though there may be some slight deviation from the world record. Since the country has no coal, oil or natural gas, the production of power becomes a matter of national concern. It must develop to the maximum its hydroelectric resources if these should prove to be competitively economical.

Any consideration of hydroelectric possibilities at once confronts the Government with competitive uses for such water and its resulting power. Where power development for general purposes is in competition with water for irrigation and its power requirements, decisions up to the present time have not rested upon strictly objective determinations of both national necessity and interest. They rest primarily with the department responsible for irrigation. In such cases it is both human and natural that first choice of water and of hydroelectric potential are generally reserved for irrigation purposes. It is quite conceivable also that this may not always be the best decision for the total economy. No neutral and objective way out of this dilemma has so far been provided.

Although data are available to a limited extent to assess the hydroelectric potential of the country, many professional workers are of the judgment that such data are inadequate to provide a reasonable picture of these possibilities. One observer in government service has even suggested that the estimates of potential hydroelectric power generally used have a validity which may vary from 50 to 100 per cent of the actual. Aside from the competitive aspects of water power development, therefore, detailed information on the future potential is decidedly inadequate.

(d) Industrial Uses

Water for industrial purposes has not been a major concern. This situation stems from the fact that hitherto industries predominating have been small in character and largely fabricating in nature. Their uses for water per unit of product are very low.

The governmental unit responsible for industrial development, for these reasons, has given little attention to the possibility that industrialization may proceed at a more rapid pace than in the past 10 years. Some signs of such a speeding up of industrial growth are already apparent in the development of new and heavy industries. These latter groups will of course be large users of water. In some instances, they may be so situated geographically as to require waters of extremely limited availability. Since provision of large amounts of water is generally the responsibility of the irrigation agency, competition between industry and agriculture for limited available water will become increasingly acute.

This situation has arisen in almost every other part of the world where industrialization has occurred. There is no reason to suppose that a similar situation will not confront Ceylon in the next 10 to 20 years. The policy and planning which should accompany decisions in such competition should not wait until disorder and confusion block the most logical development of the area. Water use should not be so frozen by premature and ill-advised decisions that the economy of the country would be embarrassed and restrained because the policies could not be reversed. The experience in other developed countries has already disclosed that competition for water among various functions goes through major changes from decade to decade. The underlying assumption in Ceylon appears to be that water for agricultural purposes must be dominant. Whether such a fixed view is warranted or even safe for the future is one of the questions to which government must give careful attention.

In like manner, the demand for water for industrial uses, now supplied in small amount by municipal water undertakings, will certainly increase. The assumption that such industrial uses will forever remain proportionately minor in total municipal use runs counter to the experience throughout the world.

(e) Navigation

In many parts of the Island canalization has already been accomplished. The ancient Dutch and Portuguese Rulers provided for water transportation by the old Dutch Canal, the Hamilton, the San Sebastian and minor artificial waterways. Some of these canals built for drainage or navigation or both, are obviously not continuously maintained. Some have fallen into disuse, while others are badly in need of dredging and perhaps extension.

No real analysis of the navigation values of the existing or even proposed canal system has been made. Such a system for water carriage may have important values in the development of the country, both in the interior and on the coastal areas. Such an evaluation should be made and a realistic appraisal of the possibilities should be recorded.

(f) Forestry, Fisheries and Recreation

The country is provided with intelligent professional workers in each of these fields. In the case of forestry, activity may be characterized as in a state of frustration. Participation by professional foresters in significant water use decisions is small. Their concern with problems of siltation, as affecting water structures, and as demonstrating the loss of soil, has not been given much scope. Current studies of silt formation and accumulation and research as to cause and effect are inadequate.

The feeling on the part of the foresters that forest cover for large acreages would be major deterrents to flood runoff is likewise in need of realistic and objective evaluation. That forestation has significant values in the protection of valuable soils is beyond debate. Relationships between forestation and water runoff, use and development, however, are not clear enough to provide guides for future activity.

The production of structures for water development do not, at this time, present important issues with respect to fish. Fish culture is primarily concerned with increasing use of streams and of reservoirs for stocking. Virtually none of the fish of the Island pose the same issues as in other countries where upstream movements may be hampered by high dams.

The well known long-range migratory fish of commercial importance, such as salmon and shad, do not occur in Ceylon waters. Only the short range type prevail with which major structures show little interference. The really high fisheries production potential resides in the development of the vast water acreage of the numerous irrigation tanks, reservoirs, village tanks and swamps. Their use, of course, poses many technical, administrative and policy questions.

(g) Flood Control

In urban and in agricultural areas, flood damage has already become of significant interest to government officials and to the citizens at large. The recurring disabilities, monetary and otherwise, in the Colombo area present an unsolved problem. A number of reports have been prepared on this issue, with special emphasis on the Colombo area. No decision has been made as to how corrective measures might be instituted and at what cost.

Minor attempts have been made to protect agricultural lands against perennial flooding. Even these minor efforts have turned out to be both costly and relatively unproductive. In this effort, again, there are many parallelisms throughout the world. Before major expenditures are made in attempts to protect agricultural land, the practices elsewhere should be reviewed to disclose the lessons learned and the policies which should guide Ceylon in this complex, erratic, expensive and sometimes useless effort.

In general, the irrigation department concerns itself with flood problems. Admittedly, it has not been able to make major progress, because of the pressure of other duties, budget deficiencies, absence of a well-defined policy and programme for both technological and financial solutions, and the perennial lack of capital money.

(h) Beach Erosion

Destruction of coastal areas by sea erosion is a matter of great public interest and concern. The Government has already learned that major amounts of money will be needed to prevent such disabilities. If the programme were successful, the amounts would be well spent. Unfortunately, the corrective measures hitherto adopted have not always stopped the erosion, which appears to be growing.

Under present procedures the local authority generally turns to the central Government, when public concern is great and when the work required for control is beyond its capacity. Parliament, in the past, has made money available for such work, which the public works agency has generally performed. A considerable amount of money has been spent in the last 10 years. The situation at Negombo continues serious.

No unit is thoroughly versed in the control of beach erosion or is in a position to provide clear and undeniably effective measures. The experience of other countries who have pursued successfully the correction of such phenomena for many years, needs to be assembled and assessed. Since the money required for these control measures is always high, the decisions as to their validity and justification should be subject to high level evaluation.

III. *Problems and Deficiencies*

(a) Basic Data

A first requisite for the most intelligent and successful use of water resources is the availability of a long term record and understanding of all of the facts regarding such resources. Because of the highly variable nature of water resources a continuing inventory of such basic data is essential. Included in such requirements are elaborate information on the flow of surface waters, their silt carrying capacity, their minimum and maximum runoff, their quality, their evaporation and infiltration; on the geological structure of the country, with particular reference to underground waters; and on the meteorological characteristics of the area in which development is proposed. Each of these features requires a continuing "bookkeeping," which would provide the essential criteria upon which the projects may be evaluated, designed and constructed. In the accumulation of such data the variations in time, geography and in land management are all matters of prime significance. Without such long term measurements and explorations, undertakings of large or small size and importance cannot be safely designed. Already examples have occurred in Ceylon where projects have been completed with limited basic data and have failed subsequently to fulfill their total design purposes and functions. Such a situation cannot and should not be perpetuated.

The hydrology branch of the Irrigation Department now measures, compiles and processes the data intelligently and efficiently. It has carried out this task, however, under severe limitations of budget, personnel and equipment, with the additional handicap of focusing its major activities upon the requirements of irrigation. Data and services are supplied to most of the official water users and developers of Ceylon. These latter cover not only the problems and necessities of irrigation, but of hydro-power, municipal water supply, flood runoff, industrial water, silt accumulation, flood forecasting and collateral functions. The significance of these services cannot be over-estimated.

The routine measurement and interpretation of basic data are insufficient for the purposes of intelligent and economical water development. Various deficiencies confront the user of data in virtually every detail of stream measurement and assessment. Although there are 478 rain gauge stations in Ceylon, only 22 of them are of the continuous recording type. Virtually all of them need rehabilitation and conversion into modern instruments.

The situation with respect to the 22 river gauging stations is likewise unsatisfactory, simply because they are inadequate in number, in modern design and in most appropriate geographical distribution.

Similar comment may be made with respect to measurements of stream currents, because of the unsatisfactory nature of the equipment provided or of the inadequacy of necessary boats to manage to read such equipment with maximum efficiency.

Sampling of silt needs elaborate extension, with the addition of more modern equipment and with an increase of the number of stations.

The number of men engaged in reading the gauge recorders is only 20, wholly insufficient to carry out the task for which they have a responsibility, even if they were to operate diligently on the existing gauging stations over the next 20 years. Travel facilities and budget for subsistence in the field are tragically inadequate.

All of these difficulties are familiar to the existing Government departments. Their officials are completely aware that the number of recording rain gauges should be more than doubled, a similar expansion is needed with current meters, the number of boats for river use should be very much increased, the number of silt samplers should be almost tripled and personnel and travel expenses should be more than doubled.

Before very long the chief and the assistant chief of the unit responsible for this highly important function will reach retirement age. There is no evidence of preparation for successors of comparable skill and competence.

The situation in respect to geologic exploration and studies is even more deficient than in hydrology. Although the general geology of the country is reasonably well understood, further development of underground waters, particularly in the Jaffna Peninsula, and of the bases for the design and construction of structures for surface waters are badly in need of extensive and detailed geological study.

The present practice consists primarily of accumulating geological information gathered through activities performed essentially for other purposes, such as for the design and construction of dams, bridges and wells. Geological studies for general water purposes are budget starved. The basic and specific information for the needs of immediate water development are essentially lacking.

The arid north-western coast, extending from Puttalam to the Peninsula of Jaffna, offers a challenge to the geologist, because of the tremendous significance of the provision of fresh water for the area. An increasing knowledge of the fresh water potential from wells in this whole area is a vital necessity for its further expansion. Ground water exploration in this region, resting upon increased geological and hydrological investigation, have inestimable potential national value.

Here, again, these delinquencies are completely familiar to the geologists. Their failure to obtain anything more than minor budgetary support over the past decades is obvious.

Sirimanne several years ago cogently summarized the water situation from the geologists' point of view in the following terms:

> Water is our most valuable mineral. Although there is an abundance of it precipitated annually on our Island, it has proved too elusive for man to harness it, to any appreciable amount. Only 8 per cent of the surface runoff is utilized by us at the present time, . . .
>
> The position in regard to ground water resources is still less satisfactory. We have no knowledge of the available resources, as only about 1 per cent of the Island's population is supplied by water from underground sources.

In the collateral field of meteorology, similar deficiencies exist. Expansion in this field should parallel those in hydrology and in geology. Budget support has been inadequate and the country will continue to pay a heavy price for the delay in the accumulation of basic information. The cost of correcting these deficiencies has been spelled out by the various governmental agencies. These additional costs have not found their way into current budgets, because in Ceylon as everywhere else, the ordinary bookkeeping of water resources is non-dramatic and unappealing. Capital investments are frequently made which cost a thousand times more than the expenditures necessary to supply essential data. The penalties for making such capital expenditures without adequate information are rarely known to the average citizen. No industrial or commercial business could survive very long if they kept no books of their resources, of their income and of their expenditures. The same principle applies with respect to water resources, where the amount, nature and behavior are all relatively unknown. The costs for the accumulation of basic data are insignificant when compared to the possible damage of millions of rupees, if their lack results in failures of projects in irrigation, hydro-power and flood control. A single mistake in the forecasting and evaluation of a flood event can and does create damages many times the cost of adequate meteorologic and hydrologic prediction and evaluation.

(b) Evaluation of Needs and of Priorities

The water problems have been canvassed from the standpoint of multi-purpose values in the field of irrigation since 1953. Similiar evaluations have been made by both the health department and public works units, in respect to municipal water supply, sewerage and drainage. Fairly broad inventories and appraisals are at hand for evaluating the potentials and the necessities in the field of electricity.

In each of these examples the establishment of priorities as to importance and as to time is a primary objective. In all of them, however, the explorations and evaluations have been made by each water unit independently. Co-ordination of inquiry, integration of departmental approaches and policies and current consultation on any or all features of programming have been distinguished largely by their absence.

The major deficiency in the planning of projects, in consultation between governmental units, and in design and construction is well understood by all the responsible officials. Their failure to accomplish integration and consultation may be attributed more to the rigid administrative structures than to the officials' unawareness of the deficiencies noted. It is even doubtful whether such integration can be accomplished, purely through the desire of officials to co-operate. Some mechanism must be provided which would assure a common meeting place for official integration. A tacit acceptance of the belief that such a philosophy should predominate, without the mechanism for its implementation, evidently does not work.

The situation is further complicated by the fact that Government itself has created agencies to perform the same or similar functions, which inevitably must be in conflict with each other. For example, as already pointed out, at least four agencies now exist which have a responsibility in the field of potable or municipal water supplies. Their consultation with each other is almost nil and their dependence for water upon a fifth agency, that responsible for irrigation, creates additional obstacles to rapid development.

All of these manifestations of growing pains are not surprising, but it is important to eliminate them before the administrative structures become so frozen that any attempt to provide for better integration will be hampered by the functional inbreeding which time produces in any department. The time is ripe not only for insisting upon collaboration, but in providing the necessary machinery to do so.

(c) Finance

No small part of the delay in moving forward with advantage in water use, is due, not only to the insufficient funds allotted for these purposes, but to the whole system of financing such projects and providing for their reimbursement.

Virtually no local unit of Government has the resources or is permitted to develop the resources to provide itself with bond issues for capital investment. The result of such a situation is that every local governmental unit must turn to the central Government for such aid. Even the largest city in Ceylon, Colombo, is in this unhappy status.

Such a situation perhaps must prevail during a transition period until local units gain financial stability and responsibility which would make them self-supporting. In this interval, the Choksy Committee recommends a central Government bond issue of relatively long term and with a rate of interest of 2 per cent, in order to stimulate local water development.

Active study, however, should be instituted to determine how the major local units may become financially autonomous and develop the resources for reimbursement, which will increasingly strengthen autonomy and stability. Such inquiries should be pursued by competent governmental units or by parliamentary inquiry committees.

Consideration should be given to the development of metropolitan districts for many water and sewerage functions. Colombo, Jaffna and Kandy have all grown to such size, within and outside their city limits, to warrant a unitary approach to their water supply, sewerage and drainage problems. The machinery for meeting such metropolitan problems has been used in many countries and should be explored and adapted to the situations of Ceylon.

In projects of national significance, such as irrigation, flood control and power, more realistic diagnoses are essential to provide for the return to Government of a considerable part of its expenditures. This is particularly true in the case of irrigation and flood control projects, where already the return to the Central Government is an infinitesimal portion of its total expenditure. Such a tendency toward little or no reimbursement will inevitably result in undertaking projects which have little or no validity or justification.

It is certainly true that some projects must be undertaken for the general welfare, even if they have little or no demonstrable economic validity. If the latter, however, is not even evaluated, the criteria for choice and priority of projects to the best advantage of the total economy will automatically be dispensed with. Such a practice can only result in wasteful expenditure of money. The sociological aspects must at least be sieved through the orthodox fiscal attributes. The decision as to choice, of course, still remains that of Government. Where local responsibility for an irrigation project, for example consists of virtually no repayment, universal pressure for ill-conceived undertakings is bound to result.

(d) Central-Local Government Relations

Part of the difficulty of expanding water use and development stems from the fact that for the most part even the larger local units have little autonomy or responsibility for planning, designing and executing works. The capacity to raise funds and to provide for charges and reimbursement is in most instances extremely low or even non-existent.

The perpetuation of a governmental system which tends to pauperize local government units has many elements of danger. The machinery proposed later herein for the guidance and development of water resources will include this governmental problem. There is some reason to suggest that the central Government should, as time goes on, remove itself from many actions in local development. This would be possible only if emphasis is placed upon raising the level of local responsibility and autonomy.

Tax and revenue sources are already available in local areas. They need nursing, adjusting and identification in order to prepare and implement a local fiscal program which will increasingly make local units less dependent upon central Government. The task will not be simple, but its solution needs to be intelligently and thoughtfully confronted.

(e) National Water Policy

It is apparent that no semblance of total national water policy now exists. A number of policies are operative. They are neither consistent with each other nor uniformly adjusted to the necessities of the country.

Competition for water resources is high. Decisions as to most appropriate uses and priorities are unintegrated. They rest primarily upon the current views and policies of individual departments, lightly tied to national policies for land development, for water use in general and for fiscal necessities.

No central agency has been assigned the task nor has assumed the responsibility for relating all water uses to each other and in turn for arranging these developments in priorities for maximum national advantage.

Priority of use has been dominated primarily by an agricultural and land policy, which tends to pre-empt the largest volumes of water. This policy in turn underemphasizes alternative uses and even fails to estimate their relative merits.

The present situation of non-integrated planning and execution, if continued for even a few more years, can only lead to waste of resources and of money. One need not labor the fact that water development in Ceylon in general has been haphazard. The period of pioneering in this manner, although completely understandable, should be brought to a close.

Ceylon cannot depend upon the current economic forces alone to provide either the diagnoses or the consequent future solutions. The continuation of unintegrated development frequently precludes the best control and utilization for the maximum welfare. Each year, conflicts in interest increase and are crystallized as between users and as between governmental agencies.

The supply of water is limited. Its planned use is a most important function of Government. No other resource so dominates the future development and existence of the country. The determination, on a broad scale, of the potential of each drainage basin and of its relation to the whole country should be established by the joint forces of those experienced in various sectors of these operations.

The development of a major plan, therefore, is a first essential. The continuing revision of the plan is of equal necessity. Both require a review machinery in government, which is non-existent.

As a prerequisite to such diagnoses and action, the present deficiency in basic data should be eliminated. Long term records, indispensable for most major decisions, must be initiated for accurate and continuing recording of precipitation, infiltration, stream flow, silt load and other significant characteristics.

iv. *The Water Resources Board*

(a) Powers and Duties

All the evidence accumulated in this study has made clear that an overlying agency is essential to accomplish the purposes discussed. The most effective way of bringing all water planning and use into integrated and continuously adjusted form is through a central government agency. Co-ordination of separate agencies, continuing readjustment and inquiry, development of standards and criteria for project evaluation, continuing determination of priorities for water use, and continuing definition and redefinition of national water policy all require a permanent unit at top level in Government. Such a Water Resources Board is recommended for Ceylon. It should encompass all of the functions related to water use, development, and finance.

It has been suggested that, if Parliament were to define the elements of a national water policy, its execution by the existing government units would automatically reach a high level of integration. Efforts to accomplish this purpose by such a simple device as a legislative act have been eminently unsuccessful throughout the world. It is difficult to define policy so specifically that it may serve as an unalterable guide for agencies, when the problem itself is not fixed and the mechanisms for developing solutions are similarly eternally in flux.

Such a Board as is here proposed, sitting regularly and frequently, would provide both the continuity and the flexibility to meet the needs. By the very nature of its activities, it will encounter problems in finance, in central-local government relationships, in functional and geographical competition for water, and in the testing of the validities of governmental action. These are day by day functions which cannot be frozen by legislative dictum, whose very wisdom and applicability may be questioned the day after its passage.

It has been further suggested that, in a small country such as Ceylon, if all water and land development were placed in one governmental unit there would be no necessity for an overlapping integrating and review board. Such reorganization gives the semblance of a solution, without its substance. Even when so consolidated, the various units tend to grow in size and in competition. In this instance, no compelling reasons are apparent for major consolidation of present units, with the important exceptions noted later herein. These exceptions deal largely with areas where functions are of a strictly similar nature. Structural and administrative consolidation throughout the whole structure of water planning and development is not recommended, except through the medium of the Water Resources Board.

(b) Composition

The membership of the Board should be composed of the key representatives of each of the agencies dealing with water problems as a primary responsibility. These representatives should be at top level administratively. Their participation in board action should not be relegated to subsidiary or secondary levels within their agencies. As a matter of fact, this requirement will undoubtedly be self-acting. As the importance of the Resources Board becomes apparent, its decisions will not be left to subordinate officials.

In addition to the governmental agency representation, the Board should have at least three non-government members. These might be chosen from the engineering, legal or general citizen areas. Alert and intelligent representation of the public viewpoint may thus be assured. The chairman of the Board should not be an agent of Government. He should be chosen from the country at large, for his wisdom, objectivity, public interest and capacity for weighing important public issues. If such an individual should happen to be an engineer, this should not be a barrier to his appointment as chairman. It might even have certain major advantages.

(c) Status in Government

The Board should be created by an act of Parliament. It should report directly to the Prime Minister. A precedent for this kind of a structure may be found in the early Water Resources Committee of the United States. Such a position assures the dignity and the significance to the deliberations and the decisions of the Board, which its responsibilities must entail.

The Board should *not* have the executive functions of design, construction and operation and maintenance of projects. These functions should remain with the existing government agencies already responsible for them. If these latter executive duties are imposed upon the Board, its major functions of integration, of planning, of study and of policy proposal become confused with the all too human desire of extending the empires of project development and construction. The two primary functions of integration and of execution should be kept rigidly separated, so that the motive and actions of an overlying Board of Review do not become confused and into competition with executive agencies.

v. *Special Reorganization Proposals*

Although no major reorganization of existing departments is proposed, certain important functions are now widely distributed in responsibility and in attitude. In three areas reconstruction, consolidation and adjustment for stronger leadership are suggested below:

(a) *Health Services*

The leadership which one would expect a central health department to provide for the stimulation of environmental sanitation in general, and domestic water supply, sewerage and drainage, in particular, has evidently failed of its purpose. Progress in these areas has been unusually slow, considering the unanimity of opinion that these requirements should and must be met as a number one priority.

Some of this lack of progress lies in the absence of a continuing leadership and educational program of the health department. The deepseated roots and causes of such delayed action are not too obvious. That unit in the health department which should have major responsibility for such leadership, namely, the public health engineering unit, has neither the status, the dignity nor the power to exercise this function to maximum advantage.

The existing public health engineering unit has been excessively burdened with design and construction activities, which divert it from its major functions of guide, leader and stimulator of sanitation projects. This design and construction function should be reduced to a minimum, with a residual no more than sufficient to provide the staff with the essential experience and qualifications for Civil Service promotion. Beyond that point, the Department of Public Works should assume all of the design and construction responsibilities in the fields of domestic water supply, sewerage and drainage.

The essential functions of a reconstituted public health engineering unit in the health department, with the appropriate status described above, should include the following:

1. It should have general supervision and control over the waters of the country, in so far as their sanitary and physical condition affect the public health or comfort.

2. It may make and enforce rules and regulations, and order works to be executed, to correct and prevent the pollution of such waters.

3. It shall investigate all sources of water and ice supply, and all points of sewage discharge.

4. It shall examine all existing public water supplies, sewerage systems and refuse disposal plants, and shall have power to compel their operation in the manner which shall project the public health and comfort, or to order their alteration, extension or replacement when deemed necessary.

5. It shall pass upon the design and construction of all public water supplies, sewerage systems and refuse disposal plants which shall be built within the country.

6. It shall consult with and advise public officials, having or about to have systems of water supply, drainage, sewerage or refuse disposal, as to the most appropriate source of water supply, and the best method of assuring its purity, or as to the best method of disposing of drainage, sewage or refuse, with reference to the existing and future needs of all communities or persons which may be affected thereby.

7. It shall also consult with and advise public officials, corporations, companies and individuals engaged or intending to engage in any manufacturing or other business whose sewage and industrial wastes may tend to pollute the waters of the country.

8. It may also conduct experiments relating to the purification of water and the treatment of sewage or refuse.

9. In no case shall the unit be required to prepare plans, specifications or detailed estimates for any improvement, unless it be specifically delegated to do so by the Parliament and adequate special appropriation be provided for the purpose. It shall, however, prepare and provide information of a preliminary nature in connection with its normal activities and duties.

10. In order to make it possible for the public health engineering unit to perform these functions successfully, legislation should be enacted to prevent the installation of a system of water supply, sewerage or refuse disposal, for public use or materially to alter or to extend any such existing system, without having a written permit from the director of health services. It is obvious also that such a permit cannot be issued until complete plans and specifications for the installation, alteration

or extension, together with pertinent information thereon, have been submitted and approved by the unit. All construction shall take place in accordance with the approved plans.

These guiding principles have stood the tests of a half-century of practice in many countries. It is by no means too early to initiate such principles and their collateral functions in Ceylon. As a matter of fact, it is essential that this be done, before systems are installed in haphazard and undesirable form, when major corrections thereto are either impossible or extravagantly costly. With the powers and duties here outlined the health department and its implementing unit, public health engineering, will be in a position to recapture the leadership essential to rapid progress in this field.

The principles listed above deal naturally with problems of water resources. They are not intended to suggest that other functions of great significance in environmental sanitation should not similarly be the responsibility of the health department and of its public health engineering unit.

(b) Public Works

A department of public works should be created which would have the responsibility for preparing the design for and for constructing the water, sewerage and drainage systems for the country. In this unit all of such duties should be centralized. In exercising this function, the department of public works should have close liaison with the public health engineering unit of the department of health services. It should be bound by the principles already listed above in connection with this latter agency.

The water works sub-department of the department of public works has completed designs for most of the major towns in the island. Even in cases where such designs have not yet been finished, a considerable amount of investigation and preparatory work has been accomplished. Virtually all of this, however, has been done either without or perhaps with only desultory consultation with the health department. This situation needs immediate and prompt correction.

The public works department has formulated a future program of reasonably modest size, but of orderly and thoughtful character and priority.

The unit has the strong conviction, which the writer of this report whole-heartedly shares, that "properly controlled and maintained the water works in the Island could, in most instances, be self-supporting without being a charge to the State. There will, of course, be rural areas and small villages, which are not in a position to maintain a water supply or pay for the installation." With this principle in mind, centralization of the functions herein discussed should be accomplished promptly and the competitive features in present practices should be equally promptly eliminated.

(c) Geological Survey

One central agency should be made responsible for collecting and reviewing the adequacy of hydrologic and geologic data. A new geological survey should be created which would have the following responsibilities in a separate water supply branch.

(1) The collection of all basic hydrologic data, both surface and underground.

(2) The exploration of the geologic features of the country and the accumulation of basic geologic data, essential for intelligent water development.

The functions briefly noted above are those which are now scattered among a variety of departments and are being performed with less than total satisfaction. They are all poorly budget supported. The centralization of collection, investigation and statistical analysis of these basic necessities for water resources development, is an essential step in an orderly approach to future water use and development.

It is well to re-emphasize that re-organization alone, in the directions noted above, without strong but modest budget support, would fall far short of either the hopes or the necessities for water resources use.

Summary of Conclusions and Recommendations

1. The Government of Ceylon now performs many functions in the field of water resources, use and development.

2. It does so through multiple independent agencies, in some instances competing with each other and in most cases performing their duties independently, without major integration of purpose, plan or priority.

3. Basic hydrologic, meteorologic and geologic exploration and data are inadequate for safe and logical design and operation of water projects.

4. Inadequacies in financing projects and in local government autonomy and responsibility, coupled with central government deficiencies in leadership and co-ordination, account for the lack of progress in important water development.

5. A unified national water policy is lacking.

6. The creation of a central Water Resources Board is recommended, to formulate national policy, to co-ordinate planning and execution, to establish criteria for the selection and financing of projects and to integrate water policy with policies for agricultural and industrial expansion.

7. Re-organization and strengthening of certain departments are

suggested for wider fulfilment of some important functions, *e.g.*, the provision of potable water, sewerage and drainage faciilties and the collection, interpretation and dissemination of basic data.

Acknowledgments

Rarely has a reviewer received such gracious, wholehearted and helpful co-operation in a study as has the present author found in Ceylon. To enumerate the names of ministers, permanent secretaries, individuals, official agencies and citizens, who have aided in this review, would require a roster of many pages. In order to avoid the omission of any of these, the writer takes this means of acknowledging and thanking publicly all of them for their courtesy, unfailing help and astonishing friendly co-operation.

Only two individuals must be singled out for daily guidance and liaison activities—almost to the extent of full time. To Engineer E. B. Anketell of the Ceylon Health Department and Dr. R. L. Tuli, of the World Health Organization, I shall be eternally grateful.

Financing Sanitary Works in the Tropics—
A Challenge*

Not quite twenty years ago, your speaker had the pleasure of watching a master at work on the identification of a tropical disease which had already attacked over 500 persons in a North American city. A profound student of amebic dysentery, he moved from a position of doubt as to the true nature of the epidemic disease to one of rapid conviction, as his tools of diagnosis and powers of clinical observation came into play. This demonstration of scientific acumen in Dr. Craig I have never forgotten.

Nor have I forgotten the modesty and proficiency with which he participated in the investigating commission's deliberations. From that field study, a major axiom appeared: that epidemic disease must have multiple causes, other than the specific organism. In the Chicago epidemic, aside from the presence of the amebic dysentery cysts, the striking collateral phenomenon in causation was the cloudy climate of administrative control of water-sewage relationships in two hotels.

The theme of this paper stems in part from that early association. It is difficult to express adequately an appreciation of the distinction and honor which your Society bestows upon me in lending to this contribu-

* Reprinted from *American Journal of Tropical Medicine and Hygiene*, Vol. 2, No. 4 (July, 1953); the Seventeenth Annual Charles Franklin Craig Lecture, one of four papers composing a Symposium on Sanitary Engineering in the Tropics held on November 15, 1952, during the Annual Meeting of the American Society of Tropical Medicine and Hygiene at Galveston, Texas.

tion the distinguished name of so scholarly an investigator in tropical medicine as Dr. Craig.

Many observers have pointed out that tropical diseases differ in no important sense from the diseases which occur in many other parts of the world. Historically, the diseases of the tropics have merely outlived their opportunities in the rest of the world. Their decline in temperate zones has been the result of artificial measures of protection, much of which has been in environmental sanitation. The lessons learned from these successes in the temperate zones may be applied with some adjustments to the diseases which still plague the inhabitants of the tropics.

The elimination of typhoid fever and other enteric diseases, the building out of insect-borne diseases and the general modification of the physical environment for the protection of man are reasonably well understood disciplines. The professional worker in the tropics, however, must take these accepted principles and determine how they may be most successfully applied to the issues which confront him in a large part of the world.

When it is found that these accomplishments are in arrears as compared with the results so far attained in more favored areas, one searches naturally for some key to the failures. This key certainly does not rest in the absence either of scientific information or of diagnosis of local condition. By and large, principles for disease control and methods for environmental sanitation correction are reasonably well understood. What are the obstacles which bar the way to introduction of these methods and to wider participation in these promised successes?

John E. Gordon (1952) has recently pointed out that disease is the result of an ecologic process. It stems from a mutual relationship of various living organisms in an environment and their reaction to animate and inanimate surroundings. He includes in this ecological world all of the factors affecting the wellbeing of the species, not only "the agent of the disease but the intricate complex of the environment." This concept of disease causation gives us a cue as to the problem in the tropics. The multiple factors of food, of physical environment, of rates of reproduction, of economic and social status, all make for a dynamic equilibrium which at the moment may be unfavorable to maximum survival and health.

The Problem of Money

Of these factors, population growth and economic status perhaps are two of the most significant restraints in the advancement of environmental sanitation.

Marston Bates (1952) has recently epitomized part of this conclusion by the comment: "Disease in the tropics is fostered more by poverty than by climate." Standard of living in the tropics, so often parallel with underdeveloped countries in general, is usually at low ebb. The introduction of sanitary facilities into such a population at once poses significant fiscal difficulties. This discussion will be devoted primarily to the major disabilities in underdeveloped countries due to the lack of financial resources. Of this population problem little will be said, since my ignorance of solutions to this issue is even greater than that in the financial sphere.

MacDonald (1950) in England, an experienced observer of the tropical scene, has emphasized the same conclusion when he stated several years ago that "We can control all the plagues in the tropics and exterminate many of them. The speed and degree of success with which we do this does not depend upon fresh advances in technical knowledge, but on the administrative arrangements to put our knowledge into practice."

Even in that vast area of mosquito borne disease control, Russell and his associates (1946) express an equally optimistic view that "adequate technique for control is available and that it is financially possible is beyond dispute, whatever myopic revenue officials may put down on minute papers."

We need not debate, therefore, that scientific knowledge is sufficiently far in advance of application to make it possible for us to reduce or even to eliminate many of the environmental diseases, provided we could produce the economic and social climate essential for the introduction of our well understood techniques. Money, therefore, becomes almost the major key to disease eradication in many of the areas of which we speak. It is not the sole source of hope, because the development of informed professional workers, of improved legislative sanctions, and of wider and more efficient administrative machinery are all essential parts of major effort. In sanitary works, however, the unavailability of money represents one of the great deterrents to progress.

The Resources

The greater part of this discussion will be devoted to this particular feature of public health effort, a function to which the health officer and the engineer too frequently devote little or no serious attention.

The questions which must be posed in this connection are simple ones: is money available in the tropical countries; can it be channeled into sanitary works; are the resources so inadequate that the only hope for development in these areas rest upon external gifts, grants-in-aid or other forms of largesse?

Consideration here will be devoted primarily to a review of the availability of resources within the country itself. The financing of sanitary works on the basis of gifts of any kind is ruled out, first because such a technique is increasingly unattractive to the recipient governments and secondly, as a long range form of financing, it is precarious to say the least. Some way must be found by which the governments of tropical countries will rely increasingly upon their own strengths and will progressively develop fiscal techniques by which indigenous resources will be channeled more and more into the important sanitary works of the country. The rate at which this use of money will move can only be determined by the growing financial strength of the country.

What is the present situation with respect to money in the under-developed countries? Fortunately a great deal of study has been devoted to this problem by a number of agencies. The International Bank for Reconstruction and Development has accumulated much experience in this area of interest. The Institute of Inter-American Affairs has shown high ingenuity and imagination in exploring and in developing local fiscal resources in Latin American countries. The United Nations (1950, 1951) through a long series of studies by its Department of Economic Affairs has disclosed a number of interesting features of financing in underdeveloped countries. The individual countries themselves have, of course, subjected their problems to intensive scrutiny. The Government of India, in the last five years has made intensive studies of its problems in this connection, both through it Planning Commission (1951) and through its Ministry of Health. The latter has issued a comprehensive report of its Environmental Hygiene Committee (1950) which devotes no inconsiderable part to its deliberation to the same problem.

Throughout all of these official and semiofficial reviews the recurrent challenge of finance is perhaps the most striking single issue to appear. In the Environmental Hygiene Report (1950) in India, the following indicative comment appears, "Water supply is the most crying need of villagers. It can be provided by capital expenditures. . . . If some financial wizard can suggest a way of raising this money, we will harness all the resources of public health engineering to achieve this to perfection." This search for the financial wizard is universal in the underdeveloped countries. Is there any reasonable hope that this search might be successful in the not too distant future? Some optimism is possible, what does that optimism rest upon?

John H. Adler (1952) of the Economic Department of the International Bank has recently reviewed this whole problem with reference to government, since in most of these countries government is the important major source of local capital formation. It is his judgment that the two factors which limit severely the level of public and private investment are first and predominantly the level of private savings and the other the lack of an organized capital market through which savings can be channeled from the private saver to the financing of public investment.

Holdings of public debt by individuals are extremely small through Asia and the Far East. In virtually all of these countries the study indicates the major problem is how to devise incentives for greater savings and investments. In many countries the hoarding of savings is particularly significant and high especially in two areas, South and Southeast Asia and in the Middle East. In these latter it is estimated the private gold hoards are sometimes as large as 10 per cent of the total national income.

Hoarding by governments as well is not an unusual characteristic because of the requirements they have set up that savings bank deposits must be backed by 100 per cent of foreign exchange.

These practices by private citizen and by government are considered to represent sources of investment money which for the moment cannot be pried loose, either because of lack of confidence in the stability of governments or by the unattractiveness of low interest rates from public investment.

Making Money Available

All of these studies suggest ways of inducing individuals to enter the public market by one or more of the following procedures for increased use of savings:

1. Increased interest rates by institutions. For the most part, these amounts are restricted to only 2 or 3 percent, insufficient to attract investment.

2. By the creation of better savings institutions.

3. By the development of well managed and regulated stock markets.

4. By attracting higher income classes to the diversion of their savings from less to more useful public purposes.

5. By reducing the private investment in land and real estate in metropolitan urban areas.

6. By a general reduction of mal-investment through improved education and governmental guidance.

7. By the compulsory reduction of conspicuous consumption by middle and higher income classes. In general, it is thought that this might be accomplished by taxation on luxury items.

8. By using the idle resources of the community, in the form of unemployed labor and some materials, in spare time work on capital improvements. This type of effort has been successsfully employed in some of the Latin American countries, particularly in the construction of sanitary works.

One cannot review these studies in various parts of the world without realizing that in many countries sanitary works are possible of accomplishment through the existing resources of the countries, provided both government and people could be persuaded that their money would be intelligently and honestly planned and spent. One of the striking deficiencies in many of the countries is the absence of adequate facilities for safe deposit of voluntary savings. Almost every investigator, however, stresses the point that a fundamental consideration in making these funds available is the safety of the deposit. It is not surprising, but it is worth emphasizing, that confidence in government institutions is so often at low ebb that one of the writers is prompted to record the economic axiom that "confidence is a tender growth."

The application of ingenuity to finance is also stressed and the suggestion is even made that in some of these countries the use of a lottery form of savings for public works should be seriously considered. The first Washington monument in the United States was built in Baltimore by such use of a lottery, but the method has long given way to more sophisticated fiscal procedures.

Another significant feature of all the inventories is the conclusion that taxation has not yet reached a burdensome level in many of the countries under discussion. The possibilities of general and special taxes are still relatively unexplored. The device used to a great extent in the United States of special assessments and of special tax authorities for such works is just beginning to be applied.

The high rate of interest is, of course, a symptom, not only of the lack of confidence, but to some extent to the lack of proper finance and credit machinery. Its existence, however, is a sharp deterrent to public works construction. It is particularly severe in rural areas where the absence of a developed credit system makes the borrowing of money almost impossible. In Haiti, for example, the effective rate of money lending to farmers may be 100 per cent or more. It is extremely doubtful whether much public works would or could be built even in the United States if interest rates varied from 20 to 100 per cent. The Planning Commission of India, in its first five-year plan issued in 1951, emphasized the fact that "The progressive substitutions of usury by organized credit at reasonable rates are also steps calculated to promote economic and social equality. The Commission recognized, however, the high importance of the relevance of tax evasion to all of its proposals."

That many of these defects have their roots in the recurrent instability of governments is confirmed in the comments of Wyman R. Stone (1952), Director of the Institute of Inter-American Affairs. He comments, "I am afraid that one of the biggest problems is essentially that of the stability of governments and the lack of confidence that people with money have toward investing in the future of their own country." He further points out that in the evolution of many of these countries there is a long tradition of siphoning out of the country a good deal of the money earned locally. The amount returned for local improvements was very small and the machinery provided for raising funds locally was virtually non-existent. This historic picture accounts for the fact that in many instances the governments are largely central in character, with a minimum of local autonomy for development of local tax resources.

Examples of Financing

It would appear, therefore, that in many of these countries resources are at hand; they are in general either kept out of circulation or are channeled into speculative and high interest bearing risks, or they move into investments outside of their own countries. Can these practices be readjusted and reversed? How may the local financing of public investment be strengthened?

In Latin America there are evidences that such trends may be reversed and that local financing can and may be increased. The experience of the International Bank is of special interest in this connection, because it exercises fairly rigid control over its own loans. It has developed a wide international experience and it attempts to subject its loans to the kind of scrutiny and criteria which would normally prevail in England or in our own country. They share the view that in many of the underdeveloped countries the amount of private savings is surprisingly high and compares not too unfavorably with the rate of private savings in the countries of Western Europe and in the United States. There are notable examples of this general pattern in Brazil, Mexico, Colombia, Chile, and India, where active markets in corporate stocks have been developed.

The International Bank itself has been able to promote successfully a great deal of local financing in connection with its own loan operations. It has a long series of such local successes in India, in agricultural and power development; in Pakistan, in agriculture; in Thailand, in irrigation and other loans; in Iraq, in flood control projects; in Ethiopia, for highway and other development; in Southern Rhodesia, in electric power development; in Mexico, in light and power development; in Nicaragua, for highway construction; in El Salvador, for hydroelectric power; in Brazil, in the development of traction facilities and power; in Chile, for both power development and the exploration of underground water resources; in Turkey, for electric power, irrigation, and flood control. These represent only examples of the directions in which these lending agencies have moved in order to strengthen the use of local fiscal resources and to increase their application to public improvements. Given time and imagination, coupled with an understanding of local financial difficulties, it is possible to develop in many of the underdeveloped countries the use of local resources to an extent hitherto unanticipated.

Without an understanding of the underlying problems of financing public works, the health official and the engineer are unlikely to make important progress in the installation of sanitary works in underdeveloped countries. They must master not only the basic difficulties in these fiscal structures but they must assist in so strengthening and orienting them that the key to the application of their technological solutions to disease prevention will be more widely available.

That this essential feature of sanitary engineering practice is of extraordinary importance was recognized by the Expert Committee on Environmental Sanitation of the World Health Organization at its very first session in September, 1949. It stated in its Report to WHO that

> WHO must make clear very early in its sanitation efforts that it is frequently cheaper to provide adequate and safe public water supply and sewerage facilities than to perpetuate individual private, costly and dangerous springs, wells, cisterns, cesspools and septic tanks. Both health officers and sanitary engineers on occasion lose sight of this important fact. This concept, however, can be applied only when ingenious but orthodox fiscal procedures and the use of local materials are carefully explored and adopted. The prevailing rates of interest payment are often more important features of fiscal programmes than are the amounts of capital investment. Excessive interest rates are common in many underdeveloped countries, where private risks may be very high. The pooling of loans, supported by more favourable governmental reservoirs of funds, may result in lower interest rates. These and other valid fiscal approaches need early study, recording and dissemination in countries requiring public facilities. Successful practices developed in financing, and they are numerous in many countries, should be the subject of a special monograph for wide distribution.

Summary

General agreement may be presupposed upon the thesis that, in preventing disease and promoting health in the Tropics, the application of solutions lags behind scientific knowledge. One of the major obstacles to the more rapid introduction of sanitary facilities lies in the presumed deficiency of money. A recognition of this deficiency, coupled with a successful search for resources, give the best promise of more rapid accomplishments.

A number of recent studies of underdeveloped countries disclose larger amounts of fiscal resources than has been normally assumed to be at hand. Their failure to be moved into the public works market rest primarily upon absence of confidence in government, of modern safe financial institutions, and of general public understanding. Because of these factors, the professional public health worker may well broaden his sphere of interest and influence to encompass these aspects of the society within which he works, if he hopes to speed up public health attainments.

It is increasingly apparent, as Balfour (1950) pointed out several years ago, that "public health programs must be coordinated with a general plan to develop all spheres of social activity, including education, agriculture, communications, and industry." To this list, this paper adds that of the economics of public works expenditures!

BIBLIOGRAPHY

Adler, John H., 1952, Personal communication, August 6.

Balfour, Marshall C., 1950, Problems in health promotion in the Far East, *The Milbank Memorial Fund Quarterly* 28(1):84.

Bates, Marston, 1952, *Where Winter Never Comes*, Charles Scribner Sons, Pub.

Environmental Hygiene Committee 1950, Ministry of Health, India, Government of India Press, Simla.

Gordon, John E., 1952, The Twentieth Century—Yesterday, Today, and Tomorrow (1920–), *The History of American Epidemiology*, The C. V. Mosby Co. Pub.

MacDonald, George, 1950, Lecture to the Royal Society of Arts, England.

Planning Commission, 1951, The Government of India, The First Five Year Plan, Commerce and Industry Press, New Delhi.

Russell, West, and Manwell, 1946, *Practical Malariology*, W. B. Saunders Co. Pub.

Stone, Wyman R., 1952, Personal communication, October 22.

United Nations, Department of Economic Affairs, 1950, Economic Survey of Asia and the Far East.

————————, 1950a, Domestic Financing of Economic Development.

————————, 1951, Measures for the Economic Development of Under-Developed Countries.

U S Water Supply Lessons Applicable
to Developing Countries*
with Herbert M. Bosch

A community water system is defined, for the purposes of this discussion, as an integrated system that delivers a safe water, in ample quantity, into the household of every member of the community. It is implied that the provision of this amenity for domestic, industrial, and sanitation purposes is on an uninterrupted basis 24 hours a day, and 365 days a year. Full pressures in the water mains are likewise presupposed, as is the sustained full-time management of a responsible local agency.

These detailed specifications are spelled out to distinguish real community systems from those intermittent water services whose product is sometimes of safe quality and is delivered at points remote from the user, often at zero pressure. Even these inadequate systems are now only sparingly available to somewhat more than two-thirds of the population of the world. They represent, however, a retrospective picture of the domestic water supply situation in the United States some 100 years ago. It is valuable, therefore, to retrace the history of community water supply development in the United States, in order to determine the means by which this advance has been effected and to measure the impact that this development has had upon the public health and upon society in general. Some of the lessons of the past have important implications for acceler-

* Reprinted from the *Journal American Water Works Association*, Vol. 55, No. 8 (August, 1963). Copyright 1963 by the American Water Works Association, Inc.

ating the installation of water facilities throughout the globe. It need no longer be demonstrated that without water civilization declines.

History of U S Community Supplies

The earliest public water supplies date from 1652 in Boston, about 1732 at Schaefferstown, Pa., and 1761 at Bethlehem, Pa. At the close of the eighteenth century, only seventeen utilities were in operation. The number did not pass the hundred mark until 1850 and the thousand mark until 1885. By 1895, the number had reached about 3,000. At the close of 1924, it is estimated that more than 9,000 water utilities were supplying about 10,000 communities.

A turn of the faucet was by then all that was necessary for thousands of people to secure either hot or cold water on any floor of a dwelling. The public water supply was already having a beneficial effect upon public health, and had rendered certain functions, such as fire protection, street sprinkling, and sewer flushing, easier and more efficient, and new ones had been found, including many industrial uses. These supplies were not only substituting safe for unsafe drinking water, but were also making water-carried-sewerage systems possible, which in turn were replacing the dangerous privy and cesspool.

The evolution of the system under private sponsorship is of interest, particularly in view of the fact that outside of the United States and in much of Europe private ownership of community water systems is frowned upon and often prohibited. Yet, in 1890 in the United States about 23,000,000 people were supplied by water systems, of which one-third were privately owned and operated. By 1925 more than 85 per cent of the people were supplied by municipally owned water systems. Although this ratio had been materially altered by 1960, it is still true that more than three-quarters of the people are served by publicly owned systems. Private capital may have a prominent role in many countries in the development of new water systems, provided government policy and the political climate in general are favorable.

At the turn of the century about 30,000,000 people had the advantages of a municipal water supply; total use was 3 bgd. In 1954, these figures had grown to more than 100,000,000 people with a total use of 16 bgd. The average daily per capita use for the country as a whole was 150 gpcd.

Today, 22,000 communities, served by 18,500 systems, provide 140,000,000 people with water. These are true community water systems as defined above.

The continuing rapid urbanization and industrialization of the United States give no basis for assuming that the provision of new water facilities is either at an end or tapering off. On the contrary, all projections for the future show major increases in population and a continued influx into urban areas. It is probable, therefore, that total demands will reach at least 29 bgd by 1980 and at least 43 bgd by 2000. Even the per capita daily use will rise with the increase in the standard of living and the wider use of water-requiring household equipment, such as the automatic clothes washers.

Cost of Facilities

Because of the long history of community water development in the United States, no truly reliable estimate is available of the total investment in these facilities. It may be assumed, however, that, for the complete systems, this investment exceeds $17,000,000,000. In 1958 alone, capital expenditures reached almost $850,000,000.

Of much greater significance than these astronomic figures is the transcendent fact that unit costs, or per capita annual costs, are surprisingly and modestly low. This salient fact needs to be emphasized and reemphasized in teaching others to apply the lessons of United States experience to the solution of this important problem in developing countries. In these regions, the staggering capital investments required frighten ministers of finance, public health, and public works. Yet such officials need to learn that the strengthening of borrowing power, the development of the principle of reimbursability, the fortifying of local responsibility in management and fiscal control, all shift the emphasis in time from total capital investment to annual costs per person. These latter amounts are not intimidating and are increasingly within the grasp of millions of people, when the realities of sound financing are understood and applied.

Costs in United States

The case history of the United States is full of confirmation of these generalizations. For example, in 1954, the latest year for verifiable data, the average annual cost per person for water was $9.79, with a high in the arid Great Basin region of $13.67 and a low in the humid Chesapeake Bay region of only $7.97. Even with the great developments in community water systems projected for 1980 and 2000, involving billions of dollars of capital expenditure, the annual costs will remain $10 or less per person, on the average.* These annual costs include operation, maintenance, interest, and amortization.

Safe water delivered into the house is a remarkably inexpensive and

* The following per capita annual costs for publicly owned utilities in the United States have been reported in the JOURNAL[17]: 1955, $10.65; 1950, $7.94; 1945; $5.98. On the basis of these amounts, the per capita cost in 1960 was $12.98.

plentiful commodity. It generally costs from 5 to 10 cents a ton. No limit should be placed on the amount furnished or the time at which it is available, provided it is not wasted or dissipated uselessly and the customer pays for it.

In general, these are the policies guiding water supply development in the United States, and, increasingly, they are being met in practice. Of equal importance, however, is the realization that such supplies have been universalized among urban dwellers almost entirely through local responsibility and local financing and repayment. So successful has this performance been for more than 100 years, that water utility bonds are among the highest-rated investments in terms of safety in the open financial market. Defaults have been rare, interest rates often are less than 6 per cent and frequently less than 4 per cent annually, and periods of repayment extend to as much as 40 years.

Such financial stability has evolved; it has not always been so. It reflects at least a half-century of local responsibility and integrity, and a climate of political stability. Without these advantages, public water systems will be slow in creation and slow to develop. Central-government subsidy or external largesse in any form rarely provides the necessary ingredients. The major lesson of the United States experience is that the present systems are predominantly products of local financing, without any significant central-government subsidy.

Uncontaminated Water

Man has pursued the quest for uncontaminated water for thousands of years. During these centuries the criteria of acceptability in water have become more complex, more quantitative, and more rigid. The search, of course, is never ending, because the world is not static. Technology is ever on the move; populations and, with them, waste products, eternally increase; hence the protection of the consumer requires more and more complex controls. Centuries ago men wanted primarily to avoid or treat turbid waters. As a matter of fact, the treatment of the earliest supplies in the United States centered on removal of mud, and the original reason for a public water supply in many instances was solely to lay the dust on unpaved dirt streets and highways.

The disease hazards of water, although empirically suspected in earlier years, were not the major motivations toward community systems. The abilitiy to conduct chemical tests long preceded their application, which has resulted in such great progress in the control of disease-producing substances in water. To these tests have now been added the diagnostic indications for the less well-known organic and inorganic substances in water, whose physiologic effects are still but dimly understood. Accompanying these growing concerns has been the ever increasing demand throughout the last century by the consumer—demands often running ahead of technology—for superior palatability. Today, the water must be intensively scrutinized and treated, if necessary, and not just stored and delivered.

These advances in the public's standards of quality were naturally initiated by the forward march of water purification methods and sewage treatment processes that guard and improve the surface and ground water sources of the community systems. The great progress in these installations, it must be remembered, was made only during the last century.

History of Water Treatment

Until 1870 no water filtration plants existed in the United States. Some so-called filters, or strainers, were in use, but they could not be dignified with the title of filters as that name is now understood. In the 1870's the Poughkeepsie and Hudson, N.Y., slow sand filters were built, followed by those at Lawrence, Mass., in 1893. In the late 1880's the earliest rapid sand units appeared. By 1897 more than 100 such installations had been built, and, by 1925, 587 rapid and 47 slow sand filters had been built, and were delivering 5 bgd.

At the turn of the century, a great forward step in water protection came about through the introduction, in 1908, of chlorination for bacterial disinfection. Chlorination subsequently became the universal resort of the sanitarian, both in water and in sewage treatment.

The building of installations for water treatment has proceeded at a high rate from 1925 to the present. Simultaneously, however, water sources have become increasingly polluted by familiar biologic and chemical materials, plus newer and less familiar types of industrial and other wastes, such as synthetic organic chemicals and radioactive materials. Many viruses and other disease-producing organisms add to the ever growing control problems.

In spite of the delays due to economic depressions and wars, progress in pollution abatement has been great in the last 40 years. By 1957 more than 7,500 sewage treatment plants had been serving 77,000,000 people. An additional 3,000 communities serving 22,000,000 people had sewerage in 1957, but they were discharging raw sewage. The population served by sewers comprised somewhat less than 100,000,000 people in less than 11,000 communities.

Table 1 shows, in chronologic perspective, the increase in population served by sewers in the United States.

The sewage pollution abatement picture, however, still remains less than satisfactory, even though United States cities spent more money in 1961 for this purpose than ever before in history. On Jan. 1, 1962, 5,290

Table 1
US Urban Population and Population Served by Sewers, 1900–80

Year	Urban	Served by Sewerage Systems
	Population—*1,000,000*'s	
1900	30	25
1920	54	50
1940	80	70
1960	126	105
1980	200*	200*

* Estimated.

communities still had inadequate or no sewage treatment facilities. The effect of the resulting pollution on drinking water quality, however, should not be exaggerated, as water treatment processes have been singularly effective. In addition, less than 4 per cent of the 5,290 communities had a population of more than 5,000.

Expenditures in 1961 for sewage treatment were $560,000,000. The federal funds included in this total equal $1 for every $5.50 of municipal money. In prior years, by far the largest expenditure had its origin locally, unsupported by central-government subsidy. For the future, the projected annual costs (operation, maintenance, and amortization of investment) for collection and treatment are $818,000,000 for 1980 and $1,200,000,000 for 2000. The projected annual costs per person are again extremely modest—less than $5 in both 1980 and 2000.

Effect on Public Health

Contaminated water has always been a carrier of disease. Contamination of watercourses, whether surface or underground, has been the rule wherever there were people. The waste products of man have invariably been indiscriminately discharged into his environment. Man has been the host of many pathogens and many of these have spent part of their life cycle in the digestive tract and have found their way into human urinary and fecal discharges. The number and variety of these organisms have been myriad. They run the gamut from the ubiquitous typhoid fever, amebic dysentery, infectious hepatitis, and schistosomiasis, to others too numerous to mention.

Not too long ago all of these diseases plagued the United States, and all are, in part, waterborne. Today, many of the diseases are relegated to the classification "tropical"—truly a misnomer, as these so-called "tropical" diseases at one time were prevalent in cold as well as hot climates. They have not, in fact, disappeared from the western world, but have been controlled by environmental sanitary measures, such as water purification. When these measures are relaxed, the diseases recur.

In most developing countries, many of which are tropical, these sanitary restraints have not yet come into play on a large scale. Until they do, the enteric diseases will continue to take a major toll in disability and in lives.

Typhoid Fever

The major lesson of the advent of community water supplies in the United States is the great accompanying reduction in waterborne enteric diseases. The disappearance of typhoid fever is a striking example of this accomplishment. This experience holds promise of equal benefits in other evolving countries. A brief review of the public health achievement of the United States is pertinent, because it represents one of the most remarkable accomplishments of the century.

Typhoid fever deaths per 100,000 in 1900 were 35.8. By 1936 they had been reduced to 2.5, whereas today it is virtually zero (Fig. 1).

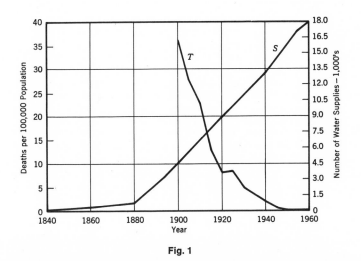

Fig. 1

Simultaneous Decline in Typhoid Fever Death Rate and Rise in Number of Community Water Supplies in the United States. Curve T is for the death rate and should be referred to left-hand scale; Curve S is for the number of water supplies and should be referred to the right-hand scale.

Minor recrudescences occur, but it is rare to see a typhoid case in a US hospital. Of equal significance is the fact that in the large cities, of, say, more than 100,000 population, the rates have consistently been notably lower than those for the nation as a whole. Safe water and pasteurized milk have undoubtedly accounted for this prideful accomplishment. It can and should be matched in the next decades in the developing countries.

The role of contaminated water in the dissemination of enteric diseases had, of course, been recognized for several years before the development of modern supply systems. Even before the great advances in bacteriology, Snow in England had shown in his classic monograph, *Mode of Communication of Cholera*, the relation between water from the Broad Street pump in London and an epidemic of cholera. That pathogens causing the diarrheal diseases of children—typhoid fever, cholera, and shigellosis—can survive in water and can cause illness in those who ingest the water is well known. In more recent years, the possibility that water has a role in the transmission of infectious hepatitis has also been studied.

Because of the comparative universality of typhoid fever, the morbidity and mortality data for this disease have been used as criteria of water sanitation, despite the fact that water is not the only mode of transmission of that disease. The increase in the number of municipal water supplies has paralleled closely the decline in typhoid deaths for more than half a century.

Effect of Chlorination

Undoubtedly, the continuous disinfection of public water supplies with chlorine accelerated this decrease in waterborne typhoid fever. A very considerable decrease in waterborne typhoid occurred, however, even before disinfection with chlorine became a common practice. This would seem to indicate that the installation of community water supplies, even though not all deliver a water of the highest sanitary quality, may be expected to have an appreciable effect on typhoid fever death rates.

Massachusetts Records

The annual reports of the Massachusetts State Board of Health prior to 1900 yield considerable evidence on the value of public water supplies in the reduction of typhoid fever, even before chlorination was adopted.

The Massachusetts department of health recognized very early the relationship between community water supplies and typhoid fever incidence. That department, the first state health department in the United States, early assumed an active role in the promotion of community water supplies and the investigation of the effect of such water supplies on the public health. The growth of water supplies and the typhoid fever death rates in the state during the period of that growth is shown in Fig. 2. The following extract from a letter by Hiram F. Mills, chairman of the Committee on Water Supply of the Massachusetts State Board of Health,

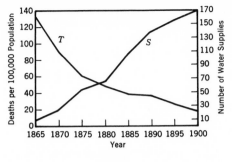

Fig. 2

Number of Community Water Supplies and Typhoid Death Rates, Massachusetts, 1865–1900. Curve T, typhoid death rate, should be referred to the left-hand scale; Curve S, number of water supplies, to the right-hand scale.

is of interest, as the data reported refer to the era before chlorination or other methods of disinfection of public water supplies were in use:

More than one-half of the cities of the state had public water supplies introduced within the years from 1869 to 1877. In the table below are given the number of deaths from typhoid fever yearly in 10,000 inhabitants, in each of the cities introducing water in the above period, for the 10 years previous to the period and for the 12 years following it:

Effect of Water Supply Systems in Typhoid Death Rate in Massachusetts Towns

Town	Mortality Rate* 1859–68	Date Water Supply Introduced	Mortality, 1878–89 Rate*	% of 1859–68
Holyoke	6.73	1873	8.93	133
Lawrence	8.34	1875	8.33	100
Lowell	6.16	1872	7.63	124
Fall River	7.78	1874	6.32	81
Springfield	9.67	1875	5.29	55
Taunton	6.12	1876	5.02	82
Northhampton	10.98	1871	4.04	37
Lynn	9.06	1871	3.87	43
New Bedford	7.77	1869	3.80	49
Newton	6.57	1876	3.65	56
Malden	8.04	1870	3.54	44
Fitchburg	10.59	1872	3.16	30
Woburn	8.29	1873	2.95	36
Somerville	4.28	1867	2.95	69
Chelsea	5.97	1867	2.89	48
Waltham	8.12	1873	2.42	30

* Rates are per 10,000, rather than per 100,000 population.

Of these sixteen cities all but three had less typhoid fever after introducing public water supplies than before; and their average number of deaths from this cause was less than one-half of the number of deaths when they used water from wells.

It is assumed that the word "wells" in the last sentence refers to individual household wells.

Importance of Ample Supply

In the incidence of typhoid fever and cholera, the principal involvement of the water supply is in connection with ingested water. In shigellosis and some of the infant diarrheas, there is increasing reason to believe that the availability of water in ample quantities may be equally or even more important than the bacteriologic quality of the supply. In a well controlled study, Hollister and others have reported on the effect of water availability of shigella prevalence in children of farm labor families in California. Their studies confirm the impression of Watt, who had postu-

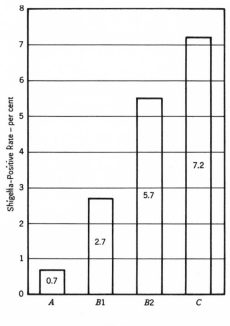

Fig. 3

Correlation of Shigella-Positive Rates With Availability of Water in Farm Labor Camps, Fresno County, Calif., 1952–55. Bar A shows the rate for those camps with water faucets inside all cabins; Bars B1 and B2 represent mixed-facility camps, and in these camps Bar B1 gives the rate for cabins with inside faucets, and B2 for cabins with outside faucets; Bar C is for camps with outside faucets with all cabins.

lated that water, even though it might be below standard, could act as a diluent and assist in the reduction of intestinal infection when used for personal hygiene purposes. Hollister and his colleagues compared the shigella-positive rates between camps that had cabins equipped with inside water faucets and camps that had a portion or all of the cabins with outside water faucets. Their data are shown in Fig. 3.

Wagner and Lanoix comment on a study carried on in Palmares, in the state of Pernambuco, Brazil, by the Special Service for Public Health. This Brazilian study showed a probable relation between the availability of water supplies and the deaths from diarrhea of infants. The study also gave some indication that the health risk was about the same whether the treated water was carried from public fountains to private houses or was taken from open, unprotected wells.

Need for Constant Vigilance

The record of the effect of water supply on disease in the United States gives no basis for assuming that control and eternal vigilance may be dispensed with once water systems are provided. The United States has a long history of the recurrence of waterborne disease when such vigilance has been relaxed. Unfortunately, the abatement of the enteric diseases does give the impression that waterborne epidemics are no longer to be feared as they were in the past. Those who hold this viewpoint must take heed of the toll exacted by these diseases since 1920, although the overall picture has been amazingly good.

It was in the period since 1920 that the largest waterborne amebic dysentery epidemic occurred in Chicago in 1933 and 1934; bacillary dysenteries and typhoid in California and New York in 1936; and jaundice in schools in Kansas and other states in 1935 and subsequently.

As if by way of reminder of the ever present waterborne menace, the typhoid epidemic in 1959 at Keene, N.H., offers a truly classic example of the results of inadequate supervision and the absence of chlorination. A rare set of circumstances, as always, produced illness of epidemic proportions. The circumstances were a carrier on the watershed, torrential rains, and a filter plant failure. It is well to be reminded that operating personnel, although conscientious, are subject to error and that facilities can and do fail.

Perhaps one stimulus to the rapid development of disinfection was the attitude of the courts in awarding damages against private and public corporations found responsible for illness resulting from pollution of water supplies. In several instances the damages were high—the city of Olean, N.Y., had to issue $350,000 in bonds to pay the costs incurred in a waterborne typhoid fever epidemic in 1929. Keene, N.H., already referred to, also paid damages aggregating thousands of dollars. An in-

complete list of such decisions includes more than two dozen instances.

Fluoridation

Another beneficial type of water treatment is now apparent in the
addition, artificially or naturally, of fluorides to public water supplies. It
has now been demonstrated that the presence of 1 ppm of fluorine in
water results in a major reduction of dental caries in children and ado-
lescents. The helpful effects on older persons are less but measurable.
Disabilities resulting from controlled application to water have been
shown to be negligible. The courts have generally sustained the validity
of fluoridation.

In 1945, the population supplied with fluoridated water was 231,920
in three communities. In 1959, the number so served had risen to
36,199,047 in 1,109 communities, and in addition, 7,000,000 people were
using waters naturally containing at least 0.7 ppm fluorine. The total
population protected therefore, was 43,000,000.

Global Implications

Recently, Abraham Horwitz, the Director of the Pan American
Health Organization, speaking of his own experience in his native Chile
and of the results of the organization's programs in North America,
Central America, and South America, made the following statement:

> If a single program were chosen which would have the maximum
> health benefits, which would rapidly stimulate social and economic
> development, and which would materially improve the standard of
> living of people, that program would be water supply with provision
> for water running into or adjacent to the house.

Despite the deficiencies in the statistics reporting enteric diseases in
many developing countries, it is clear that in all of them the mortality
from typhoid fever, gastritis, enteritis, and so forth is excessively high.
Such mortalities are in the range prevailing in North America in the last
period of the nineteenth century. As a matter of fact, for all age groups,
and particularly for infants and children 1–4 years of age, the diarrheal
diseases rank either first or in the first five of the principal causes of
disability and death.

As Horwitz points out, and as is generally accepted by most health
officials, a major reduction in these diseases is possible, quite independent
of etiologic and sociologic differences in countries or regions, by the provision of potable water in sufficient quantities for it to remain free from
gross bacteriologic contamination and in a manner conveniently acces-

sible to people. Thus, safe water for the the thirsty is not the sole objective; greater quantities of water must be provided for all the amenities of urban living.

Central and South America

The situations in two regions of the world may illustrate both the public health need and the deficiencies in community water service. In some countries of Central and South America, the death rate from the enteric diseases is still higher than 200 per 100,000 and rates in excess of 100 per 100,000 are common. Of the sixteen countries of Latin America, diarrheal diseases were the leading cause of death in the 1–4-year-old age group in eleven countries and among the first five principal causes in the remaining five countries.

Community water service, as defined above, is sadly deficient in Central and South America. Of 75,000,000 people in cities of more than 2,000 population, 29,000,000 are without such service. Almost 50 per cent of the people in cities of 10,000–50,000 are in the same category. More than 70 per cent are without service in cities of 2,000–10,000. In rural areas, matters are even worse. Of the 107,000,000 peoples in these areas far more than 70 per cent are without water service.

The leaders of these countries are, of course, well aware of these deficiencies and of the snail's pace in their correction. This understanding is well reflected in the Charter of Punta del Este, which calls for the provision of adequate water supply, sewerage, and excreta disposal in the next 10 years for at least 70 per cent of the urban and 50 per cent of the rural population. To accomplish this, strong support will be required for the prompt and continuous adoption of the fiscal, engineering, and managerial principles that have resulted in such great progress in the United States.

India

In another part of the globe, India, similar disease problems and water deficiencies confront the policy maker. The issues are the same as those discussed above. They are well recognized. Impatience with the slow pace of community water development over the last 20 years drives this country toward the realization that a new look at an old problem is demanded.

This new look was completed in 1961 by a committee created by the Indian Ministry of Health in an order dated Apr. 28, 1960. The inquiry resulted in conclusions and recommendations issued in 1962 by the Committee on National Water Supply and Sanitation. Its findings warrant a brief summary:

1. Of the urban population of 78,000,000, 34 per cent were judged to be adequately served with water, 26 per cent inadequately, and 40 per cent not served.

2. For the same urban population, adequate sewerage service was available for 21 per cent and no service for 68 per cent.

3. In the rural areas, defined by the committee as encompassing 300,000,000 people, progress toward the goal of 500,000 individual well installations was significant, but unduly slow.

The solution of these sanitation problems in India, it is recognized officially, will require that:

> ... a new path ... be cut if the program is to succeed and move on its own momentum. Local bodies should be encouraged to promote urban water supply and sewerage schemes as a self-paying industry, just as electricity undertakings are promoted and operated. The method of financing of such schemes should be patterned after the procedure and practice which have succeeded and established themselves in the more advanced countries, with such modifications as are dictated by conditions in this country.

Conclusions

The conclusions to be garnered from the experience of the United States and to be rapidly applied in the emerging countries of the world are well stated in the Indian report, in the following terms:

> The panel has therefore no misgivings on the outcome of such a venture if pursued vigorously by all the states. A certain amount of initial education and leadership would be necessary in order to wean the urban citizen and the local body from their established conventional notions that drinking water should be provided as a partial gift by the government.

BIBLIOGRAPHY

1. *Water Works Practice.* AWWA Manual. Am. Wtr. Wks. Assn., New York (1926).

2. Baker, M. N. *The Quest for Pure Water.* Am. Wtr. Wks. Assn., New York (1948).

3. Future Water Requirements for Municipal Use. Committee Print No. 7, Senate Select Committee on National Water Resources. US Govt. Printing Office, Washington, D.C. (1960).

4. Pollution Abatement. Committee Print No. 9, US Senate Select Committee on National Water Resources. US Govt. Printing Office, Washington, D.C. (1961).

5. Hollis, M. D. The Water Pollution Problem. Proc. Natl. Conf. Wtr. Pollution, USPHS. Washington, D.C. (1961).

6. Wolman, A. & Gorman, A. E. *The Significance of Waterborne Typhoid*

Fever Outbreaks 1920–30. The Williams & Wilkins Co., Baltimore, Md. (1931).

7. Gorman, A. E. & Wolman, A. Waterborne Outbreaks in the United States and Canada and Their Significance. *Jour. AWWA,* 31:225 (Feb. 1939).

8. Annual Reports 1–29, Massachusetts State Board of Health, Boston (1869–99).

9. Hollister, A. C., Jr., et al. Influence of Water Availability on Shigella Prevalence in Children of Farm Labor Families. *Am. J. Public Health,* 45: 354 (1955).

10. Watt, J., et al. Diarrheal Diseases in Fresno County, California. *Am. J. Public Health,* 43:728 (1953).

11. Wagner, E. G. & Lanoix, J. N. *Water Supplies for Rural Areas and Small Communities,* Monograph No. 42, World Health Organization, Geneva, Switzerland (1959).

12. Healy, W. A. & Grossman, R. P. Waterborne Typhoid Epidemics at Keene, N.H. *J. NEWWA,* 75 :38 (1961).

13. Task Group Report. Status of Fluoridation in the United States and Canada, 1959. *Jour. AWWA,* 52 :1513 (Dec. 1960).

14. Horwitz, A. *Facts in Health Problems.* Pan. Am. Health Organization, Washington, D.C. (1961).

15. Wolman, A. Technical, Financial, and Administrative Aspects of Water Supply in the Urban Environment in the Americas. *Boletin de la Officina Sanitaria Panamericana,* 47:5 (Nov. 1959).

16. Report of the National Water Supply and Sanitation Committee. Ministry of Health, New Delhi, India (1960–61).

17. Seidel, H. F. & Baumann, E. R. A Statistical Analysis of Water Works Data for 1955. *Jour. AWWA,* 49 :1531 (Dec. 1957).

Technical, Financial, and Administrative Aspects of Water Supply in the Urban Environment in the Americas*

In theory, at least, a health officer determines where to put major public health emphasis after a careful appraisal of the causes of disease and death. Such a review provides him with the guide lines by which his activities are to be defined. Practical adjustments are then made necessary by political, financial, or emotional considerations. Before discussing the central subject matter of this paper, therefore, it is reasonable to assess the public health situation in the Americas in order to learn what the objectives of a public health program should be.

The Health Situation

In spite of the difficulties, with inaccuracy of reporting disease in many countries, it is helpful to know what people die of and what the implications of such causes of death are for future programming.

Complete or fairly complete mortality data are available for Argentina, Canada, Chile, Costa Rica, Guatemala, Mexico, and the United States. For the remaining countries, registration is apparently incomplete. The estimated death rates for all ages for those countries with incomplete registration range between 15 and 20 per thousand population.[1]

* Reprinted from *Ingeniería Sanitaria*, November 1959, pp. 1–31.

Despite the deficiencies of the data, it is apparent that excessive mortality occurs in early childhood. A summary of health conditions in the Americas as reflected by the death rates for all ages, infants, and children 1–4 years of age, appears in Table 1.

Table 1
Number of Deaths and Death Rates for All Ages, Under 1 Year, and 1–4 Years
in the Countries of the Americas, 1956

Country	All ages		Under 1 year		1–4 years	
	Number	Rate[a]	Number	Rate[b]	Number	Rate[c]
Argentina	159,191	8.2	27,143	58.5	6,499	3.8
Bolivia	32,639*	10.1	10,113[d]	92.7	8,114[d]	...
Brazil[e]	71,158	11.9	18,131	100.3	· 6,140	11.7
Canada[f]	131,585	8.2	14,259	31.7	2,317	1.5
Chile	83,744	12.7	27,509	109.1	7,118	10.4
Colombia	171,984	13.3	55,912	103.8	34,277	20.3
Costa Rica	9,518	9.6	3,685	71.6	1,240	9.8
Cuba	36,321	5.8	...	...	...	...
Dominican Republic	23,728	9.1	8,183	77.2	4,901	13.5
Ecuador	56,390	14.8	18,181	101.8	2.108[g]	18.7
El Salvador	28,127	12.4	7,486	70.3	6.096	22.7
Guatemala	66,280	19.8	14,499	88.8	17,066	38.8
Haiti	...	...	...	...	...	...
Honduras	17,397	10.2	3,702	58.4	3,462	16.8
Mexico	368,877*	12.1	101,360*	71.0	87,473[h]	24.0
Nicaragua	9,792	7.6	3,342	63.5	1,455	9.3
Panama	8,268	9.3	2,007	55.7	1,161	10.2
Paraguay[i]	7,260	4.5	1,802	81.7	790	3.8
Peru	59,782*	6.8	29,705[h]	94.8	19,087[d]	19.6
United States	1,564,476	9.3	108,183	26.0	16,603	1.1
Uruguay	18,421*	7.0	2,212*	73.0	353	...
Venezuela	59,369	10.3	18,538	66.7	9,501	12.5

* Provisional. . . . Data not available. (a) Per 1,000 population. (b) Per 1,000 live births. (c) Per 1,000 popultaion 1–4 years of age. (d) Year 1954. (e) Federal District and seven State capitals. (f) Excluding Yukon and Northwest Territories. (g) Capital cities of provinces only. (h) Year 1955. (i) Registration incomplete.

For children 1–4 years of age, the group of diarrheal diseases was the leading cause of death in 17 countries. In 5 countries, the diarrheal diseases were among the first five principal causes.

While death rates from specific causes do not indicate the extent of the problem, due not only to inadequate registration but to incompleteness of medical certification, the death rates from typhoid fever and gastritis, enteritis, etc., are high in many of the countries. These conclusions are well illustrated in Tables 2 and 3. Comparison of many of these death rates with the corresponding figures in Canada and the United States dramatizes the fact that these diseases take an extraordinarily massive toll of life and of disability in most of the Americas.

Although the number of typhoid fever cases reported in the past three

Table 2
Number of Deaths from Typhoid Fever and Gastritis and Enteritis with Rates
per 100,000 Population in Countries of the Americas, 1956

Country	Typhoid fever		Gastritis, enteritis, etc.	
	Number	Rate	Number	Rate
Argentina	133	0.7	2,552	13.1
Bolivia[a]	92	2.9	685	21.7
Brazil[b]	94	1.6	9,421	157.1
Canada[c]	9	0.1	905	5.6
Chile	149	2.3	5,645	85.7
Colombia	561	4.3	15,638	120.9
Costa Rica	16	1.6	1,221	123.6
Cuba	. . .	. . .	. . .	. . .
Dominican Republic	104	4.0	2,509	96.2
Ecuador	900	23,7	3,928[d]	106.4
El Salvador	45	2.0	3,521	155.2
Guatemala	328	9.8	8,489	253.5
Haiti	. . .	. . .	. . .	. . .
Honduras	84	4.9	609	35.6
Mexico	3,666	12.0	56,336	184.5
Nicaragua	47	3.6	1,191	92.5
Panama	3	0.3	490	55.3
Paraguay[e]	13	0.8	264	16.5
Peru[a]	214	2.6	2,029	24.9
United States	54	0.0	7,508	4.5
Uruguay	23	0.9	524	20.0
Venezuela	63	1.1	5,577	96.6

. . . Data not available. (a) Year 1954. (b) Federal District and seven State capitals.
(c) Excluding Yukon and Northwest Territories. (d) Year 1955. (e) Registration incomplete.

years shows fluctuations, some 40,000 cases are known to have occurred each year in the 22 countries listed. An interesting illustration of the comparative situations in two countries of the Americas appears in Table 4 in a study made by Gabaldon, Berti, and Jove. From diarrhea and enteritis mortality data, these authors make clear in Table 4, that Venezuela still remains some 40 to 50 years in arrears in the prevention of these diseases. Table 5, from the same paper further demonstrates this unfavorable situation.

Dr. Gabaldon emphasizes the significant difference between the problems in such a country as his and in the United States by Figure 1 (page 239). This simple graph provides a striking basis for differentiating between the public health action required in one country and that in another with different public health problems.

This is not the place to extend the detailed consideration of the causes of death and illness, but enough has been presented to make clear that undoubtedly those diseases closely related to and reducible by environmental sanitation represent either the first cause or fall among the first five causes of death.

With these basic facts in mind, even a cursory canvass of the countries

Table 3
**Number of Reported Cases of Typhoid Fever with Rates per 100,000 Population
in Countries of the Americas, 1956–1958**

Country	1956 Number	Rate	1957 Number	Rate	1958 Number	Rate
Argentina	1,830	9.4	1,884	9.5	1,474	7.3
Bolivia	309	9.6	156	4.8	209	6.3
Brazil[a]	2,355[b]	24.9	. . .	. . .	. . .	. . .
Canada	377	2.3	279[b]	1.7	304[b]	1.8
Chile	4,172	60.1	5,371[b]	75.4	5,086[b]	69.7
Colombia[b, c]	12,864	108.3	11,643	96.8	12,696	100.2
Costa Rica	224	22.1	194	18.4	220	20.0
Cuba	1,065	17.0	241	3.8	331	5.1
Dominican Republic	211	8.1	178	6.6	. . .	. . .
Ecuador	1,569[b]	41.3	1,958	50.3	2,046	51.1
El Salvador[c]	817	74.7	654	57.1	771[b]	61.1
Guatemala	503[b]	15.0	354	10.3	402	11.3
Haiti	249	7.4	155	4.6	944	27.6
Honduras	. . .	. . .	. . .	. . .	374	. . .
Mexico	5,130	16.8	4,683	14.9	6,004	18.6
Nicaragua	184	14.3	134	10.1	351	25.5
Panama	53	5.6	47	4.9	66	6.6
Paraguay	128	8.0	55	3.4	129	7.7
Peru[b, c]	5,067	115.1	7,162	150.2	6,527	133.0
United States	1,700	1.0	1,231	0.7	1,076	0.6
Uruguay	399	15.1	359	13.4	280	10.3
Venezuela[c]	1,322[b]	38.4	695	19.3	979	25.4

* Provisional. . . . Data not available. (a) Federal District and State capitals. (b) Including paratyphoid fever. (c) Reporting area.

Table 4
**Deaths from Diarrhea and Enteritis per 100,000 Population in United States and
Venezuela and the Year in Which the Mortality in the United States
is Similar to that in Venezuela**

Age (years)	UNITED STATES 1900	1910	1920	1930	1940	VENEZUELA 1952	Year in U.S.A.
Under 1	4429.8	3778.8	1625.9	836.9	407.0	2844.1	1911
1- 4	303.0	271.8	141.3	95.6	30.2	445.4	Before 1900
5-14	8.8	6.1	4.1	3.0	0.9	13.3	
15-24	5.7	1.9	1.7	1.1	0.7	3.1	1905
25-34	7.5	3.2	3.0	1.5	1.0	3.7	1908
35-44	10.5	5.0	4.3	2.2	1.6	5.7	1911
45-54	18.6	9.3	7.4	3.6	1.9	11.6	1903
55-64	49.3	23.9	12.7	7.2	3.4	23.0	1910
65-74	130.4	74.3	32.7	16.7	7.0	45.2	1915
75-84	316.9	230.7	107.5	59.5	23.0	77.6	1922
85 and over	676.1	584.5	258.3	173.5	71.1	343.4	1915

Source: Gabaldón, A. Berti, A. L., and Jove, J. A. "El Saneamiento en La Lucha Contra La Gastroenteritis y Colitis" from *I Congreso Venezolano de Salud Pública y III Conferencia de Unidades Sanitarias.*

in question discloses the tremendous area of activity still to be covered in order to provide in the next five years a more significant reduction of disease than over the past five to ten years. Progress has undoubtedly

Table 5
Comparison Between the Mortality by Age Group for Some Communicable
Diseases in Venezuela and United States in 1947.
The rates for the United States are also expressed as percentages
of the Venezuelan rates.

Age (years)	Country	Diarrhea and enteritis	Tuberculosis	Pneumonia	Whooping cough
	Venezuela	3259.4	86.2	1086.9	360.4
Under 1	U.S.A.	152.8	10.5	343.5	41.9
	%	4.7	12.2	31.6	11.6
	Venezuela	531.7	71.7	170.4	7.9
1 - 4	U.S.A.	5.8	6.6	21.7	3.9
	%	1.1	9.2	12.7	4.9
	Venezuela	47.6	34.7	25.1	9.1
5 - 9	U.S.A.	0.5	1.9	4.2	0.3
	%	1.0	5.5	16.7	3.3
	Venezuela	9.2	69.3	9.0	0
10-19	U.S.A.	0.4	9.5	3.4	0.1
	%	4.4	13.7	37.8	—
	Venezuela	12.8	178.9	12.6	0.2
20-29	U.S.A.	0.8	31.8	4.8	0
	%	6.2	17.8	38.1	—
	Venezuela	16.5	233.7	14.0	0
30-39	U.S.A.	0.9	36.4	8.1	0
	%	5.4	15.6	57.9	—
	Venezuela	30.7	275.7	25.9	0.4
40-49	U.S.A.	1.1	46.6	17.7	0
	%	3.6	16.9	68.3	—
	Venezuela	37.5	292.8	41.2	0
50-59	U.S.A.	1.4	58.6	34.6	0
	%	3.7	20.0	83.2	—
	Venezuela	86.5	389.2	100.9	0
60-69	U.S.A.	3.2	71.6	75.8	0
	%	3.7	18.4	75.1	—

Source: Gabaldón, A., Berti, A. L., and Jove, J. A. "El Saneamiento en La Lucha Contra La Gastroenteritis y Colitis" from *I Congreso Venezolano de Salud Púplica y III Conferencia de Unidades Sanitarias.*

occurred, but one cannot take pride in the reduction of these leading causes of death.

The Environmental Sanitation Situation

The following factors play a noteworthy part in the control or reduction of the diarrheal diseases.

1. The provision of a safe, ample water supply under pressure within or immediately adjacent to each house.

2. The provision of sanitary methods for excreta disposal within each dwelling, so that fecal pollution is removed from human contact.

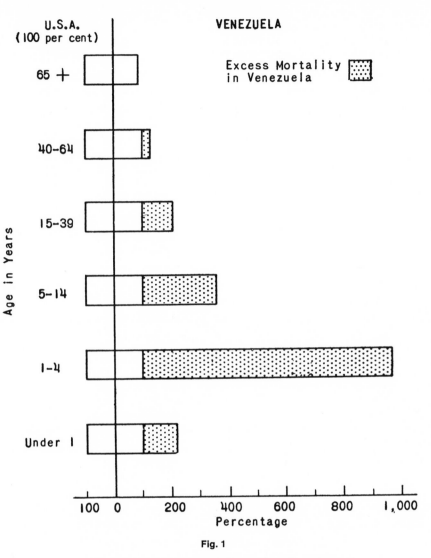

Fig. 1

Mortality Rates from All Causes in Venezuela as Percentages of
Mortality Rates in the United States, by Age Group

Source: A. Gabaldon

3. The control of disease-bearing vectors, the provision of adequate housing, and the sanitary control of milk and food.

4. The use of water and of the sanitary facilities provided to attain clean bodies, clean homes, and clean communities.

Detailed observations in California, Georgia, Kentucky, Guatemala, Korea, and elsewhere demonstrated that shigella infections and other diarrheal diseases are universally associated with the lack of sanitary facilities, poor housing, limited or no water supply, and poor personal hygiene.

If a single program were to be chosen for maximum public health dividends, the provision of safe and ample water, not only for drinking but for personal cleanliness, would be first in priority. This conclusion is well confirmed in one of the recent studies of the enteric diseases by the Pan American Sanitary Bureau. In general, all of the studies suggest that, quite irrespective of etiologic and sociologic differences, approximately 30 to 60 per cent reduction in diarrheal diseases may be expected by providing a potable water supply in sufficient quantities and conveniently accessible to people.

Almost universal acceptance of these conclusions has prevailed in the Americas over many decades. Hardly any health worker contests the significance and desirability of providing a safe water. Active programs based upon these conclusions, however, have invariably fallen behind the lip service accorded them. In the past the health officer's activity has been dissipated over a variety of fronts sometimes influenced more by emotion or political expediency than by the realities of the situation. At times, he has been lured into activities singularly appropriate for some other country but quite inappropriate for his own.

The Expanding Necessity for Water

Safe water for the thirsty is not the sole objective. Water is necessary, in addition, to make it possible for a person to keep clean. This requires an ample quantity of water easily available to the individual. As Wood of Nigeria has recently pointed out, it is an insult to ask people to be clean when they have no water for bathing or when they must walk several blocks to a half mile in order to obtain a jug of water. Water is equally necessary in order to make public housing of any value from the public health standpoint. Public housing in which provision for water and sewerage is minimal or non-existent is less than a health asset.

The emerging urbanism and industrialization in every country of the Americas have already run away from the parallel provision for water. Water development is a pre-requisite to economic development. The assumption that a country may proceed with industrialization and that water facilities will follow, places the cart before the horse.

A historical block to the rapid introduction of water facilities, either into or immediately adjacent to the house lies in the almost universal "rural psychosis" of public officials. This emotional devotion to the tiny village or isolated rural house has literally prevented them from objectively appraising the overall water necessities and their public health implications. Deliberate exclusion of any attention to the water problems and service for aggregates of population, wherever they are or whatever the occupation of their inhabitants may be, has resulted in millions of people remaining without this facility. This conscious neglect stems from the erroneous assumption that the urbanized communities of whatever size could and would take care of themselves.

The Water Situation

What are the realities of the water situation in the Americas? The PASB has collected data on the availability of water to people in the various countries of the Americas. One of the lessons learned from even this first inventory is that most of the countries are unaware of their water service conditions. If the survey does nothing more than arouse officials to an evaluation of their problem, it will have accomplished one of its major objectives.

With all of the disabilities and inadequacies of information now available, certain significant data have been accumulated which are presented in Tables 6 through 11 (pages 242–246). These tables indicate for a number of the countries the degree to which these populations now are lacking in water service.

Water service in this discussion is defined as the provision in the home or in the immediately adjacent courtyard of a water connection to a community piped water supply. Approximately 182 million persons live in the countries covered by this inquiry. Of these, 75 million live in cities with at least 2,000 inhabitants. Twenty-nine million persons or 39 per cent of the people in these urban areas were without water services in 1958. It is difficult to reconcile this finding with the common assumption that urban areas usually take care of themselves.

Cities of 50,000 or more inhabitants have the best service but frequently more than 25 per cent of the inhabitants do not have water service as defined here. In fact the population without water service in major cities goes as high as *100%*. Almost 50 per cent of the people living in cities of 10,000 to 49,999 are without such service. In cities of 2,000 to 9,999 over 70 per cent are not served.

Another 107 million persons who are not classified as urban inhabitants live either in smaller communities than 2,000 or in rural areas. Of these, 107 million, far more than 70%, are without water service and yet many live in community groups where the density of living demands community piped water and sewerage systems. This latter group, virtually urban in character and living in well constructed homes, has been almost completely neglected because by definition they are usually considered to be rural, and attention has been diverted from the economic and sanitary convenience of community facilities to the individual well and privy.

Table 6

Estimated Number and Per Cent of Population Lacking Water Service[a] in Cities of 18 Latin American Countries[b] in 1958 by Country and Size of Cities

Country	Estimated population (July 1, 1958) (thousands)	Cities of 50,000 or more inhabitants					Cities of 10,000–49,999 inhabitants					Cities of 2,000–9,999 inhabitants				
		No. of cities	Total population Number (thousands)	Per cent	Population without water service Number (thousands)	Per cent	No. of cities	Total population Number (thousands)	Per cent	Population without water service Number (thousands)	Per cent	No. of cities	Total population Number (thousands)	Per cent	Population without water service Number (thousands)	Per cent
Total	149,509	114	34,848	23.3	7,813	22	507	12,639	8.5	5,907	47	2,402	12,581	6.4	8,861	70
Argentina	20,256	26	9,158	45.2	1,241	14	84	2,241	11.1	732	33	375	2,053	10.1	1,439	70
Bolivia	3,305	4	557	16.9	160[c]	29[c]	4	118	3.6	83	70	40	182	5.5	136[d]	75
Brazil	62,725	33	12,259	19.5	3,006	25	187	4,973[e]	7.9	3,039	61	950	5,260[e]	8.4	4,153	79
Chile	7,314	9	2,457	33.6	1,035	42	39	1,050	14.4	488	46	80	474	6.5	238	50
Colombia	13,522	14	3,189	23.6	669	21	42	923	6.8	266	29	254	949	7.0	413	44
Costa Rica	1,072	1	135	12.6	3	2	6	92	8.6	—	0	16	73	6.8	1	1
Dominican Republic[f]	2,791	2	429	15.4	99	23	7	146	5.2	72	49	27	166	5.9	103	62
Ecuador	4,007	3	839	20.9	126	15	9	174	4.3	63	36	49	257	6.4	157[g]	61
El Salvador	2,434	2	289	11.9	62	21	10	164	6.7	59	36	43	181	1.4	142	78
Guatemala	3,549	1	370	10.4	74	20	4	83	2.3	59	71	83	418	11.8	314	75
Haiti	3,426	1	199	5.8	88	44	6	82	2.4	37	45	22	110[h]	3.2	105	95
Honduras	1,822	1	97	5.3	52	54	4	88	4.9	54	61	29	136	7.5	94	69
Nicaragua	1,376	1	175	12.7	63	36	8	169	12.3	83	49	21	107	7.8	75	70
Panama	995	2	198	19.9	—	0	3	45	4.5	23	50	21	92	9.2	30	32
Paraguay	1,672	1	240	14.4	100	42	3	51	3.1	51	100	40	168	10.0	161	96
Peru	10,213	3	1,437	14.1	114	8	22	762[i]	7.5	134	18	151	962[i]	9.4	735	76
Uruguay	2,710	1	850	31.4	150	18	28	594	21.9	218	37	43	187	6.9	123	66
Venezuela	6,320	9	1,970	31.2	771	39	41	884	14.0	446	50	158	806[j]	12.8	442	55

(a) Water service is considered to be lacking in houses which have no connection in either the house or its adjacent courtyard to a piped community water supply. (b) Two countries excluded: data for Mexico not available by size of cities; no data from Cuba. (c) Estimated from reporting in three of four cities. (d) Estimated from reporting in 22 of the 40 cities. (e) Population estimated on assumption of yearly increase of 4.5 per cent of census figure. (f) Population estimated on assumption of yearly increase of 10 per cent of census figure in cities over 50,000; 5 per cent in all other cities over 2,000. (g) Estimated from reporting of 12 of 49 cities. (h) Population estimated on assumption of yearly increase of 2.5 per cent of census figure. (i) Population estimated on assumption of yearly increase of 4 per cent of census figure. (j) Estimated from proportion of total population in this group at last census.

Table 7

Estimated Population in Thousands of Urban[a] and Rural Areas with the Estimated Number and Per Cent of Urban Residents Lacking Water Service[b] in 19 Latin American Countries in 1958

Country	Total population	Urban population Total	Number	Per cent	Rural population Total	Per cent of total population
Argentina	20,256	13,452	3,412	25.4	6,804	33.6
Bolivia	3,305	857	379	44.2	2,448	74.1
Brazil	62,725	22,492	10,198	45.3	40,233	64.1
Chile	7,314	3,981	1,761	44.2	3,333	45.6
Colombia	13,522	5,061	1,348	26.6	8,461	62.6
Costa Rica	1,072	300	4	1.3	772	72.0
Dominican Republic	2,791	741	274	37.0	2,050	73.5
Ecuador	4,007	1,270	346	27.2	2,737	68.3
El Salvador	2,434	634	263	41.5	1,800	74.0
Guatemala	3,549	871	447	51.3	2,678	75.5
Haití	3,426	391	230	58.8	3,035	88.6
Honduras	1,822	321	200	62.3	1,501	82.4
Mexico	32,348	14,678	6,628	45.2	17,670	54.6
Nicaragua	1,376	451	221	49.0	925	67.2
Panama	995	335	53	15.8	660	66.3
Paraguay	1,672	459	312	68.0	1,213	72.5
Peru	10,213	3,161	983	31.1	7,052	69.0
Uruguay	2,710	1,631	491	30.1	1,079	39.8
Venezuela	6,230	3,660	1,659	45.3	2,660	42.1
Total	181,857	74,746	29,209	39.1	107,111	58.9

(a) Urban areas usually defined as cities of 2,000 or more inhabitants; 2,500 or more in Mexico.

(b) Water service is considered to be lacking in houses which have no connection either in the house or in its adjacent courtyard to a community piped water supply.

Table 8

Per Cent of Population Lacking Water Service[a] Within City Limits and in Metropolitan Areas Outside City Limits, in 11 Cities of Latin America in 1958

Country and city	Population within city limits Total	Per cent without water service	Metropolitan population outside city limits Total	Per cent without water service
Brazil: Niteroi	260,000	27	140,000	14
Colombia: Bogota	930,000	20	30,000	50
El Salvador: San Salvador	213,000	23	37,000	80
Panama: Panama City	139,000	0	38,000	0
Paraguay: Asunción	240,000	42	15,000	73
Peru: Lima	1,186,000	5	200,000	100
" Arequipa	122,000	40	40,000	100
" Callao	129,000	9	20,000	100
Uruguay: Montevideo	850,000	18	152,000	67
" Salto	44,000	36	14,500	72
" Paysandu	33,000	18	15,800	54

(a) Water service is considered to be lacking in houses which have no connection in either the house or its adjacent courtyard to a piped community water supply.

Table 9

Per Cent of Population with Water Service in Houses or Courtyards and in Courtyard Only in Six Latin American Countries in 1958, by Size of Cities

Country	Cities of 50,000 or Greater			Cities of 10,000–49,999			Cities of 2,000–9,999		
	Estimated population (July 1, 1958)	Per cent with water in house or courtyard	Per cent with water in court-yard only	Estimated population (July 1, 1958)	Per cent with water in house or courtyard	Per cent with water in court-yard only	Estimated population (July 1, 1958)	Per cent with water in house or courtyard	Per cent with water in court-yard only
Bolivia	557,000	71	40	118,000	30	15	164,000	25	20
Brazil	12,259,000	75	15	4,973,000	39	20	5,260,000	21	10
Costa Rica	135,000	98	33	92,000	100	36	73,000	99	37
Dominican Republic	429,000	77	53	146,000	51	33	166,000	38	26
El Salvador	289,000	79	58	164,000	64	45	181,000	22	10
Paraguay	240,000	58	48	51,300	0	0	168,000	4	0

Table 10

Number and Per Cent of Population Lacking Water Service in Cities of Four Territories in the Americas, by Territory and Size of Cities in 1958

Country	Estimated population (July 1, 1958)	Cities of 50,000 or more inhabitants					Cities of 10,000–49,999 inhabitants					Cities of 2,000–9,999 inhabitants				
		No. of cities	Total Population Num-ber	Per cent	Population without water service Number	Per cent cities	No. of cities	Total Population Num-ber	Per cent	Population without water service Number	Per cent cities	No. of cities	Total Population Num-ber	Per cent	Population without water service Number	Per cent
Barbados,	231,000	1	100,000	43.3	61,000	61	3	62,600	27.1	44,500	71	...	...	...	...	...
British Guiana	533,000	1	99,200	18.6	—	0	1	14,700	27.6	—	0	...	...	...	...	...
French Guiana	31,000	0	—	—	—	—	1	15,000	48.4	2,000	13	1	...	...	...	...
Surinam	241,000	1	100,000	41.5	18,200	18	0	—	—	—	—	4	15,200	6.3	7,000	46

. . . No information.

Table 11
Number and Per Cent of Population Lacking Water Service
in Cities of 21 Latin American Countries

Country, city, and year of population estimate	Estimated population (thousands)	Per cent without water service	Country, city, and year of population estimate	Estimated population (thousands)	Per cent without water service
Argentina: 1958			Brazil: 1959 (cont.)		
Buenos Aires	3,805	0	Maceio	150	53
Rosario	566	12	Juiz de Fora	150	47
Cordoba	472	20	Natal	120	33
General San Martin	420	77	Manaus	120	25
Avellaneda	375	7	João Pessoa	120	33
La Plata	350	11	Duque de Caxias	120	17
Lanus	332	13	Campina Grande	120	67
Mar del Plata	305	17	Ribeirão Preto	120	25
Tucuman	264	18	Pelotas	116	31
Quilmes	242	15	São Luis	115	35
Vicente Lopez	210	13	Petropolis	110	9
Sante Fe	204	15	Sorocaba	102	29
Moron	198	59	Aracajú	100	30
Lomas de Zamora	185	19	Campos	100	5
Bahia Blanca	173	19	Rio Grande	94	23
San Isidro	165	23	Nova Iguaçu	90	11
San Justo	160	100	São Caetano do Sul	80	25
Mendoza	136	0	Teresina	80	60
San Juan	113	0	Neves	78	14
Parana	104	2	Bauru	70	29
Salta	94	19			
Resistencia	81	38	Chile: 1958		
Godoy Cruz	76	13	Santiago[a]	1,580	16
Santiago del Estero	75	6	Valparaiso[a] and		
Corrientes	71	7	Viña del Mar[a]	380	26
Concordia	64	19	Concepcion	150	20
			Antofagasta	78	...
Bolivia: 1959			Talco	69	26
La Paz	345	20	Talcahuano	68	28
Cochabamba	95	30	Chillan	66	33
Oruro	70	...	Temuco	65	30
Santa Cruz	50	86			
			Colombia: 1958		
Brazil: 1959			Bogota	930	20
Rio de Janeiro	3,000	23	Medeilin	497	10
São Paulo	3,400	15	Cali	428	6
Recife	700	29	Barranquilla	388	25
Salvador	500	40	Bucaramanga	159	31
Porto Alegre	500	10	Cartagena	140	59
Belo Horizonte	500	40	Manizales	110	18
Fortaleza	400	60	Pereira	109	17
Belém	300	33	Cucuta	93	36
Niteroi	260	27	Palmira	76	14
Santos	250	16	Armenia	73	9
Curitiba	200	20	Ibague	71	49
Santo Andre	180	33	Pasto	64	30
Campinas	150	13	Buenaventura	51	49

Table 11 (cont.)

Country, city and year of population estimate	Estimated population (thousands)	Per cent without water service	Country, city, and year of population estimate	Estimated population (thousands)	Per cent without water service
Costa Rica: 1957			Nicaragua: 1957		
San Jose	134	2	Managua	167	36
Dominican			Panama: 1957		
Republic: 1950			Panama City	139	0
Ciudad Trujillo	182	20	Colon	58	0
Santiago	57	32			
			Paraguay: 1958		
Ecuador: 1958			Asuncion	240	42
Guayaquil	427	10			
Quito	380	20	Peru: 1958		
Cuenca	50	20	Lima	1,186	5
			Arequipa	122	40
El Salvador: 1957			Callao	129	9
San Salvador	213	23			
Santa Ana	67	17	Uruguay: 1958		
			Montevideo	850	18
Guatemala: 1959					
Guatemala City	380	20	Venezuela: 1958		
			Caracas[a]	977	29
Haiti: 1959			Maracaibo	332	58
Port-au-Prince	200	44	Barquisimeto	148	41
			Valencia	117	33
Honduras: 1957			Maracay	91	24
Tegucigalpa	94	54	San Cristobal	73	22
			Cumana	64	57
Mexico[b]: 1958			Cabimas[c]	69	100
Mexico City[a]	4,700	11	Maiquetia	58	49

(a) Includes metropolitan area outside city limits. (b) For remaining cities of 50,000 or more inhabitants in Mexico the data were not given by city. (c) System under construction.

Table 12
Per Cent of Population without Water Service in Cities of 100,000 or More Inhabitants Included in Greater Buenos Aires, 1958

City	Estimated population in 1958 (in thousands)	Per cent without water service
Buenos Aires	3,805	0
Avellaneda	375	7
General San Martin	420	77
Lanus	332	13
Quilmes	242	15
Vicente Lopez	210	13
Moron	198	59
Lomas de Zamora	185	19
San Isidro	165	23
San Justo	160	100

The situation within metropolitan areas and in the surrounding fringe areas is dramatically illustrated in Table 8. Although the data are limited they shed light by showing that the percentage of population without water service in certain major cities runs as high as 42. In the metropolitan areas outside the city limits the percentage is as high as 100.

Inadequacy of reporting makes it almost impossible to elaborate upon these findings, particularly within the emerging great metropolitan areas. The innumerable communities surrounding each of the country capitals have grown at a very much higher rate over the last 20 years than the capitals themselves. This excessive rate of growth has aggravated the water service problem, which was already great, and has resulted in large numbers of people living with almost primitive water conditions, even though residing in areas where water is assumed to be available. Table 12 gives a typical example of the nature of this problem in the metropolitan areas surrounding Buenos Aires. This situation may be paralleled in many metropolitan areas. Most have large portions of the population without modern water service.

These data do not downgrade the remaining problem of the population living in communities of less than 2,000 people. Their number is great. However, for a given unit of effort, more success is likely to be obtained in a period of five to ten years in a major attack on the heavily populated urban areas from 2,000 people and up, than by the devotion almost exclusively of all effort to the populations living in aggregates of 2,000 and under. That these latter groups cannot and must not be neglected, everyone must agree. That they should be chosen for major effort to the exclusion of urban groups can only result in a dismal failure to reduce disease in any measurable degree. It may well be pointed out that historically sanitation like other public improvements has moved from the larger urban areas outward to the rural, never the reverse.

The force of these comments is well illustrated in the case of Mexico where there are 24 communities of over 50,000, 135 of 10,000 to 50,000 and 824 of 2,500 to 10,000. The number of communities of less than 2,500 is 97,607. Simple arithmetic would indicate that a public agency devoting its attentions *exclusively* to the last group, at the present rate of accomplishment, could well use 75 to 100 years and still not cover the needs of any large number of people.

If the objective of the health department is to increase rapidly the number of lives saved, the first dominant areas for public health attack are in the aggregate population communities in excess of 2,000 people each. The vast opportunities for fruitful endeavor in such urban areas are illustrated in Tables 6 and 11.

If one applies reasonable criteria to the choice for a public health activity in the field of environmental sanitation, that function should be chosen which best complies with the following criteria:

a) It brings potentially the greatest public health, comfort, and economic returns;

b) It affects the greatest number of people;

c) The program can be dramatically *sold;*

d) It gives more than reasonable expectation of easy and prompt
execution;

e) It requires for promotion a minimum expenditure of time and
energy;

f) It rests to a major extent upon the resources of the people;

g) It requires a minimum education of all the people;

h) It requires little or no additional research.

A Program for Providing Water

South of the border of the United States, at the present rate of
installation of water facilities, it will take anywhere from 50 to 100
years to provide the bulk of the people in community aggregates with
this important and necessary service. The present rate of installation in
many instances is barely keeping pace with the increase in population
growth and in some instances is even losing ground.

No single cause, of course, is responsible for this slow pace, but the
desire for perfectionism along the entire environmental front was certainly one of the obstacles to past progress. A philosophy of all or nothing,
even though for sound public health purposes, has not paid the maximum dividends.

The extraordinary emphasis placed upon the rural problem has
already been commented upon, but it needs to be emphasized that
many workers in the field of health still cling to this purpose as their
major objective. As long as they persist it is doubtful whether large
numbers of people will obtain water systems with any rapidity. The
best promise for increasing the pace of service is the determination for
greatest effort in working in urban areas.

The provision of water at a public tap in the street should not be
accepted as a major public health asset. Water which must be carried
from some central square does not meet essential conditions for the protection of the public health of the community.

Since the installation of water systems will require large amounts of
capital investment, this cost has created great fears in the minds of many
public health administrators. A proper understanding of the significance
of source and methods of repayment of capital will do much to eliminate
this fear. The large amount of capital required is less important than the
annual amounts required for interest and amortization. These annual
costs are the costs that need to be understood and stressed since in many
instances these are well within the normal resources of the community.

An equally persistent obstacle to progress is the firm conviction both of the public and of some officials that water should be provided to all people free of charge. This assumption has been variously described as an essential characteristic rooted in the culture and history of the people. Such views, however, are not paralleled by the realities in many places in Latin America. Many leading citizens insist upon exactly the contrary philosophy. Many communities have so acted and have been able to transfer water service from the concept of free to one of complete or almost complete reimbursability or repayment.

This emphasis upon *free water* has forced most countries to look to central or national governments for the money with which to provide such services. Such a practice has always resulted in less and less availability of large capital funds. In recent years when these demands upon the central government for capital funds have grown greater and greater by many additional competitive requirements of national life, the amounts of money for sanitary purposes in general and water service in particular are at a greater premium year by year. The hand-writing is on the wall; as long as this central government source is made necessary through the perpetuation of the principle of free water the rate of installation of new service will undoubtedly be small and become smaller from year to year. This will require that Ministries of Health, local health officers, volunteer health agencies, and all possible sources of help must be marshalled, under the leadership of the health teams, to educate, indoctrinate, persuade, cajole, influence, and lead people to the point of agreeing to accept their obligations for the water bill. This will be one of the foundation stones on which the success of this program will rest.

Lastly, as long as major officials in health activity give an intellectual acceptance to the necessity of water, but do not match this acceptance with an emotional enthusiasm for its development, progress will be retarded. Leadership by public health officials in this field, hitherto not militantly at hand, is a prime prerequisite to the development of this program. In environmental sanitation, first things should come first. When water has been provided to the degree herein discussed, other features of environmental sanitation historically have always followed. Broader public health developments likewise become easier of acceptance, particularly when money is released from central government sources by the rapid acceptance of the repayment character of water service.

With these negative attributes understood and avoided, the positive characteristics of the urban water supply program are stated below.

1. *Technology*

In the development of water service, technological or scientific understanding of the methods and principles of design, construction, and operation has been available for many decades. One need not wait upon further technological advance to push a program as rapidly as possible. Obviously, new concepts will appear as time goes on, but absence of new knowledge does not retard immediate and rapid progress.

The need to strengthen the technical potential of Health Organizations at all levels is immediately apparent. There are some governments which have extremely weak engineering services in their Health Ministries. There are others who have a limited number of competent engineers at national level but none at lower levels of government. In almost every country, the total number available is inadequate and the organizational structure needs strengthening.

Governments should not overlook the place of private engineering firms and private consultants in an expanded water program. Because of the ability of such private companies to increase or decrease this activity with local demand, a much greater flexibility of engineering service can be provided than where government itself tries to do the work of design and construction. This is not to minimize the place of engineers in the Ministry of Health whose function it should be to not only stimulate all Ministries, agencies, and parties to build more water systems, but also to review and approve the plans, supervise the operation, and maintain the needed public health control over all water and sanitary facilities. Engineers in private practice while in short supply in most Latin American countries, should be encouraged and assisted.

That sufficient technologic skills are not available in other Ministries in every country is likewise true. The water program therefore must encompass training of practitioners in order to make the effort continuingly successful. The program, however, should not wait upon the development of all the skills in all of the countries, since personnel is already available to initiate and to pursue the objectives in mind. The education and training of skilled professionals will probably go on forever, as populations grow and as problems emerge. The perfect state of affairs rarely, if ever, attained, is not a good reason for deferring active work.

2. *Administrative Structure*

The actual design, construction, and operation of water works is carried out usually by departments of public works, on a national level. A number of examples, however, are at hand where the development of local facilities is largely in the hands of either a municipality or an autonomous local authority. The number of municipal agencies responsible for water service is unfortunately small. Generally, even very large communities wait upon the central or the national government both for funds and for execution of projects. No good reason exists, other than custom, for permitting local groups to remain quite helpless and without responsibility in this important activity. Each situation, of course, needs to be reviewed within its own setting, but it is undoubtedly true that greater strength and responsibility must be increasingly placed upon large communities for working out their own water salvation.

Striking examples of these local possibilities are available in Guatemala City, the Federal District of Mexico, the Puerto Rico Authority, and in earlier years in the Argentine.

Multiple central agencies often have responsibilities in the field of water development. This has resulted in a certain degree of confusion and in strange partitioning of function among various agencies. The functions sometimes allocated to various agencies have been determined upon the basis of population groups. In any event, some increasing integration of effort, both for reasons of economy and for reasons of speed, with consequent consolidation of activity, would certainly appear desirable. Emphasis upon the desirable integration of central government functions should not lead, however, to further delay in program execution. Already this effort at integration, exclusive of all other practical activities, delays the program, while the search for the perfect governmental structure holds maximum attention.

Examples are likewise at hand where the Ministry of Health has responsibilities for design and construction of water facilities. In general, it is important that such activities should normally not be the responsibility of Ministries of Health. Where this is the case, the major function of the Ministry of Health suffers, namely, of stimulating other agencies in the installation of water facilities.

No single type of administrative structure is suggested for any particular country. In principle, however, public works departments would appear to be the natural agency to design, construct, and operate systems. Ministries of Health similarly should strengthen their forces and their objectives in the area of leadership and promotion of water facilities, without dissipating energies in the actual execution of projects, normally small in number and equally small in impact. Increasing responsibility and autonomy are essential for local aggregates of people, beginning with those groups in excess of 100,000 each and rapidly extending that responsibility to groups down to even 2,000 in population.

It is desirable to stress again the leadership role which Ministries of Health must accept. This will require a strengthened environmental sanitation division in all Ministries and a new administrative approach in working with other Ministries and agencies of government. It will be difficult in many countries to exercise the influence and exert the pressure necessary to make the water program a dynamic force in those countries where the engineering services of the Health Ministry are maintained at a token level. Ministries of Health must decide if they want to get into this activity, and if they decide in the affirmative, they must take immediate action.

3. Financial Considerations

The practice of providing money for water service via national or central government is well nigh universal. The wide use of such practice is well exemplified in Table 13. Even where Table 13 indicates that municipal sources of capital are available, this rarely means that capital is raised largely via municipal sources. It often means that large amounts of money are allocated by the central government to the district or municipality for expenditure or that the central government remains the arbiter for the issuance of local bonds.

Table 13
Main Source of Capital for Water System in Cities of Latin American Countries by Country and City Size

Country	Cities with 50,000 or more inhabitants	Cities with 10,000– 49,999 inhabitants	Cities with 2,000– 9,999 inhabitants
Argentina	National	National	National
Bolivia	National–Municipal	National–Municipal	National
Brazil	...	...	...
Chile	National	National	National
Colombia	Municipal	...	...
Costa Rica	National–Municipal	National	National
Dominican Republic	National	National	National
Ecuador	Municipal	Municipal	Municipal
El Salvador	Municipal	Municipal	Municipal
Guatemala	Municipal–Private	National, Municipal, or Private	National
Haiti	National	...	...
Honduras	National–Municipal	Municipal	Municipal
Nicaragua	National	Municipal	National–Municipal
Panama	National–Private	National	National
Paraguay	National–Municipal	None	Private
Peru	National	National	National
Uruguay	National	National	National
Venezuela	National	National	National or State

... No information

It is rare indeed that municipalities have full autonomy with respect to the fiscal aspects of water service, including direct responsibility for the issuance of bonds resting upon the credit of the local entity. The absence of such authority has brought unfortunate results in that major cities in many instances are unable to meet the requirements of existing populations or of those populations which have grown up in the metropolitan areas adjacent to them. The hopeless pressure for more capital on the national government accounts for the general hope that some mysterious source of capital may be found, either in loans or grants from agencies external to each country. Since charges for water service are not only variable, but in some instances close to non-existent, capital investment is obviously unattractive to either private or public lenders. Since relatively long term bonds at low interest rates are necessary for water supply facilities, this demand is rarely met through public or private lending agencies.

The income from most water systems in South and Central America hardly ever pays for the interest or amortization of capital invested. In fact, it is quite rare that such income supports even the annual cost of maintenance and operation. A commodity, therefore, such as water, which has no sales value or income, is unlikely to be an attractive investment. No government, no matter how humanitarian its instincts, has successfully supplied its people with clothing, food, houses, and services without any hope of repayment.

The health officer, therefore, must confront himself with the necessity of bringing new conviction to governments and to peoples that water service, a first pre-requisite for public health returns, must be converted into a commodity service. The cost of this service must be reimbursable in part or in total, as each community may gradually be raised to such a level of self-support. In other words, the mythology that a commodity which costs money to produce and to deliver is as free as the air must be rapidly expunged from the minds of officials and people. This conversion of attitudes has already taken place with large numbers of people in Latin America, even in those areas where officials still fall back upon this reasoning to justify the delay in the development of water service.

People pay for water in every one of the countries under discussion. When the housewife travels great distances to the public square to purchase a small can of water, she often does so at a cost ten times the cost of a safer water in greater quantity available to the house. Yet when water is piped into the house the great plea is made for extending this service free of charge.

Acceptance of the "free water" gospel is by no means universal. It is the line of least resistance, but it is breached even in a single country. In the same countries, water is often paid for in some communities, while adjacent ones hide under the cloak of past history in avoiding payment.

It is worth pointing out that almost nowhere is electric power provided free and when the bill is unpaid, the electricity is turned off. "Free" service apparently has different connotations in the same country for different public services—and cultural anthropology should not be invoked to justify only the bad practice.

Charges for water use, partial payment for water investment via property taxes, and revenues from other sources, have all been used in the Latin countries for the financing of water systems, in whole or in part. It is only rarely, however, that both capital charges and maintenance and operation are fully provided for.

In many very large and reasonably well-to-do communities, the charges for water border on the ridiculous. Courageous correction of these situations is essential in preparation for the long term program. The evidence supplied in Table 14 gives reasonable indication that many

Table 14

Method of Establishing Payment Scales for Water Consumers in Cities of 18 Latin American Countries by Size of City

Country	Cities of 50,000 or greater								Cities of 10,000–49,999								Cities of 2,000–9,999								General payment scale (U.S. dollars)
	No. with water	Flat rate	Meter	Meter and flat rate	Rate per faucet	Proportion of rent	No charge	Not stated	No. with water	Flat rate	Meter	Meter and flat rate	Rate per faucet	Proportion of rent	No charge	Not stated	No. with water	Flat rate	Meter	Meter and flat rate	Rate per faucet	Proportion of rent	No charge	Not stated	
Argentina	25					25								a			...					a	19		6.75 per cent of monthly house rent. Payable every 6 months.
Bolivia	4	2	1	1					4	a							...	a							$.90 to $1.50 per year. Very little revenue collected.
Brazil	33							33	...							a	...							a	Not stated.
Chile	9		9						...		a						...		a						Not stated.
Colombia	14		9					5	30							30	180		a					180	Range from $.014 to $.031 per cubic meter.
Costa Rica	1			1					6	2	2	2					16	12	3	1					Not stated.
Dominican Republic	2		2						...		a						...		a						$3.50 for the first 20 cubic meters and $0.10 for each additional cubic meter.
Ecuador	3		1					2	9		2	1					...		3						$.026 to $.033 per cubic meter.
El Salvador	2			2					10	9		1					42	37						5	Not stated.
Guatemala	1		1						4	4							62	61		1					Not stated.
Haiti	1				1				...				a				5				5				$.80 to $8.00 per month depending on number and size of faucets.
Honduras	1		1						5			4				1	22				3			19	$.04 to $.075 per cubic meter or $0.50 to $1.50 per faucet per month.

(cont.)

Table 14 (cont.)

Country	Cities of 50,000 or greater								Cities of 10,000–49,999								Cities of 2,000–9,999								General payment scale (U.S. dollars)
	No. with water	Flat rate	Meter	Meter and flat rate	Rate per faucet	Proportion of rent	No charge	Not stated	No. with water	Flat rate	Meter	Meter and flat rate	Rate per faucet	Proportion of rent	No charge	Not stated	No. with water	Flat rate	Meter	Meter and flat rate	Rate per faucet	Proportion of rent	No charge	Not stated	
Nicaragua	1	1	1						8	5	2	1					9	7	2						Flat rate $1.42 to $2.13 per month.
Panama	2		2						3		1	2					20	1	2	13				4	$.10 to $.12 per cubic meter. Flat rate $1.00 per month per connection.
Paraguay	1		1						0								...					a			(1) Monthly minimum $5.00 for 40 cubic meters, or (2) Included in rent.
Peru	3	1	2						...	a							...	a							Not stated.
Uruguay	1		1						...		a						...		a						Each month: $.054 per m³ for first 10 m³; $.11 per m³ for 2nd 10; $.13 per m³ for next 80; $.14 per m³ for next 100; $.16 per m³ for next 300; and $.18 per m³ for all over 500 m³.
Venezuela	8		6	2					39	13	23				3		112	93	11				B		Not stated.

... Information not available.

(a) General statement as to basis for payment—number of cities using this basis not specified.

consumers in Latin American countries pay something for water. These amounts no matter how low represent real milestones along the road toward self-support.

Mr. Eugene R. Black, President of the International Bank for Reconstruction and Development, has summarized this situation perhaps better than almost anyone else in the following terms:

> A steadily expanding supply of essential public utility services is a requisite of economic growth in all underdeveloped countries today. Over the next decade, many thousands of millions of dollars in capital for these services must be found. There is simply no practical way to raise this money unless a substantial part of it is generated by the utilities themselves through adequate charges to the users of their services.
>
> The Bank has been laboring this point for a very long time. We have held it is dangerous for a developing country to be sentimental or practically expedient about things like railroads and power plants; that policies based on these attitudes only create an intolerable drain on the savings which are the lifeblood of every country's future prosperity. We have said that adequate utility rates are especially important in a country where there is no organized capital market. By 'adequate' rates we have meant rates which enable utilities not only to cover the real cost of their services, but also to retain out of earnings substantial sums each year to help finance the expansions which inevitably will be needed to sustain future growth. And we have made no distinction in advocating adequate rates between privately owned and publicly owned utilities.
>
> I feel the Bank's insistence on sound utility finance is being vindicated today by events in many member countries. All over Latin America and in many other parts of the underdeveloped world, officials charged with the job of finding capital for development are themselves struggling to get a recognition of the simple principle that utilities should pay their way.

One of the important results of the enforcement of the principles on reimbursability herein discussed is that central government money is then released for other important public purposes which do not lend themselves easily to the application of the repayment principle. If water service and the capital required therefor is eliminated from the drain on central government funds, the central government dollar is so stretched that more money is made available for the general services in health, education, medical care, hospitals, etc. These latter now are in competition with required water facilities which are not, but should be, self-supporting.

4. *Sources of Funds*

The hard fact that programs for resources development must be financed through local sources, is very well understood by ministers of finance and economics in every one of the Latin countries. The fruitless search for easy sources of money, either within the country or preferably from some external source, is unfortunately one of the major efforts of officials.

For certain kinds of water development, such as irrigation and hydroelectric power, external sources of money, often in the form of loans, are available. A list of these sources is shown in Figure 2 (Banker's Trust Company pamphlet on foreign trade). The World Bank or an international finance corporation rarely makes extensive loans for community water service. This does not mean that such sources of capital are not available under certain conditions. No money is available, however, for loan purposes from most of these agencies, unless there is a clear demonstration of the total economic validity of the purposes of the loan and equally convincing demonstration that there is more than a reasonable chance that the loan will be repaid and that maintenance and operation of the facilities will be adequately provided for through appropriate rates.

The recently created Inter-American Bank to promote development of Latin America may offer less stringent sources of development money. The charter for this bank was accepted in April, 1959, and provides for two complementary agencies. The first and larger one will be the Inter-American Development Bank. It will make most of its loans in dollars. The loans will be reimbursable in the currencies in which they are made and the terms will be those of regular commercial banks.

The second agency will be a fund for special operations. It will make loans normally regarded as non-acceptable bank risks. These loans will finance projects that are socially useful, though not necessarily self-liquidating. Such loans will have easier terms and will be repayable in local currencies.

The Inter-American Bank will also provide finance, managerial and technical experts to assist the countries in moving toward stronger administrative and fiscal status.

None of these sources, however, should be considered as substitutes for the rapid development of local sources of funds based upon the principle of self-support and repayment. It is particularly important to recognize that the development of water service in Latin America will rest upon the maximum utilization of local resources of manpower, materials, and money.

The kind of program here visualized will only become effective when a new and imaginative approach is made to fiscal support by means of maximum local loans at low interest rates and with long amortization periods. Judicious and restrained use, for stimulation purposes, of grants-in-aid, and the rapid development of the principle and the reality of complete financial self-support, are the keys. Many water systems throughout the world pay for themselves by property taxes, charges for

Fig. 2a

United States Agencies That Help to Finance Foreign Trade
(Prepared by Bankers Trust Company)

	United States Agencies		
	Export-Import Bank	*Export-Import Bank Cooley Amendment Funds*	*Development Loan Fund*
Purpose	To promote U. S. exports.	Economic development; expansion of markets for U. S. agricultural products.	To finance productive projects in less developed countries having a great capital need.
Nature of Loans	Lends in dollars only. Agricultural commodities, 12–15 months; machinery and equipment, 3–5 years; projects or development, 5–15 years.	Lends in local currencies at local interest rates 3–15 years; loans must be acceptable to the foreign country.	Lends in dollars repayable usually in local currencies; 3–40 years. Loans in local currencies will be available later. Rates: Private Sector—same as Export-Import Bank; Public Sector—3½% per annum. Foreign government guarantee not required.
Who Can Borrow	U. S. private enterprises; foreign private enterprises and governments of friendly countries qualifying under the Battle Act.	For business development: U. S. private enterprisers. For agricultural markets expansion: private enterprisers of U. S. or country whose currency is borrowed.	Private enterprises of U.S.; government or private enterprises in any country qualifying under the Battle Act.
Where the Funds Must Be Spent	United States.	Recipient countries, which must have signed agreements with U. S. Department of Agriculture.	Any friendly country.
Private Participation in Loans of the Agencies	Commercial banks and other financial institutions welcomed.	No.	Welcomed.
Must Seek Private Capital First	Yes.	No.	Yes, and also Export-Import Bank, World Bank, and International Finance Corporation capital.
Must Ship Only in United States Vessels	Yes, unless waived by Maritime Administration.	Yes, unless waived by Maritime Administration.	Yes, unless waived by Maritime Administration.

Fig. 2b

International Agencies That Help to Finance Foreign Trade
(Prepared by Bankers Trust Company)
International Agencies

Commodity Credit Corporation	*World Bank*	*International Finance Corporation*
To promote export of U.S. surplus agricultural commodities.	To finance projects helping to build the foundations of economic growth in less developed countries.	To finance private enterprises contributing to economic development of member countries.
Credits up to 3 years supported by confirmed letters of credit of U. S. banks.	Lends in dollars and other currencies. Term, 5 to 25 years, depending on project. Present rate, 5¾% per annum. Government guarantee required.	Makes loans to industrial and mining ventures, with convertibility to or rights to acquire capital stock. Lends in dollars; local currency loans will be available later. No government guarantee required.
Export firms in the United States.	Public or private entities in member countries.	Private enterprises in member countries.
	Member countries, normally other than that in which project is located.	Member countries, normally other than that in which project is located.
United States.	Commercial banks and other financial institutions welcomed.	Welcomes financial institutions in member countries.
Not applicable. See "Nature of Loans."	Yes, and other public capital.	Yes.
See "Nature of Loans."	Not applicable.	Not applicable.
Not applicable.		

water used, special assessments, or by combinations thereof. Their lessons must be applied in whole or in part to all of Latin America, with appropriate adaptation to local practices, cultures, and fiscal attitudes.

If one waits upon the availability of vast amounts of international aid, the program will wait a very long time. Local and national resources, infrequently supplemented by bi-lateral and international funds, can provide the bases for rapid extension of water to the people.

If the provision of community water is always to be viewed through the spectacles of the past, success is unlikely. That it need not be viewed on the basis of the status quo has been demonstrated already in many areas in Latin America, for water essentially is cheap and can well pay for itself. People can and do learn why this must be so, if one takes the pains to make the principle understood.

Elements for Implementation

Assuming general acceptance of the desirability of a program for urbanized water facilities, the following steps for action are indicated. They are noted in maximum simplicity because their detailed elaboration would require a separate monograph. They are divided into two major divisions and it would be reasonable to assume that action could proceed in both simultaneously.

I. *The Organization and Administrative Action*
Each country should:

1. Initiate a study of the best type or types of organization for carrying out the national water program.
2. Enact such laws and enabling legislation, and adopt such procedures as are required to implement a program of sound, well managed, well operated, adequately financed water systems.

II. *The Technical Action*
Since it may be expected that changes in organization and administrative structure require time, it is urged that no country wait for success in those activities before proceeding with the following technical actions. Every country should:

1. Have a reasonably complete inventory of the water service situation in community aggregates of people throughout the country.
2. Have a classification of areas unsupplied with water according to sizes of communities.
3. Make a selection of the areas which are the largest, which have

the greatest need, and which will offer the fewest obstacles to immediate success.

4. Prepare a preliminary design and cost estimate for servicing each of the areas selected. This should include new sources, treatment plant, pumping facilities, etc., if required.

5. Prepare for each area a rate structure, encompassing property taxes, consumption charges, special assessments, or other sources sufficient to pay annually charges for interest on and repayment of loans, for maintenance and operation, and for new additions.

6. Provide for establishment of the managerial instrument to execute, finance, and administer the project, whether national or local.

7. Provide for the creation of the administrative unit to be responsible for total water development and finance in the large capital and other metropolitan areas.

8. Prepare the legislation required to implement the items delineated above.

9. Arrange for the continuing collection of pertinent experience of other areas to provide for the education of officials, general public, industrialists, economists and financiers, and water consumers.

10. Delineate each proposed project in great detail—from its engineering elements to the charge for water to each class of consumer in order to sell its value and low cost to the public.

11. Prepare and distribute authoritative and sound literature spelling out examples of successful water service, self-supported, in other countries.

In selecting the area or areas where the initial effort is to be made, one should be chosen where obstacles will be the least. This will provide a background for experience. It will permit development of the channels and mechanisms by which the later, more difficult areas can be approached.

These steps in the early action program represent in virtually every instance a direct, almost daily, cooperative effort of the Ministries of Health, of Public Works, and of Finance. They entail likewise an early grasp of the inner workings of both national and local political units, in order to formulate procedures best adapted to each country and its subdivisions.

Summary

The extension of water facilities to the people, not only for the thirsty, but to provide cleanliness and expand industry, housing facilities, and tourism must be one of the great public health endeavors for the next 5 to 10 years. The past success in making such facilities available is incredibly small. It is not keeping pace even with the annual increment of population growth. At the present rate of development, water will be made available to 75 per cent of people in the countries of Latin America only after 50 to 100 years.

If one waits until all of the theoretical requisites for such a program are at hand, one will wait forever. Technologic skills, improved administrative structure and new devices for financing, with strong self-liquidating features, are all sufficiently well understood now to make the initiation of a militant program practicable at once.

The success of such a program is contingent upon the leading health officers of every country not only accepting the theoretical validity of the program, but giving it more than lip service to carry it forward successfully.

A joint attack upon this problem by the Ministries of Health, of Public Works and of Finance is essential. Reorientation of the activities of virtually all of the departments of health must precede these objectives.

PASB/WHO and ICA have major responsibilities in providing leadership in the education of officials in the administrative, technologic, and finance features; the national and international banking units in the development of credit; and the national and local political units in the responsible execution of the projects. Sharp divisions of responsibility are impractical and academic. PASB/WHO and its national governing members must supply the spearhead for strengthening the inter-relationships among all of the groups noted above.

That the provision of community piped water to the people is a worthy public health endeavor is perhaps best summarized in the opening statements by WHO Director General, Dr. M. G. Candau, at the Twelfth World Health Assembly in 1959. He there stated:

> Water predominates as the major constituent in practically every phase of an individual's physical, social, and economic life. Experience has proved that making potable water available to the individual is the foundation on which rests the health and economic progress of the community. Because of the basic public health importance of community water supplies, WHO cannot remain aloof from its obligation to supply the stimulation and assistance needed to bring about their construction.
>
> It is disheartening to record that in 1959 in many major cities and their densely urbanized satellites many millions of people are still dependent upon individual wells, springs, or itinerant purveyors for this life-giving commodity. Cities, ranging from two to seven or eight million people, not only fail to furnish water through pipes to households of several hundreds of thousands of their inhabitants, but even

to those directly connected to the system they supply an unsafe water, often on a rationed basis of a third each day or less. This significant fact is often ignored in determining environmental sanitation programs.

The labour involved in drawing water and transporting it for a long distance, a task which often falls to the lot of the women, results in their virtual enslavement. Frequently as much as one-half of their time, day after day, month after month, is taken up with this essential chore. A very simple calculation will show that there is no more efficient means of transporting water than by a pipe. A small pipe, one inch in diameter, will deliver in a day, without human effort, as much water as can be carried by 150 women working steadily for eight hours. Even in the most advanced countries there are still great deficiencies.

For such a programme to be successful it should move rapidly beyond lip service to real effort, including budgetary allotments, increases in skilled personnel, and actual operating programmes. Its success would demand of ministries of health a militant and continuing leadership and a far closer co-operation with departments of public works than now generally exists. It is sound to separate the stimulative functions of a health department from the executive functions of a public works department. Such administrative separation, however, does not justify each in going its own way. Their co-operation is essential in carrying forward a water supply programme.

Acknowledgment

I should like to express my appreciation to the Director of PASB and his headquarters staff, to the Zone representatives and engineers, and to the many people of the Ministries of Health in the countries of this Region who have assisted me in providing, collecting, and consolidating information and who have so willingly given of their time and effort.

REFERENCES

1. United Nations, Report of the World Social Situation, p. 16, 1957.

COMPREHENSIVE

PLANNING

FOR

HUMAN ENVIRONMENT

Man and His Changing Environment*

The past several decades have been characterized in contrasting terms, depending upon the optimism or cynicism of the observer. We live in an era of profound change, whether such change is measured in biophysical terms or in the stresses of social and political reconstruction. It is a time of great conflict between scientific development and social and political adaptation.

Whatever the choice of philosophy, the world presses upon man the necessity for accepting change and the challenges and hazards which necessarily accompany it. Because man faces significant issues with no obvious solutions does not detract from the fact that this is still a golden era of intellectual opportunity. Charles V. Chapin, half a century ago, aptly phrased the health officer's obligation to adjust to change in the following terms:

> To do our duty day by day is, indeed, a pleasure, to abate nuisances, to isolate contagious diseases promptly, to examine school children, to license hogs, to listen patiently to complaints, to diagnose doubtful cases, to record births and deaths, to distribute milk for

* Reprinted from *American Journal of Public Health*, Vol. 51, No. 11 (November, 1961), pp. 1,631–37. Copyright by the American Public Health Association, Inc. Presented before the Association Symposium of the American Public Health Association at the Eighty-Eighth Annual Meeting in San Francisco, Cailf. Oct. 31, 1960.

babies, to vaccinate, to kill mosquitoes, give out antitoxin, to inspect baby farms, to examine dogs' brains, to distribute circulars, to make blood tests, to back up the family physician, to keep the reporters good-natured, to answer fool questions, are all in the day's work. . . . But the health officer however faithful, who gets into a rut is not doing his full duty.[1]

Characteristics of Our Age

When one deliberately attempts to assay the world in which the public health worker now functions, he will soon discover that no single characteristic is universally applicable. He must consider geography, economic and social period, and the status of disease. This is not a uniform world with a uniform display either of conditions or of hazards. It has been said, for example, that the communicable diseases have well-nigh disappeared, that morbidity is on the increase in certain age groups, that life expectancy has reached perhaps a plateau of some 70 years. These phenomena are true for the most part only in the Western Hemisphere. Most of the statements are equally untrue for more than half of the total population of the globe. One is confronted, therefore, with two worlds of contrasting disease aspect and hence of differing necessities and programs.

For this discussion, I am restricting myself primarily to the Western world and more specifically to the United States of North America. Such a narrowing of geographical scope is essential for the purposes of this symposium. If one were to embrace the world as a whole, each description, each judgment and each prophecy, no matter how circumscribed, would have to be posed in multiple forms.

Innumerable areas of activity may illustrate what has been happening in the environment over the last several decades. Their listing would not only confuse the situation, but detailed documentation is already in print.[2] A few examples for establishing a setting are, however, noted in the following.

Water Supply

The ingenuity of the engineer will be pressed in the next quarter of a century to exercise increasingly skillful control and management of water resources. These resources will be ample for the future if intelligently and logically planned and developed. In the consummation of these tasks central issues are already apparent.

Specific synthetic organic chemicals are one of the major characteristics of our era. They are finding their way increasingly into our public water supplies. They may originate in the wastes of the population, as, for example, in the detergents. Fertilizers, insecticides, and other agricultural poisons provide them on the land. Deliberate application to waters for plant or fish control is not uncommon.

Although we are aware of a mosaic of stable organic materials, our tools of examination and of identification are still much too inadequate to provide the quantitative information necessary either to determine toxic aspects or methods of removal.

Whether a limit exists or will be attained at which human accommodation to such substances may be exhausted is still in the realm of speculation.

Similar concern and confusion are obvious with the assessment of the public health aspects of viruses in the water environment. Here, too, we wait upon improved methods for recovery, identification, enumeration, and particularly, epidemiological assessment of public health significance.

Water Pollution

Excessive abuse of receiving bodies of water from the waste waters which reach them will require increased attention. The reclamation and re-use of waste waters are probably dominant necessities of the future, not only because of acute shortages of fresh water in some areas, but because of increasing demand and pollution even in fairly rich water areas. The recapture of the once used or spent water supply presents a significant technological challenge. This challenge is unlikely to be met by even the most economic methods for desalting sea water. On the contrary, the cost of reclaiming used fresh water, with a tiny fraction of the soluble materials present in sea water, appears to offer more satisfying prospects.

To the orthodox processes of primary and secondary treatment one may well expect the addition of tertiary and even quaternary degree treatment and polishing of domestic and industrial wastes.

The investigator in this field, therefore, has an exciting future of research. High on the list would be the necessity for greatly improved analytical methodologies, diagnoses of effects of long-term persistence of wastes on water uses, the development of simple and short-term bioassay procedures, and extensive inquiries into the technics for removal of larvicides, algaecides, piscicides, and other economic poisons.

Air Pollution

Although tremendous progress has been made, particularly in California, in the baffling aspects of air pollution and its control, far more remains to be resolved than has so far materialized from the sharp attention in recent years to the physical and biological sciences, engineering, public health, economics, and the law. For virtually the same reasons as in water supply and in stream pollution, rapid industrialization and urbanization, coupled with the geographical and meteorological disabilities of some areas, have pushed forward more rapidly the necessity for detailed exploration in air pollution than might have been the case in a more leisurely developing technology. The increase in air-borne wastes, with either familiar or new kinds of pollution, plagues the health officer in expanding areas of the country.

As in so many pollution situations, man soon discovers the variability of his so-called natural environment. The Southern Californian who prides himself on the excellent climate pays a price for the meteorological peculiarities which dominate the fate of his industrial and domestic air-borne wastes. Many years ago Horace Walpole touched upon this controlling feature of the environment when he observed that "the French can never have as beautiful landscapes as ours in England, till they have as bad a climate."

Many questions remain unanswered. What standards of air cleanliness are to be maintained and for what reason? What are the effects of air pollution upon man, plant, and animal life? Are they the results of short or long exposure and are they likely to do major harm to biological life? The intuitive assumptions that a polluted atmosphere is not conducive to the best health still lack either strong statistical or epidemiological support. A tremendous amount of painstaking and costly research over a long period of time is to be anticipated.

The details of this specific area of research need not be delineated here except to re-emphasize that knowledge must be extended in clarifying the chemistry of air pollution systems, the chemistry of sulfur compounds, the physiological effects of aerosols in atmospheric reactions, and the physiologic and toxicologic effects of specific pollutants.

Food Technology

The increase in the number and variety of processed foods is considered by some to be synonymous with a better and easier life. It seems to be assumed that most individuals for one reason or another are unwilling to accept foods in their natural state. Hence every conceivable effort has been made to modify color, taste, structural appearance, texture, stability, nutritive value, and substituted commodities. Such successful efforts to supplement, modify, and conceal nature introduce innumerable problems of identification, of evaluation, of control, and of assessment of long-term biological effects. To the orthodox problems of biological hazards in food, industry has added the major issues of chemical, biochemical, physical, and other adjustments. The natural and artificially induced shifts in food habits, new methods of food technology, and the intentional and inadvertent use of additives find the health officer confronted with a baffling set of conditions unheard of even a decade ago.

Occupational Health

In man's work-environment we find difficulties similar to those encountered in the fields already mentioned. Hundreds of threshold limiting values have already been established in industry to protect man against hazardous chemical, biological, and physical agents. Over the full working lifetime of an individual fewer criteria are at hand, because no one has been willing to assume that the short-term threshold limit values may be applied with safety to lifetime exposures.

The same situation applies with equal force to all of the emerging problems in the field of radiation, whether for medical, industrial, research, or other purposes. On land, on sea, and in the air, these problems will increase and extensive research will be essential in order to arrive at reasonable restrictions for protecting life.

Debate as to the reliability of all of our permissible limits will continue for years. The development of methods for evaluating occupational hazards will press more and more upon us. The responsibility for carrying out these tasks has not yet been fixed, but that the health officer will have and must have a prime position in this responsibility no one can gainsay.

In the decision as to whether man becomes and remains a victim of his own technology or uses it to the advantage of mankind, the members of the American Public Health Association will have much to say. It need not follow that man will be lost in his own machinations. To protect him against his own wisdom and success in industrial application will not be easy, but the health profession certainly cannot sanction failure to control the environment.

Where Do We Go from Here?

Much of the discussion up to this point is really preliminary to the central question—what do we do in this world of changing environment? That this environment will increasingly impose a hazard must be accepted as a reasonable basis for any new or expanded professional activity.

The mere listing of the baffling problems already confronting us has led some, in answer to where we go from here, to suggest recourse to the psychiatrist. A better alternative must be found than this one of despair. Public health administrative practice throughout history has an impressive record of improvisation to meet the known and the unknown challenges of man's environment. Life has always been a competitive adventure. As Dubos so well points out, "The very process of life is a continual interplay between the individual and his environment, often taking the form of a struggle resulting in injury or disease." That the environment is more complex than it was a half century ago offers no basis for losing heart. That scientific evidence, measurement, and evaluation are far less complete than desired is also no reason for retreat. This has always been the case. Improvement in the health of man in the 19th century, for example, was undoubtedly without the benefit of the best advice which medicine and the germ theory of disease might have provided if knowledge had been at hand. Success antedated precise knowledge.

Another factor in our favor lies in the tremendous capacity which man has exhibited over thousands of years for natural adaptation and for artificial adjustment to his environment.

More and more we are aware of the fallacy of the "doctrine of specific etiology of disease" and of the truth that "Most disease states are the indirect outcome of a constellation of circumstances" (Dubos). The recognition of the impact of external stresses upon man and disease provides the health practitioner with a broader, even though a more difficult, arena for investigation. In such an arena the significant questions are not whether or not scientific investigation should proceed, but what guides the public health worker may be expected to choose in his professional conduct. It is to these guides that much of this symposium perhaps should be devoted.

Choices of Guides for Administrative Action

The public whom the sanitarian serves is often a hard task master. The man on the street and his invariable companion, the social reformer, have an impatience with inaction. The objectionable atmosphere, the unsightly stream, the mysterious tastes and odors of water and food, and the esoteric characteristics of radiation, all demand attention and control. Abstruse explanations of the inadequacies of scientific knowledge, of unexplored epidemiological worlds, and of insufficient data fall upon deaf ears. In such not unfamiliar dilemmas, what should a practitioner in public health do? Some choices are listed for debate. To steer a middle course between the known, the unknown, the less than frank, and the politically expedient is the unhappy but often the successful lot of the health officer.

The Madison Avenue or Propaganda Route

The changing environment has many dramatic features which so easily lend themselves to the "soft sell" in the modern parlance. The use of suggestion, as a mask for scientific ignorance, and of implication, as a substitute for epidemiologic evidence, are great temptations for bolstering budget, for focusing public attention, and for providing action even if ill-defined.

To the scientist this route is obviously highly suspect. To the politician it is a rich method of raising popular interest and hence "getting something done." To the columnist, on the prowl for the dramatic and plausible, if not the accurate, the route is fruitful.

The health officer undoubtedly looks at this guide with a jaundiced eye for fear that the unproved may be a dangerous boomerang weapon. Examples of such discredited recent efforts are all too numerous. Only the threat of libel suits prevents a partial listing here of these abortive pronouncements.

The Statistical Route

John W. Tukey at Princeton University recently referred to the "characterization of a statistician as a man who draws straight lines from insufficient data to foregone conclusions." The bio-metrician in public health has however a firmer heritage than this. His tools have been eminently useful in providing some underpinning for public health action. This useful route is certainly one to which the health worker will turn in the search for policy support.

The Epidemiologic Route

In much of the attack on the problems of environmental control, the epidemiologist holds important keys. It is unfortunate that in the past he has not seen fit to put too much investigative effort in the field of which we speak. His long-term devotion to the orthodox problems of communicable disease is understandable. The dependence, however, of the health officer upon wider epidemiologic inquiry into the subtle impact of environment upon man is so great that the investigator should increasingly apply his tools to such areas as the impact of air pollution upon respiratory disease, of minor concentrations of chemical constituents in food and water upon long-term disease, and of the whole virus complex in its relation to environmental routes for disease causation.

The Research Route

Perhaps the outstanding block to a better understanding of the impact of the environment upon man and the more intelligent efforts at control lies in the delayed research exploration of all the factors involved. As always, administrative action waits upon scientific proof. The route is slow, fumbling, and difficult of formulation. As a prime ingredient of ultimate intelligent policy and action it perhaps takes first place. Action obviously will proceed, while the leaven of new scientific discovery perennially and, it is hoped, promptly adjusts day-by-day practice.

The Route of Intuition

A student of public health accomplishment in the past century cannot help but be impressed with many advances in environmental control which preceded scientific verification. In many instances, the lay social reformer was a militant forerunner of the professional public health worker in pressing for major improvement in the physical way of life of masses of people, often in actions unsupported by scientific evidence and on important occasions contrary to such evidence.

Useful results in public health were often obtained by these measures and the failures were perhaps meager prices to pay for the successes. In modern society, so often speeding along an ever wider highway of general welfare, the public acts upon intuition and is impatient of delay in action. There is something to be said for a public policy which demands clean air, clean streams, and decent houses, per se, even if the coefficients of correlation with morbidity and mortality are either nonexistent or of a low order of magnitude.

After all, we are still a long way off from an analytical technic of measurement of the physiologic-psychologic merits of green grass and trees. No biochemical criteria for such an impact upon man appear even in the offing. Yet Sir Arcot Mudaliar of India, at the World Health Assembly in Minneapolis, wisely bemoaned the fact that no health officer included in his official agenda an interest or an influence in preserving or creating open spaces in the rapidly urbanizing areas of the world. Perhaps the engineers who plow under vast green areas for the super-super-highway and who pile brick upon brick in urban and suburban areas devastated by the excavating machine are as subtly destructive to man as our once familiar Typhoid Mary was.

The route of intuition in public health practice deserves dignified appraisal, if for no other reason than it gives free rein to "the driving power of mercy"! (that happy phrase of Sir Arthur Newsholme).

The Integration of Multidisciplines

Major progress in curbing the vicissitudes of a changing environment will require the best that all the scientific disciplines can and will supply. The problems confronting us are not the exclusive jurisdiction for understanding or abatement of any single professional group. The engineer, it is true, has the age-old obligation of translating concept into structure and facilities, but in performing this significant task he must move forward simultaneously with the physiologist, chemist, physicist, biochemist, and other scientific workers.

The task of centering these disciplines upon the environment is almost completely unfulfilled. There is hardly a health department that provides the setting for such interdisciplinary attack. Such an effort must come within the compass of the sanitarian's thinking, even if the opportunities for such broad approach may be limited to only a few departments of health.

General Summary

The environment of man has changed profoundly in the last quarter of a century. Added to the earlier hazards of living organisms in water, air, and food, our technology has contributed new chemicals, new biologics, new physical contaminants. The effects of these changes upon life are little understood whether they be long or short term in manifestation. That the changes cannot be ignored by the health practitioner is obvious.

Guides for action are posed for discussion. One or more of these must be accepted for policy and performance. The wise brew of scientific knowledge, epidemiologic verity, public demand, and rare intuition, with the inevitable seasoning of budgetary restraint, will no doubt be the choice.

REFERENCES

1. Chapin, Charles V. Address to the American Public Health Association, Winnipeg, Canada, September, 1908. J.A.M.A. 52 :686–687 (Feb. 27), 1909.

2. Proceedings of the Conference on Man Versus Environment, May 5–6, 1958. Washington, D.C.: Public Health Service (Jan.), 1959.

The Metabolism of Cities*

The metabolic requirements of a city can be defined as all the materials and commodities needed to sustain the city's inhabitants at home, at work and at play. Over a period of time these requirements include even the construction materials needed to build and rebuild the city itself. The metabolic cycle is not completed until the wastes and residues of daily life have been removed and disposed of with a minimum of nuisance and hazard. As man has come to appreciate that the earth is a closed ecological system, casual methods that once appeared satisfactory for the disposal of wastes no longer seem acceptable. He has the daily evidence of his eyes and nose to tell him that his planet cannot assimilate without limit the untreated wastes of his civilization.

No one article could describe the complete metabolism of the modern city. Moreover, many of the metabolic inputs such as food, fuel, clothing, durable goods, construction materials and electric energy present no special problem. Their supply is handled routinely, in part through local initiative and in part through large organizations (public or private) that operate about as effectively in one city as another. I shall be concerned therefore with three metabolic problems that have become more acute as cities have grown larger and whose solution rests almost entirely in

* Reprinted with permission. Copyright © 1965 by Scientific American, Inc. All rights reserved.

the hands of the local administrator. Although he can call on many outside sources for advice, he must ultimately provide the solutions fashioned to the unique needs of his own community. These three problems are the provision of an adequate water supply, the effective disposal of sewage and the control of air pollution.

That these three problems vary widely from city to city and that they are being managed with widely varying degrees of success is obvious to anyone who reads a daily newspaper. It is ironic, for example, that New York City, which houses the nation's (if not the world's) greatest concentration of managerial talent, should be running short of water while billions of gallons of fresh water flow past it to the sea. It is not easy for people living in arid countries, or even for those living in the southwestern part of the U.S., to have much sympathy with New York's plight.

This summer, while New Yorkers were watching their emptying reservoirs and hoping for rain, Californians were busy building an aqueduct that would carry water some 440 miles from the Sacramento River, near Sacramento, to Los Angeles and other cities in the southern part of the state. And thanks to earlier examples of foresight, people in southern California were watering their lawns and filling their swimming pools without restriction, while in New York and New Jersey lawns were dying and pools stood empty. In the water-rich Middle Atlantic states water shortages are largely the result of delayed action and failures of management—sometimes exacerbated by political jockeying.

If American cities have had such unequal success in supplying their citizens with water, it is hardly surprising that some should have an even less satisfactory record in controlling water and air pollution, areas in which the incentives for providing remedies are much weaker than those that motivate the supplying of water. To make matters worse, pollutants of water and air often do not respect state boundaries. For example, the wastes of five states—Michigan, Indiana, Ohio, Pennsylvania and New York—have contributed to the accelerated pollution of Lake Erie. "The lake," according to the U.S. Public Health Service, "has deteriorated in quality at a rate many times greater than its normal aging process." The fourth-largest and shallowest of the five Great Lakes, Lake Erie is the main water suppy for 10 million U.S. citizens as well as for the huge industrial complex that extends for 300 miles along the lake's southern shore from Detroit to Buffalo. The combination of treated and partially treated municipal sewage and industrial wastes that enters Lake Erie directly, and also reaches it indirectly through a network of rivers, has disrupted the normal cycle of aquatic life, has led to the closing of a number of beaches and has materially changed the commercial fishing industry. Last month the five states, in consultation with the Public Health Service, reached agreement on a major program of pollution abatement.

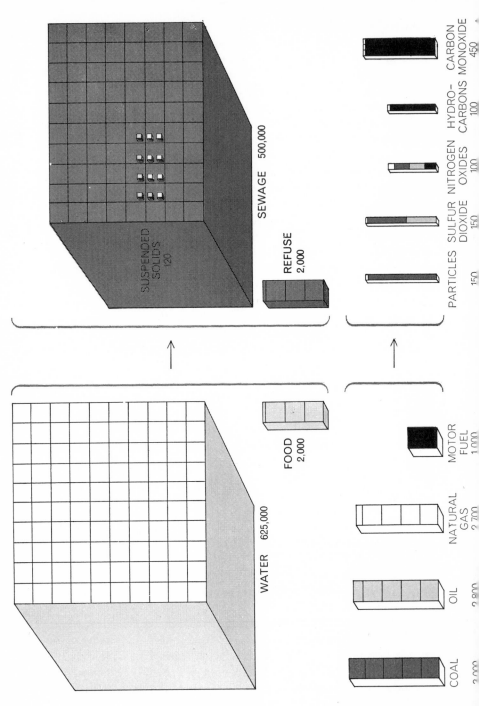

Chart 1

Metabolism of a city involves countless input-output transactions. This chart concentrates on three inputs common to all cities, namely water, food and fuel, and three outputs, sewage, solid refuse and air pollutants. Each item is shown in tons per day for a hypothetical U.S. city with a population of one million. Water, which enters the city silently and unseen, overshadows all other inputs in volume. More than .6 ton (150 gallons) must be supplied to each inhabitant every day. After about 20 per cent of the water has been diverted to lawns and other unrecoverable uses, it returns, contaminated, to the city's sewers. The city's most pervasive nuisance, air pollution, is accounted for chiefly by the combustion of fuels. (If refuse is burned in incinerators, it can also contribute heavily, but that contribution is not included here.) The various air pollutants are keyed by shading and black to the fuel responsible. Most of the particle emission (soot and fly ash) is produced by coal burned in electric power plants, and in well-designed plants more than 90 per cent of the particles can be removed from the stack gases. For this hypothetical city one may assume that 135 of the 150 tons of particles produced by all fuel consumers are removed before they reach the atmosphere. All other emissions, however, pollute the atmosphere in the volumes shown. Sulfur dioxide is based on use of domestic fuels of average sulfur content.

Although engineers concerned with water supply, sewage disposal and air pollution are accustomed to thinking in terms of large volumes, few laymen quite appreciate the quantities of water, sewage and air pollutants involved in the metabolism of a modern city. Chart 1 expresses these quantities in the form of inputs and outputs for a hypothetical American city of one million population. The input side of the chart shows the requirements in tons per day of water, food and fuels of various kinds. The output side shows the metabolic products of that input in terms of sewage, solid refuse and air pollutants. The quantities shown are a millionfold multiplication of the daily requirements of the average city dweller. Directly or indirectly he uses about 150 gallons (1,250 pounds) of water, four pounds of food and 19 pounds of fossil fuels. This is converted into roughly 120 gallons of sewage (which assumes 80 per cent recovery of the water input), four pounds of refuse (which includes food containers and miscellaneous rubbish) and 1.9 pounds of air pollutants, of which automobiles, buses and trucks account for more than half.

As of 1963 about 150 million out of 189 million Americans, or 80 per cent, lived in some 22,000 communities served by 19,200 waterworks. These 150 million people used about 23 billion gallons per day (b.g.d.), a volume that can be placed in perspective in several ways. In 1960 the amount of water required for all purposes in the U.S. was about 320 b.g.d., or roughly 15 times the municipal demand. The biggest user of water is irrigation, which in 1960 took about 140 b.g.d. Steam electric utilities used about 98 b.g.d. and industry about 60 b.g.d. Since 1960 the total U.S. water demand has risen from about 320 b.g.d. to an estimated 370 b.g.d., of which municipalities take about 25 b.g.d. [see Chart 2].

Thus municipalities rank as the smallest of the four principal users of water. Although it is true that water provided for human consumption must sometimes meet standards of quality that need not be met by water used in agriculture or industry, nevertheless throughout most of the U.S. farms, factories and cities frequently draw water from a common supply.

For the country as a whole the supply of available water is enormous: about 1,200 b.g.d. This is the surface runoff that remains from an average daily rainfall of some 4,200 b.g.d. About 40 per cent of the total precipitation is utilized where it falls, providing water to support vegetation of economic value: forests, farm crops and pasture lands. Another 30 per cent evaporates directly from the soil or returns to the atmosphere after passing through vegetation that has no particular economic value except insofar as it may prevent erosion of the land.

It is obvious that one cannot expect to capture and put to use every drop of the 1,200 b.g.d. flowing to the sea. The amount that can be captured depends on what people are willing to pay for water. One recent estimate places the economically available supply at somewhat less than

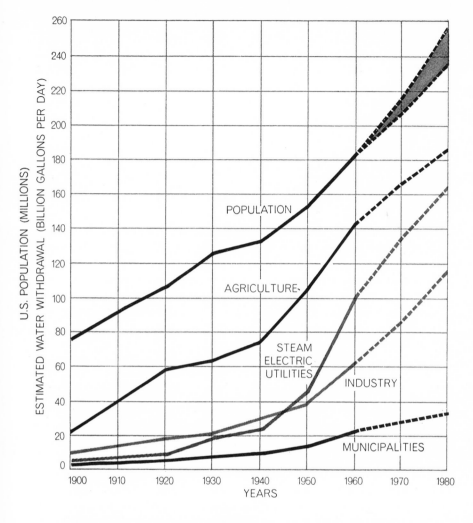

Chart 2

U.S. water requirements will be 53 per cent greater in 1980 than in 1960, according to the most recent estimates of the Department of Commerce. Virtually all water used by agriculture is for irrigation; nearly 60 per cent of all irrigated land in the U.S. is in five Western states (California, Texas, Colorado, Idaho and Arizona) where water tends to be scarcest. Steam power plants need water in huge amounts simply to condense steam. In 1960 municipalities used about 22 billion gallons per day (b.g.d), which represented only about 7 percent of the total water withdrawal of about 320 b.g.d. The important distinction between water "withdrawal" and "consumptive use" is shown in Chart 3.

half the total, or 560 b.g.d. In my opinion this estimate is too conservative; I would suggest a figure of at least 700 b.g.d.

Even this volume would be inadequate by the year 2000—if all the water withdrawn for use were actually consumed. This, however, is not the case now and will not be then; only a small fraction of the water withdrawn is consumed. In 1960 "consumptive use," as it is called, amounted to about 90 b.g.d. of the 320 b.g.d. withdrawn. Most of the remaining 230 b.g.d. was returned after use to the source from which it was taken, or to some other body of water (in some instances the ocean). A small fraction of the used water was piped into the ground to help maintain local water tables.

Estimates by a Senate Select Committee a few years ago projected a consumptive use of about 120 b.g.d. in 1980 and of nearly 160 b.g.d. in the year 2000, when total demand may reach 900 b.g.d. It will be apparent in Chart 3, where these projections are plotted, that agriculture accounts for the biggest consumptive use of water. It is conservatively estimated that 60 per cent of the water employed for irrigation is lost to the atmosphere as the result of evaporation directly from the soil or indirectly by transpiration through the leaves of growing plants. (The amount of water incorporated into plant tissue is insignificant; roughly 1,000 gallons of water is needed to produce about 10 cents' worth of crop.) In contrast, from 80 to 98 per cent of the water withdrawn by municipalities, industry and electric utilities is available for reuse. It is for this reason that the projected withdrawal rate of 900 b.g.d. in the year 2000 should not prove difficult to meet, whether the economically available supply is 560 b.g.d. or 700 b.g.d. Of the 900 b.g.d. that may be required in A.D. 2000 to meet human, industrial and agricultural needs, approximately 740 b.g.d. should be available for reuse.

These estimates, moreover, are pessimistic in that they make only minor allowances for reductions in industrial or agricultural demands as a result of technological changes and in that they provide for no significant increase in the cost of water to hasten such changes. Thus we must reasonably conclude that for many years beyond A.D. 2000 total water shortages for the U.S. as a whole are highly improbable.

If water is going to remain so plentiful into the 21st century, why should New York and other cities find themselves running short in 1965? The immediate answer, of course, is that there has been a five-year drought in the northeastern U.S. With the completion in 1955 of two new reservoirs in the upper reaches of the Delaware River, and with the extension of the Delaware aqueduct to a total distance of more than 120 miles, New York City believed it could satisfy its water needs until the year 2000. This confident forecast reckoned without the unprecedented drought.

There is no point in criticizing New York's decision to depend so heavily on the Delaware watershed for its future needs. The question is what New York should do now. As long ago as 1950, in an earlier water shortage, New York was advised to build a pumping station on the Hud-

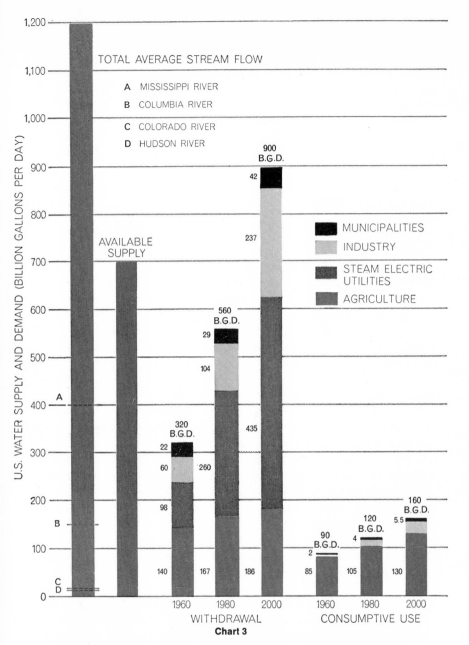

Chart 3

U.S. water supply consists of the approximately 1,200 b.g.d. that flows to the sea through the nation's waterways. This is the streamflow that results from an average precipitation volume of some 4,200 b.g.d. About 70 per cent of all precipitation returns to the atmosphere without ever reaching the sea. The average flow of four important rivers is marked on the streamflow column. The author estimates that about 700 b.g.d. of the total streamflow can be made available for use at a cost acceptable to consumers. The estimates of water withdrawal and consumptive use for 1980 and 2000 are (with slight rounding) those published a few years ago by a Senate Select Committee. The 1980 estimate is 13 per cent higher than that of the Department of Commerce shown in the illustration on the preceding page. "Consumptive use" represents the amount of water withdrawn that subsequently becomes unavailable for reuse. Except for irrigation, consumptive use of water is and will remain negligible. Thus a 700-b.g.d. supply should easily meet a 900-b.g.d. demand.

son River 65 miles north of the city to provide an emergency supply of 100 million gallons per day, or more as needed. (New York City's normal water demand is about 1.2 b.g.d. The average flow of the Hudson is around 11 b.g.d.) The State of New York gave the city permission to build the pumping station but stipulated that the station be dismantled when the emergency was over. By the time the station was built (at a point somewhat farther south than the one recommended) the drought had ended; the station was torn down without ever having been used. This July the city asked the state for permission to rebuild the station, a job that will take several months, but as of mid-August permission had not been granted.

Meanwhile there has been much talk of building atomic-energy desalination plants as the long-term solution to New York's water needs. The economic justification for such proposals has never been explained. New York now obtains its water, delivered by gravity flow to the city, for only about 15 cents per 1,000 gallons (and many consumers are charged only 12 cents). The lowest predicted cost for desalination, assuming a plant with a capacity of 250 million or more gallons per day, is a highly optimistic 30 to 50 cents per 1,000 gallons. Since a desalination plant would be at sea level, its entire output would have to be pumped; storage and conveyance together would add about 20 cents per 1,000 gallons to the basic production cost. Recent studies in our department at Johns Hopkins University have shown that if desalinated water could be produced and delivered for as little as 50 cents per 1,000 gallons, it would be cheaper to obtain fresh water from a supply 600 miles away. (The calculations assume a water demand of 100 million gallons per day.) In other words it would be much cheaper for New York City to pipe water 270 miles from the St. Lawrence River assuming that Canada gave its consent, than to build a desalination plant at the edge of town. New York City does not have to go even as far as the St. Lawrence. It has large untapped reserves in the Hudson River and in the upper watershed of the Susquehanna, no more than 150 miles way, that could meet the city's needs well beyond the year 2000.

Few cities in the U.S. have the range of alternatives open to New York. The great majority of inland cities draw their water supplies from the nearest lake or river. Of the more than 150 million Americans now served by public water supplies, nearly 100 million, or 60 per cent, are reusing water from sources that have already been used at least once for domestic sewage and industrial waste disposal. This "used" water has of course been purified, either naturally or artificially, before it reaches the consumer. Only about 25 per cent of the 25 b.g.d. now used by municipalities is obtained from aquifers, or underground sources. Such aquifers supply about 65 b.g.d. of the nation's estimated 1965 requirement of 370 b.g.d. Most of the 65 b.g.d. is merely a subterranean portion of the 1,200 b.g.d. of the precipitation flowing steadily to the sea. It is estimated, however, that from five to 10 b.g.d. is water "mined" from aquifers that have been filled over the centuries. Most of this mining is done in West Texas, New Mexico, Arizona and California.

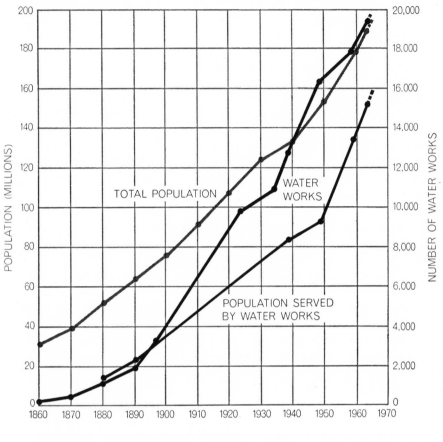

Chart 4

Growth of municipal water supplies accelerated after 1880, when less than a fourth of the U.S. population was served by waterworks. By 1939 the number served by waterworks exceeded 60 per cent and by 1963 the figure had reached nearly 80 per cent.

The fact that more than 150 million Americans can be provided with safe drinking water by municipal waterworks, regardless of their source of supply, attests the effectiveness of modern water-treatment methods. Basically the treatment consists of filtration and chlorination. The use of chlorine to kill bacteria in municipal water supplies was introduced in 1908. It is fortunate that such a cheap and readily available substance is so effective. A typical requirement is about one part of chlorine to a million parts of water (one p.p.m.). The amount of chlorine needed to kill bacteria and also to "kill" the taste of dissolved organic substances—many of which are introduced naturally when rainwater comes in contact with decaying vegetation—is adjusted by monitoring the amount of free chlorine present in the water five to 10 minutes after treatment. This residual chlorine is usually held to about .2 p.p.m. In cases where unusually large amounts of organic compounds are present in the water, causing the public to complain of a bad taste, experience has shown that the palatability of the water can often be improved simply by adding more chlorine. Contrary to a widely held impression, free chlorine itself has little taste; the "bad" taste usually attributed to chlorine is due chiefly to organic compounds that have been too lightly chlorinated. When they are more heavily chlorinated, the bad taste usually disappears.

Throughout history impure water has been a leading cause of fatal disease in man; such waterborne diseases as typhoid fever and dysentery were still common in the U.S. less than a century ago. In 1900 the U.S. death rate from typhoid fever was 35.8 per 100,000 people. If such a rate persisted today, the deaths from typhoid would far exceed those from automobile accidents. By 1936 the rate had been reduced to 2.5 per 100,000, and today the disease is almost unknown in the U.S.

In underdeveloped nations, where many cities are still without adequate water supplies, waterborne diseases are among the leading causes of death and debility. In Central and South America more than a third of 75 million people living in towns or cities with a population of more than 2,000 are without water service. Similarly, in India about a third of the urban population of 80 million are without an adequate water supply. The city of Calcutta is regarded as the endemic center of cholera for all of southeast Asia.

No general prescription can be offered for bringing clean water to the vast urban populations that still lack it. I have found in my own experience, however, that the inhabitants of communities both large and small can do much more to help themselves than is customarily recognized. If the small towns and villages of India and elsewhere wait for their central governments to install public water supplies, most of them will wait indefinitely. It is surprising how much can be accomplished with local labor and local materials, and the benefits in health are incalculable.

In the larger cities, where self-help is not feasible, municipal water systems can be built and made to pay their way if an appropriate charge is made for water and if the systems can be financed with long-term loans, as they have been financed traditionally in the U.S. Such loans, however, have only recently been made available to underdeveloped countries. A few years ago, when loans for waterworks had to be paid off in six to 12 years, the total value of external bank loans made to South American countries for water supply and sewerage projects was less than $100,000 in a six-year period. Under the leadership of the Pan-American Health Organization and the U.S. Agency for International Development bankers were encouraged to extend the repayment period to 28 or 30 years. Today the total value of bank loans made to South American countries for waterworks and sewerage systems has surpassed $660 million.

Outside the U.S., as within it, adequate water resources are generally available. The problem is to treat water as a commodity whose cost to the user must bear a fair relation to the cost of its production and delivery. The total U.S. investment in municipal waterworks is about $17.5 billion (replacement cost would approach $50 billion), or about half the nation's investment in telephone service. More significant than investment is the cost of service to the consumer. The average American family pays about $3 a month for water, which it cannot live without, compared with about $7.30 for telephone service. One might also note that the average household expenditure for alcoholic beverages is more than $15 a month. It should be clear that Americans can afford to pay for all the water they need.

The question of fair payment and allocation of costs is even more central to the problem of controlling water pollution than to the problem of providing water. Whereas 150 million Americans were served by waterworks in 1963, only about 120 million were served by sewers [see Chart 5]. Thus the wastes of nearly 70 million Americans, who live chiefly in the smaller towns and suburbs, were still being piped into backyard cesspools and septic tanks. When these devices are properly designed and the receiving soils are not overloaded, they create no particular hazard. Unfortunately in too many suburban areas neither of these criteria is met.

The principal pollution hazard arises where sewage collected by a sewerage system is discharged into a lake or river without adequate treatment or without any treatment at all [see Chart 6]. As of 1962 the wastes of nearly 15 million Americans were discharged untreated and the wastes of 2.4 million received only minor treatment. The wastes of 32.7 million were given primary treatment: passage through a settling basin, which removes a considerable portion of the suspended solid matter. Intermediate treatment, which consists of a more nearly complete removal of solids, was applied to the wastes of 7.4 million people. Secondary treatment, the most adequate form of sewage treatment, was applied to the wastes of 61.2 million people. The term "secondary treatment" covers a variety of techniques, often used in combination: extended aeration, activated sludge (an accelerated form of bacterial degradation), filtration through beds of various materials, stabilization ponds.

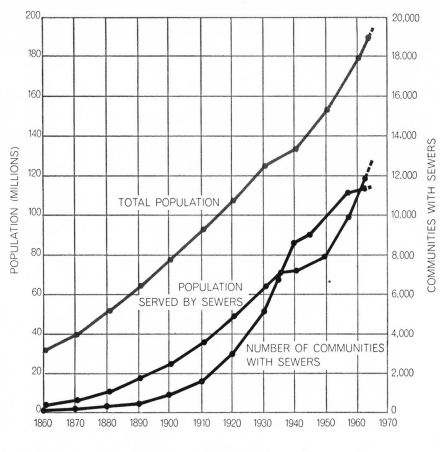

Chart 5

Growth of sewerage facilities has lagged behind the growth of community water supplies, chiefly because people are reluctant to pay taxes for what long seemed a nonessential service. Nevertheless, 63 per cent of the population was served by sewers in 1962.

It can be seen in Chart 6 that appears on page 289 that although there was a significant improvement in sewage treatment in the U.S. between 1942 and 1962, a big job remains to be done. Only in the past five years of this period did the rate of sewer installation begin to overtake population growth. The present U.S. investment in sewers and sewage-treatment works is about $12 billion (again the replacement value would be much higher). The Public Health Service estimates that replacing obsolete facilities, improving the standard of treatment and providing for population growth will require an annual investment of more than $800 million a year in treatment works for the rest of the decade. This does not

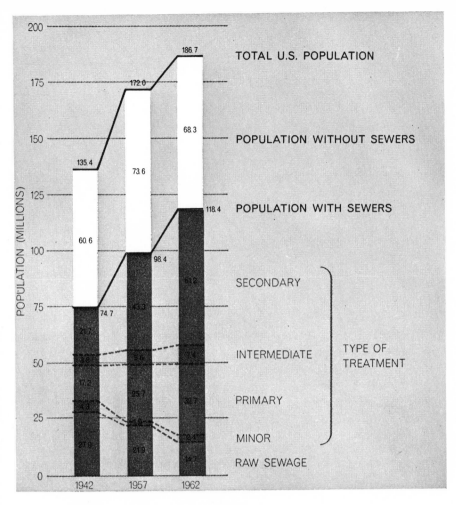

Chart 6

Race between sewers and population growth is depicted in this chart. Between 1942 and 1957 population outstripped the increase in sewerage service. Between 1957 and 1962 sewerage service grew slightly faster than population. People without sewers do not necessarily contribute to the water pollution problem if they use effective septic tanks and cesspools. The principal pollution is caused by communities—and by industries—that discharge wastes into waterways with little treatment or no treatment at all. Data for this chart and the two preceding ones were supplied by the U.S. Public Health Service.

include the cost of extending the sewage-collection systems into new urban and suburban developments. This may add another $800 million to the annual requirements, making an approximate total of more than $1.6 billion a year.

Unfortunately some municipalities have not found a satisfactory or painless method for charging their residents for this vital service. Many simply float bonds to meet capital costs and add the cost to the individual's bill for property taxes. In Baltimore (where the tax bill is completely itemized) it was decided some years ago that sewerage costs should not be included in the citizen's *ad valorem* taxes but should be made part of his water bill. In the Baltimore system the charge for sewerage service is half the water service charge. A good many other cities charge for sewerage service on a similar basis.

Cities, of course, account for only a part, and probably not the major part, of the pollution that affects the nation's waterways. Industrial pollution is a ubiquitous problem. Industrial pollutants are far more varied than those in ordinary sewage, and their removal often calls for specialized measures. Even in states where adequate pollution-control laws are on the books, there are technological, economic and practical obstacles to seeing that the laws are observed. The Federal Water Pollution Control acts of 1954 and 1962, which enlarged the role of the Public Health Service in determining the pollution of interstate waterways, have sometimes been helpful in strengthening the hand of local law-enforcement agencies.

My final topic—air pollution—is much harder to discuss in quantitative terms than water pollution, which it otherwise resembles in many ways. It is never going to be possible to provide a collection system for air pollution emissions, almost all of which result from combustion processes. Every house, every apartment, every automobile, truck, bus, factory and power plant is vented directly into the open air and presumably will have to remain so.

There are perhaps only three general approaches to controlling the amount of pollutants entering the atmosphere. One is to switch from a fuel that produces undesirable combustion products to one that produces fewer such products. Thus fuel oil produces less soot and fly ash than bituminous coal, and natural gas produces less than either. The second expedient is to employ a new technology. For example, atomic power plants produce none of the particulate and gaseous emission that result from the burning of fossil fuels. One must then decide, however, whether the radioactive by-products that are released in the environment—either in the short run or the long—by an atomic power station are more or less hazardous than the fossil-fuel by-products they replaced. The third recourse is to remove the undesired components from the vented gases. Fly ash, for example, can be largely removed by suitable devices where coal or oil is used in large volume, as in a power plant, but cannot readily be removed from the flue gases of thousands of residences. The problem of dealing with many small offending units also arises in trying to reduce the unburned hydrocarbons and carbon monoxide emitted by millions of automobiles.

At this point it is worth asking: Why should air pollution be considered objectionable? Many people enjoy the smell of the pollutants released by a steak sizzling on a charcoal grill or by dry leaves burning in the fall. The cigarette smoker obviously enjoys the smoke he draws into his lungs. In other words, a pollutant per se need not necessarily be regarded as a nuisance. If by accident or design the exhaust gases emitted by a diesel bus had a fragrant aroma (or worse yet, led to physiological addiction), not many people would complain about traffic fumes.

The criteria of what constitutes an objectionable air pollutant must therefore be subjectively defined, unless, of course, one can demonstate that a particular pollutant is a hazard to health. In the absence of a demonstrated health hazard the city dweller would probably list his complaints somewhat as follows: he objects to soot and dirt, he does not want his eyes to burn and water, he dislikes traffic fumes and he wishes he could see the clear blue sky more often.

Many conferences have been held and many papers written on the possible association of air pollution with disease. As might be expected, firm evidence of harmfulness is difficult to obtain. The extensive epidemiological data collected in the U.S. on smoking and human health suggest that in general place of residence has a minor influence on the incidence of lung cancer compared with the smoking habit itself. British statistics, however, can be interpreted to show that at times there is something harmful in the British air. In any event, it will be difficult to demonstrate conclusively—no matter how much one may believe it to be so—that air pollution is associated with long-term deterioration of the human organism. Eric J. Cassell of the Cornell University Medical College recently summarized the situation as follows: "I do not think that it is wrong to say that we do not even know what disease or diseases are caused by everyday pollution of our urban air. . . . We have a cause, but no disease to go with it."

Two diseases frequently mentioned as possibly associated with air pollution are chronic bronchitis and pulmonary emphysema. In Britain some investigators have found strong associations between chronic bronchitis and the level of air pollution, as measured by such indexes as fuel use, sulfur dioxide in the air and sootfall. In California the death rate from emphysema increased fourfold in the seven-year period from 1950 to 1957. This increase may indicate nothing more than the fact that older people go to California to retire, but there is objective evidence that emphysematous patients in Los Angeles showed improved lung function when allowed to breathe carefully filtered air for 48 hours.

In response to mounting public concern, and the urging of President Johnson, Congress two years ago passed the Clean Air Act, which states in its preamble that "Federal financial assistance and leadership is essential for the development of cooperative Federal, state, regional and local programs designed to prevent and control air pollution." The regulatory abatement procedures authorized in the act are similar to those found in the most recent Water Pollution Control Act. When an interstate pollution problem is identified, the Public Health Service is empowered, as a first step, to call a conference of state and local agencies. The second step is to call a public hearing, and the third step, if needed, is to bring a court action against the offenders.

The Clean Air Act takes special cognizance of air pollution caused by motor vehicles; it requires the Secretary of Health, Education and Welfare to report periodically to Congress on progress made on control devices. He is also invited to recommend any new legislation he feels is warranted. Eventually the secretary may help to decide if all new U.S. motor vehicles should be equipped with exhaust-control systems, such as "afterburners," to reduce the large amounts of unburned hydrocarbons and carbon monoxide that are now released.

California studies in the 1950's showed that exhaust gases accounted for 65 per cent of all the unburned hydrocarbons then produced by motor vehicles. Another 15 per cent represented evaporation from the fuel tank and carburetor, and 20 per cent escaped from the vent of the crankcase. As a first step in reducing these emissions California began in 1961 to require the use of crankcase blowby devices, which became standard on all U.S. cars beginning with the 1963 models.

A new California law will require exhaust-control systems on all 1966 automobiles and light trucks sold in the state. The law is intended to reduce by 70 or 80 per cent the amount of hydrocarbons now present in exhaust gases and to reduce the carbon monoxide by 60 per cent. All the carbon monoxide is generated by combustion and is now released in the exhaust. The steady rise in carbon monoxide vented into the atmosphere of Los Angeles is plotted in Chart 7.

No one questions that an affluent society can afford to spend its money without a strict accounting of benefits received. Any reasonable expenditure that promises to improve the quality of life in the modern city should be welcomed. It is not obvious, however, that any American city except Los Angeles will be significantly benefited by the installation of exhaust-control systems in motor vehicles. The cost of these systems will not be trivial. At an estimated $40 to $50 per car, such systems would add more than $300 million to the sales price of new cars in an eight-million-car year—and this does not include the annual cost of their inspection and maintenance. If one objective of reducing air pollution caused by automobiles is to increase the life expectancy of the city dweller, or simply to make his life more pleasant, it can be argued that $300 million a year could be spent more usefully in other directions.

In most large cities, for example, the electric utilities consume up to half of all fuel burned. Most utilities have made reasonable efforts to reduce the emission of soot and fly ash; virtually all new power plants,

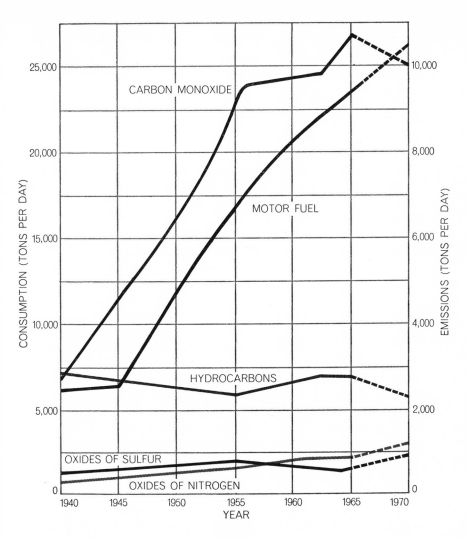

Chart 7

Los Angeles air pollution is tied closely to the steep rise in automobile use in Los Angeles County. This chart compares gasoline consumption with the computed output from all sources of carbon monoxide, hydrocarbons, oxides of nitrogen and oxides of sulfur. Motor vehicles produce only small amounts of the last two substances and their output has been controlled chiefly by curbs on the emission of pollutants by industry. Carbon monoxide and hydrocarbon emissions should decline when cars start carrying exhaust-control systems.

and many old ones, are now equipped with devices capable of removing a large fraction of such emissions. Utilities, however, are still under pressure, both from the public and from supervising agencies, to use the cheapest fuels available. This means that in New York and other eastern-seaboard cities the utilities burn large volumes of residual fuel oil imported from abroad, which happens to contain between 2.5 and 3 per cent of sulfur, compared with only about 1.7 per cent for domestic fuel oil. When the oil is burned, sulfur dioxide is released. Recent studies show that the level of sulfur dioxide in New York City air is almost twice that found in other large cities.

Sulfur dioxide is difficult to remove from stack gases, but it is estimated that for about $1 a barrel most of the sulfur could be removed from the oil before it is burned. For the volume of oil burned by the Consolidated Edison Company in New York City the added cost would come to about $15 million annually. If the cost were divided among Consolidated Edison's three million customers, the average electric bill would be increased about $5 per year. One would like to know how this expenditure would compare in improving the quality of New York City's air with New York's pro rata share of more than $300-million-a-year investment that would be required by the installation of exhaust-control systems in motor vehicles. That share would be on the order of $8 million a year. Perhaps New Yorkers should insist on both investments. But these are only two of many options, all of them expensive. It is the responsibility of the public health officer to make choices and assign priorities, even while admitting that air pollution is never beneficial.

One must also recall that when large-scale changes are contemplated, the whole spectrum of society is involved. Rarely do all forces march forward in step, particularly where public policy and scientific verity are not crystal clear. Competitive forces delay correctives until public opinion rises in wrath and pushes for action on an *ad hoc* and intuitive basis.

Let me sum up by observing that in the case of water supply the accomplishments of the U.S. have been extraordinarily good, not only in the prevention of waterborne and water-associated diseases but also in providing water generously for comfortable living in most places at most times. The prospect for the future is likewise good. The realities are that we are not running out of water and that we are capable of managing our water resources intelligently.

In the area of water and air pollution our successes are only partial. Rapid urbanization and industrialization have intensified the problems of controlling both. At the same time one must concede that there is much stronger scientific justification for mounting vigorous programs to abate water pollution than to abate air pollution. Nevertheless, public pressure on behalf of the latter is increasing, and as has happened so often in the past, we may find action running ahead of knowledge. This is not necessarily to be deplored.

My own view coincides with that recently expressed by P. B. Medawar of University College London at a symposium on the interaction of man and his environment. "We are not yet qualified," he said, "to prescribe for the medical welfare of our grandchildren. . . . I should say that present skills are sufficient for present ills."

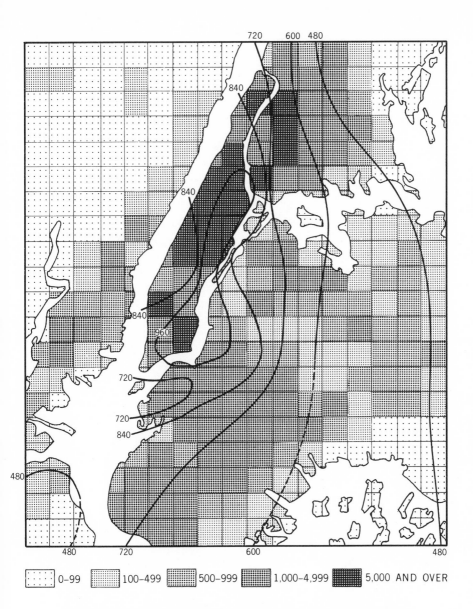

New York air pollution contains large components of sulfur dioxide and particulate matter (soot and fly ash). The grid shows for the central part of New York City the computed output of sulfur dioxide per square mile in tons per year based on fuel used for space heating and producing hot water. About 55 per cent more sulfur dioxide is released into the atmosphere by such "point sources" as power stations and industrial plants. The total figure for the entire city is estimated at more than 600,000 tons a year. The grid is taken from a larger map prepared under the direction of Ben Davidson of the Geophysical Sciences Department of New York University. The contour lines show the average dustfall levels in tons per year as measured by New York City's Department of Air Pollution Control.

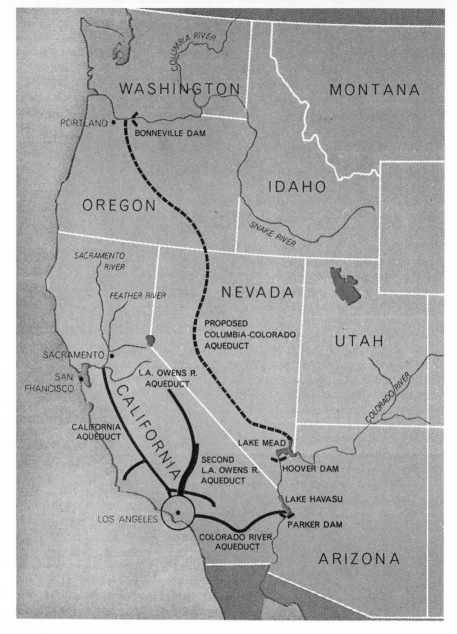

Distant transportation of water has been practiced in the West for many years. Los Angeles now has three major sources of supply to meet its daily demand of 470 million gallons. About 15 per cent comes through the 300-mile Colorado aqueduct, completed in 1941, about 21 per cent is pumped from local wells and the remainder, 64 per cent, comes from Owens Valley, 340 miles to the north. An enlargement of the Owens Valley supply system is nearly completed. Meanwhile the state is building a new 444-mile aqueduct that will deliver water from the Sacramento River to southern California. Proposals are now being made to move water from the Columbia River, which accounts for more than 12 per cent of total U.S. streamflow, to the arid Southwest. The water might be taken from below Bonneville Dam and diverted some 800 miles to Lake Mead on the Colorado River, following the general route shown (*broken line*).

Values in the Control
of Environment*

Progress in the public health movement has much in common with the development of any other movement. It is marked by rapid changes of concept in some periods, by slow methodical advance in others, by changing standards and by fetiches and taboos. It is important, therefore, to stop in one's activities at reasonable intervals long enough to take stock of such varying methods, standards and concepts as are in use, in order to evaluate specific forms of work in their relation to the general program.

In any historical review of a subject or a movement, it is frequently convenient and sometimes valuable to divide progress into chronological eras. In so doing in our own field, the era of environmental sanitation is commonly assigned to the latter half of the nineteenth century. We are now living in the era of personal hygiene. Between the two we rode blithely through the era of infectious disease work. In some circles, we take pride in having left behind us such vestiges of the dark ages as control of water supplies or the control of communicable diseases. When a new era arises, all "progressive" workers must climb aboard the band wagon and throw over the sides the accumulated experience of past eras. Although the monetary system (disease) remains the same, the standard

* Reprinted from *American Journal of Public Health*, Vol. 15, No. 3 (March, 1925), pp. 189–94. Copyright by the American Public Health Association, Inc. Read at the General Sessions of the American Public Health Association at the Fifty-third Annual Meeting at Detroit, Michigan, Oct. 22, 1924.

bearers changing from gold to silver standards, or vice versa, have the fond hope that the currency of the realm has thus been improved.

There appears to the writer to be a serious fallacy underlying attempts to subdivide progress into eras, when such subdivisions are used as the bases of future activity and education. The fallacy lies in the assumption that the recognition of the causes of a particular disease is equivalent to the elimination of the effects of that disease.

The serious outcome of such a method of discrete, rather than consecutive, historical progress as outlined briefly above may be, and sometimes is, a relaxation in the control of environment, and not an adjustment of control with a revaluation of control measures. The profession is thus in danger of losing the fruits of past accomplishments by chasing, too exclusively, the will of the wisps of the future. In other words, the thesis which this paper seeks to emphasize is embodied in the biblical injunction: "these things ye should do, while not leaving these other things undone." The mutual exclusiveness of activity at various eras is neither intelligent nor does it take cognizance of the errors in the teachings of the past. With these philosophical observations behind us, we may pass to a more definite analysis of our problem.

Every undertaking has a past, a present and a future aspect. It is important in evaluating the significance of any procedure, therefore, to indicate its advantages in the past, its accomplishments in the present and its promise for the future. The control of environment appears to me to merit such a threefold review, for it has great achievements to its credit in the past; it demands a maintenance of efficiency and, in some communities, an initiation of efficiency, in the present; and it holds forth a bright vista for the future.

One method of developing the above theme would be to launch upon an elaborate statistical procedure in which the various major causes of death and sickness would be quantitatively assigned to the realms of adjustment by attack upon environment or upon the individual. Such a procedure would give delight to the watchful biometrician and geneticist, whose principal pursuit in life appears to be to leap from ambush upon the youthful and innocent wanderer in the forest of numbers, for, although frequently willing to acknowledge some of the fruits of labor in control of environment, they are stricken stark mad at some of the other claims in public health work.

In order to avoid this ambuscade, the writer prefers to select the major causes of sickness and death and to discuss in general their relation to environment and to point out where past performance has made and future promise may make their impress. It should be emphasized that the discussion of the control of environment and its effects should not be confused with the rather useless attempt at evaluation of personnel, for the part which engineer, laboratory worker, statistician, physiologist or physician has played or is to play in the environmental program is regulated by the time, the place and the nature of the problem involved. We are concerned here with the principles of activity rather than with the professional titles of the persons who are to do the work, although obviously the nonmedical sanitarian has had and should continue to have the training and experience necessary for the major part of this type of work.

Barring the comfortable plan of assigning all accomplishments in health improvement to improved human stock, and all future victories to further favorable hereditary influences, it is usually admitted that the major nondebatable fruits of conscious effort in past decades are those of sanitation, *e.g.*, the provision of safe water supplies, the adequate disposal of sewage, the eradication of mosquitoes, the control of milk and other food supplies and similar so-called elementary undertakings. It is not usually a matter of controversy that some of the major achievements of the past—the control of typhoid fever, dysentery, cholera, yellow fever, typhus fever and plague (in so far as this last disease has been controlled)—have been made primarily through the attacks upon the environment of man. It is not necessary, therefore, to dwell upon past achievements, but it has not been so frequently pointed out that these past accomplishments have many future implications.

Although in 1920 the typhoid fever death rate had reached a figure of less than 8 per 100,000 in the Registration Area of the United States, there are still literally hundreds of communities in this country and elsewhere which are confronted with excessive typhoid fever death rates. When we compare our own figures in the Registration Area with those in some foreign countries, we have little reason for complacent abandonment of communal sanitation. In addition we cannot help realizing that it is becoming increasingly difficult to retain even what has been gained in the case of typhoid fever when we consider the enormously increasing pollution of our streams by human wastes. Few health officers appear to realize the enormous problems confronting the American public in the situations arising in such streams as the Ohio and Illinois rivers, where the number of persons contributing to the sewage pollution and the areas under consideration are not matched by any other stream in the world. The growth of population in this country has been rapid in past decades. We are now in the period of increasing dependence upon the more highly polluted streams for drinking water. The increasing use of large rivers and lakes as sources of municipal drinking water is superimposing new problems of water and sewage treatment upon the older and more familiar difficulties. Most of us engaged in this work are well aware of the necessities of developing more complete methods of water and sewage treatment than any now available. The subjecting of waters to double treatments and the ever-increasing refinement of sewage purification are direct results of the dwindling resources of safe water.

Those future difficulties and defects in past practices offer to-day fields for experimentation and research in water and sewage treatment which should delight the most fastidious of searchers for new truths. The control of situations involved in the important public health problems associated with but a single food in man's daily needs is hardly made easier by the ill-advised public statements of some health officers that "water as the transmitter of typhoid fever has been much exaggerated; the real offenders are lettuce salads." As if to warn us of our human frailties, every now and then the ugly head of enteric fever epidemic arises in water-borne form, in various sections throughout the country.

Even assuming that, in such environmental diseases as typhoid fever, we have reached in some areas a degree of successful control, we must not ignore the obvious fact that many communities, aggregating millions of people are still without the most elementary requirements of safe drinking water and of adequate disposal of human excreta. It is doubtful whether there are any states in the Union in which even 75 per cent of the population are safeguarded beyond the necessity of improved water and sewerage equipment to meet even moderately desirable standards.

Aside from the need for these new installations, it is well to emphasize most strongly the obvious importance of maintaining the present degree of control where it has reached a successful point. The maintenance of an environmental advantage in public health can certainly not be secondary to the original establishment of this advantage. We are well aware of the skeletons of plants erected which were abandoned through public neglect. The ghosts of environmental diseases may have been safely laid in literature, but certainly not in fact. Typhoid fever, plague and cholera still take their thousands in toll. Knowledge as to their control is at hand, but their elimination is still an active part of the health worker's day.

Probably one of the most remarkable demonstrations in public health accomplishment in this country is the malaria prevention work in the southern and southwestern states. No single disease causes more discomfort or more economic loss than malaria. The primary attack upon it has been made through measures directed at changes in environment. Although the disease itself is ages old, the developing technology of its control in different areas is one of the most interesting and novel of demonstrations of to-day in preventive medicine.

The relative adjustments of large scale drainage projects, oiling measures, fish culture, house screening, domestic animal screens, larvicides and quinine prophylaxis measures to meet the manifold exigencies of a thousand and one areas are both amazing in their complexity and in their fruitfulness for further study. The incidence of malaria covers the globe, with millions afflicted in India, in the Ukraine, in Russia, in Italy, in Greece, in Palestine and in South America. It is interesting to reflect upon the importance of malaria control when we realize that for over 25 years in Russia alone not less than 3,000,000 cases have been reported each year, with almost 5,000,000 in the first nine months of 1923. Although quinine prophylaxis has been available for many years as a means of attack upon malaria, mosquito control through community measures survives as a major procedure. The prevention of malaria to-day remains a branch of environmental sanitation and of public administration. Certainly in this field the future holds no darkness for engineer, biologist or statistician.

If we follow man from birth to death over the bridge of life, we encounter many enemies to life and well-being which offer future prospect of partial or complete subjugation by environmental measures. The greatest percentage of mortality to-day is during the first five years of man's existence and the major causes of this mortality are the diseases of the respiratory and enteric group. A careful review of existing literature and statistical data warrants the view that at least part of these tolls, and by no means a minor part, are closely correlated with environmental influences, an important one of which is the relative concentration of human beings within the home. Tuberculosis of children under five, a possible sequel of rickets, and pneumonia have in recent laboratory and large scale experimentation been sufficiently closely identified with absence of sunlight and adequate ventilation to warrant inclusion in the diseases susceptible to partial control and alleviation by environmental improvement. Recent summaries of the experience of the United States Children's Bureau and the New York Association for Improving the Condition of the Poor indicate markedly the profound influence on infant and child mortality of congestion within the living quarters. With artificial feeding, race and nativity, frequency of birth, employment during pregnancy carefully corrected for, the statistical data appear to indicate major correlations of infant mortality with housing congestion.

In adolescence and early maturity, tuberculosis in its various forms is the outstanding wielder of the scythe of misery. The tremendous influence of social and physical environment on the development of this endemic disease has been pointed out for decades. Lack of fresh air and sunlight and overcrowding, with its attendant spreading of mass infection, are certainly factors to be reckoned with in the control of the disease.

More recently, in the Year Book for 1922 and 1923 of the Association of Tuberculosis Clinics of Greater New York, Inc., the influence of better housing conditions in raising resistance to tuberculosis is strikingly brought out by comparative statistics for similar populations, independent of race and color. For example, the Jews, with well-established resistance, in the same year show a death rate from tuberculosis of 70 per 100,000 in the group living in the old tenements of the Manhattan lower east side of New York, of 59 in the central Tremont District of the Bronx

where there is better housing and of only 39 per 100,000 in the Browns-
ville District of Brooklyn, an area of spaciousness and individual homes,
this last "a rate as low as that of Framingham, Massachusetts, the seat of
the well-known tuberculosis control demonstration of the National Tuberculosis Association."

Even the Italian and colored populations show the advantages of the
modern planning and housing in the Corona district of Queens Borough,
with a rate of 69, and in the district around Jamaica, noted for its individual home development, with a rate of 64. Here we have large-scale
demonstrations of a situation normally not available for proof. It is
reasonable to suppose that at least one factor in the spread of tuberculosis
may be associated with environment, although we must be particularly
cautious in correlating two such intricately connected social conditions
as housing and health.

Although the control of the respiratory diseases has not advanced
sufficiently far to warrant claims of any kind, there is still some evidence,
much of it debatable and requiring more careful confirmation, that
housing, ventilation and adequate provision of fresh air may be salutary
aids in reducing mortality.

During man's productive life, he is confronted with hundreds of industrial hazards, whether at work in the mine, in the steel mill, in the
shop, in the office or in the open air. All of these hazards, whether specific
in the process or remotely associated with the occupation, have environmental implications. The elimination of the hazards of mining, of pot-
teries, of printing presses, of Bessemer furnaces, of glass work, of dyestuffs
and chemical manufacture, of caisson and tunnel work, all require the
joint efforts of engineer, chemist, physicist and physiologist. They are
not susceptible to the usual vaccine and sera prophylaxes and therapies.
They must be improved through the aid of these in part, but in the majority of instances the attack upon them must have its approach through
the modification of industrial mechanisms and processes, supported by
the personal hygiene of the worker.

Industry obviously is primarily the working ground of the engineer.
Upon him rests the development of process, the introduction of new
equipment, the elimination of the hazards of the old methods, machinery
and materials. Although the medical officer has frequently ignored the
importance of this amazing environmental field of public health effort,
unfortunately the engineer all too frequently has also avoided trespassing
therein. The improvement of working conditions in industry, by developing standards through research and by introducing resultant improvements in lighting, ventilation and sanitation, must be in major part the
province of the engineer.

When we consider the study of the elimination of the "process hazards," such as dusts, poisons, infections, heat and humidity, excessive

cold, compressed air work, noise and vibration, the engineer's contribution in the team play of physiologist, chemist and physician is much greater than the engineer himself has sensed. The problems are new, complex and important. They await attack.

In all that has so far been said, the importance of environmental control for the present and the future has rested upon a narrow definition of environmental activity. I should like, for a moment, to expand upon the possibilities of the future by envisaging a physical environment delicately adjusted to the optimum physiological requirements of the individual. Heretofore, we have emphasized the control of the negative side of environment by attempting to eliminate and prevent those "accidents" of this mundane sphere to which man has been exposed, such as typhoid fever, malaria, yellow fever, industrial accidents, acute infections, etc. Little or nothing has so far been contributed to the positive phase of environmental control; that is, the maintenance of a higher level of physiological efficiency at all times by the proper adjustment of the factors in environment. Obviously, our knowledge of the underlying principles of the positive effects of such adjustments of housing, ventilation and heating, upon man are exceedingly meager, but no one will question that the individual's adaptation to this world may be improved by changing the individual or by modifying his physical environment. How far this latter form of control may be extended we do not predict, but its limitations at present are in the almost complete absence of positive adjustment of environment, and the very fragmentary knowledge of the relation which the controllable physical world actually bears to physiological function. Both of these limitations time must necessarily remove, for they are limitations of inertia and ignorance.

We are even a longer distance away from an understanding and control of that environment of Krause which "includes every mundane experience which, directly or indirectly, may exert an effect on the constitution and function of tissues." But to state that we are far away in understanding and control is no barrier to our striving toward an accomplishment which will be immeasurable in its results for human welfare.

The conservative conclusion appears to be that, as long as man does not carry on his existence "in vacuo"; as long as he is in continual contact with his own and other environment; as long as his resistance to many diseases is dependent upon the improvement of his environment; as long as we may fortify man's natural defensive mechanisms by artificial bolstering; just so long will the control of environment be an important element in public health progress. It is undoubtedly true that to do the things enumerated above in the most logical and economical fashion will require continual adjustment of method and of thought with advances of knowledge. It certainly is not true that any axioms developed since the

latter half of the nineteenth century should cause a cessation of environmental control. They should cause modifications, revaluations and retest-
ing in a few instances, but certainly not abandonment of past successful
accomplishments and future promises.

Experience and experiment will demonstrate in increasing measure
the advantage of providing for man from birth to old age a healthy dwelling, in a carefully planned city, with protected food supplies, safe working conditions, and protection against insects, rodents and bacteria and
their ravages. The acceptance of the above pronouncement does not
involve any reflections of doubt upon the efficacy of diphtheria antitoxins,
of smallpox vaccines, of annual medical examinations, of the large number of other extra-environmental accomplishments which are such amazing forerunners of a public health millennium. It is conceivable that the
scientist may continue to attack disease through two media, environment
and individual, with greater results than by abandoning each one in turn
when new standard bearers appear in succeeding years. The public,
volatile in mind and in action, delights in changing flags. It is the scientist
who should apply the brakes to skidding principles of action.

In closing, I may be pardoned a parting word to my conferees in the
field of environmental sanitation. Much emphasis has been given in the
preceding discussion to the failure of some workers to recognize the
present and future possibilities of environmental control in public health
work. It cannot but fail to appear, after study of this situation, that this
same failure to take advantage of the fruitful opportunities before us has
been the striking characteristic in many instances of both pedagogic and
the practicing engineer. Engineering in public health has connoted water
supply, sewage and refuse collection and treatment in most of its history.
Engineering pedagogy has followed orthodox practice by devoting most
of its energies to the elucidation of the principles of these restricted fields.

The intent of this paper is not only to indicate a fruitful continued
field for environmental control in the public health program, but to point
out to the engineer the wonderful prospect for the application of intelligent research, careful practice and interesting accomplishment awaiting
him in the fields of malaria control, housing design, city planning, industrial hygiene and sanitation, food handling, etc., in the adjustment of the
environment to the maximum advantage of the individual. Perhaps the
mistaken coma in environmental control has had its origin in the unconscious state of that foremost exponent of environmental regulation of past
decades, the sanitary engineer himself.

Changing Public Health Practices
and Problems*

Within the last 2 weeks an important professional group in the United States attempted to formulate certain primary principles regarding the development of a national health program. As its major bases it assumed that (1) the health of the people is a direct concern of government and a national public health policy directed toward all groups of the population should be formulated; (2) adequate medical care is an essential element of public health and local, state, and federal governments need to supplement present efforts of the medical profession to provide it; and (3) the problem of economic need and the problem of providing adequate medical care are not identical and may require different approaches for their solution.

The crystallization of the recognition of these principles in 1937 is perhaps more important than the principles themselves, for after all they were succinctly summarized as far back as 1854 by Sir John Simon in the City of London Reports when he first recommended the creation of a national Ministry of Public Health, to care, as he put it, for "the physical necessities of human life." It is likewise no novelty to accept with increas-

* Reprinted from *American Journal of Public Health*, Vol. 27, No. 10 (October, 1937), pp. 1,029–1,035. Copyright by the American Public Health Association, Inc. Read before the Annual Conference of Health Officers and Public Health Nurses, Saratoga Springs, N.Y., June 24, 1937.

ing seriousness the old concept that the saving of lives or the postpone-
ment of death are the major purposes of health work. When we couple
with these objectives the maintenance or evaluation of physical and
mental.efficiency, we have established for the present at least the basic
goals of public health service. The definition of these services, the evaluation of technics for accomplishing and providing them, and the criteria
of progress in accomplishment, are again subject matters which have
long held the attention of the public health profession.

What is important in the pronouncement of the principles noted
above, is that the time has apparently arrived for a universal agreement
upon objectives, tacitly accepted by some and publicly rejected by others
in past years. Let us discuss, for a moment, their implications for public
health practice.

In less than 100 years the expectation of life at birth has increased
from 35 to between 60 and 65 years in the United States. The major part
of this increase in expectancy has been accomplished largely in the control
and reduction of communicable diseases.

Concurrently with this change, profound changes in population distribution, both as to age and as to numbers, have taken place. The leading causes of death have in less than a quarter of a century shifted in
major aspects.

That these changes should have reached a critical turning point in
the last few years has been emphasized to a greater extent than ordinarily,
largely because we have just passed through a depression and post-
depression period. Striking prophecies as to the problems of public health
of the future, however, antedated the depression. For example, in the
evaluation of the Cattaraugus County Health Demonstration in 1931,
Winslow pointed out with uncanny vision the following forerunners of
the principles of 1937:

> 1. The one great outstanding lesson of the Cattaraugus County
> Health Demonstration is the urgent importance, the great difficulty,
> and the high cost of adequate health service for rural communities.
> 2. There is obviously but one way out of this difficulty—state aid.
> 3. Surely the most prosperous nation in the world's history must
> find a way to equalize the distribution of the fruits of medical and
> sanitary science through all its areas.

These conclusions were written before and not during one of the
worst depression periods which this country has experienced. Strangely
enough, the depression period, through the emphasis on the necessity of
supplying adequate medical care for the indigent poor, has given the
fillip to the crystallization of principles enunciated in the early part of
this paper.

To put these principles into action, it is important to summarize the changes in concept regarding disease prevention which have occurred in the last 25 years and upon the basis of which future perspective and method must rest. Fortunately, within the past 2 years, critical analyses of these questions have been made on each level of government and by voluntary groups interested in the scientific methodology of disease prevention and the promotion of health. Selected examples of these recent investigations may elaborate certain of the problems of the future.

Minnesota

Within the past year the Minnesota State Planning Board, through a subcommittee on public health, has attempted an evaluation of its public health practices and an exposition of its public health program for the future. The findings of that committee in general terms are applicable to the problems elsewhere in the United States.

It places emphasis, first of all, upon the fact that the 7 leading causes of death in Minnesota today are, in the order of their quantitative importance:

1. Heart disease
2. Cancer
3. External causes
4. Cerebral hemorrhage
5. Pneumonia
6. Nephritis
7. Tuberculosis

The committee further emphasizes that these were not always the 7 leading causes of death as is illustrated in the tabulation listed in the report and reproduced in this paper as Table 1.

The changes in causes of death have come about because of radical changes in the character of population. This in turn is the result of the fact that the group of communicable diseases which once took a heavy toll of life has now become of relatively slight importance. When to these diseases we add accomplishments in the reduction of smallpox, diphtheria, and typhoid fever, we find a population of a changing age composition that has escaped the hazards of infancy and contagious diseases, and has entered a period of life when it is confronted by hazards of a totally different character.

Of the 7 major causes of death, only 2, tuberculosis and pneumonia, are communicable in character and it is unfortunately true that of the entire group of leading causes of death only these 2 show a downward trend.

The remaining 5 present a public health problem radically different from those which the public health profession has attacked in the past.

Table 1
Seven Leading Causes of Death
(Report of Minnesota State Planning Board, December, 1936)

Rank	1910	1915	1920	1925	1930	1935
1	Tuberculosis	Heart Disease	Heart Disease	Heart Disease	Heart Disease	Heart Disease
2	Heart Disease	Tuberculosis	Cancer	Cancer	Cancer	Cancer
3	Pneumonia	Pneumonia	Tuberculosis	External Causes	External Causes	External Causes
4	External Causes	External Causes	Pneumonia	Pneumonia	Cerebral Hemorrhage	Cerebral Hemorrhage
5	Cancer	Cancer	External Causes	Cerebral Hemorrhage	Pneumonia	Pneumonia
6	Diarrheal Diseases of Children	Nephritis	Influenza	Nephritis	Nephritis	Nephritis
7	Nephritis	Cerebral Hemorrhage	Nephritis	Tuberculosis	Tuberculosis	Tuberculosis

These causes are in the degenerative diseases group, comparable with the obsolescence and depreciation of physical equipment with which the engineer has been familiar for years. They do not lend themselves to the simple mass community attack so familiar in the sanitation field and to a lesser degree in the field of communicable disease control. Their very nature, however, makes them more amenable to preventive measures, wherever these are understood, and to alterations in the hygiene of the individual.

As the Minnesota report so strikingly concludes, the leading causes of death today "represent the field of adult hygiene, a field of medicine the interest of which to both the individual and the state must be, for some time to come, a matter of increasing concern and importance."

Massachusetts

In the report of the Special Commission to Study and Investigate Public Health Laws and Policies of the Commonwealth of Massachusetts (December 2, 1936), the commission cautions the citizens of Massachusetts not to rest too easily upon the public health achievements of the past and the favorable conditions of the present. It, too, points with pride to the enviable records in the control of smallpox, typhoid fever, and diphtheria, in the remarkable reductions in tuberculosis and infant mortality, to the first state cancer and pneumonia programs, to an excellent syphilis control program, and to the very successful operations in the milk and sanitation and sewage disposal fields.

Although the commission takes great pride in these achievements, it warns that the governmental structure upon which public health programs of the future are to be constructed must be adapted to the changing needs and problems of society.

In Massachusetts, as in Minnesota, strengthening of local public health administration with increasing influence of the state, both in administration and in financial responsibility, is suggested.

As in most other instances the commission takes great care to indicate that it is not opposed to the theory of the greatest possible degree of local autonomy, "but believes that in certain matters it must be amended lest it fall into disrepute and disappear."

In Massachusetts, as elsewhere, renewed emphasis appears on the need for greater coordination of public health activities, voluntary and official, to avoid duplication and conflict.

A demand for increased professional ability of persons employed in public health work is given equal importance with the governmental structure under which they labor. In this precept the Massachusetts Commission's findings parallel those of other investigations.

As to the scope of proper public health activity it recognizes that:

> Within recent years there has been a progressive broadening of the
> scope of public health. It is equally apparent that with the changing
> social and economic structure it becomes impossible to define what
> should be the desirable limits of public health activity. It seems inevit-
> able, however, that government will more and more render certain es-
> sential services, and it is therefore important that there should be a
> guiding philosophy as to the relationship between these personal serv-
> ices and the private practice of medicine.

Maryland

The Rockefeller Foundation has just completed for the State of Maryland a review of its public health administration, carried out under the
general direction of a sub-committee of the Maryland State Planning
Commission.

The purposes of this review were to assemble sufficient information
to give a composite picture of the present status of state and county health
administration in Maryland in its relation to government in general, to
closely allied official agencies, and to nonofficial agencies engaged in
rendering important health services. Preeminent in the findings are the
emphases upon the necessity of trained and efficient personnel, upon the
functional integration of the component parts of the state organization
and of the local subdivisions thereof, upon the desirability of extensive
service in health education, and upon the developments of comprehensive venereal disease and tuberculosis programs.

It emphasizes, as in Minnesota and in Massachusetts, the great importance of so integrating the public health activities of the state as to
curtail and prevent the scattering through various state agencies of activities which should be functions of the health department.

So important did the investigators find the interrelation of public
health activities with other governmental necessities and duties that
they recommend strongly the creation of an experimental county undertaking, for the development of an integrated public administration
unit, wherein the various services of government, such as public health,
education, social welfare, economic welfare, etc, may be administered as
interrelated members of a unified county program. Their recognition of
the inter-competitive phases of public health activities with all the other
demands upon government led to the desirability of developing such an
experimental county administrative unit. One of the major needs in
Maryland as elsewhere would appear to be a horizontal uplifting of these
several services of government, rather than an undue emphasis on the
vertical uplift of individual services. As the public health demands upon
government funds increase, this integration of collateral governmental

operations with public health activity will assume an increasingly important position. The development of such integration is strongly recommended in the Maryland report. It is an effort to anticipate the results of undue competition for public money and service rather than to pay at a later date the penalties of the failure to recognize their significance.

Federal

The great impetus given to the public health movement by the financial aid included in the Social Security Act is best exemplified by the 6 point program of activity which Dr. Thomas Parran, Surgeon General of the U.S. Public Health Service, has recently announced. On the federal level of government this program supports and parallels the thinking represented in the state surveys herein summarized. Dr. Parran proposes—

1. To finish the job of wiping out tuberculosis.
2. To wipe out the dread disease syphilis, "the end results of which crowd our jails, our poorhouses, and our insane asylums."
3. To make available to people everywhere facilities for the proper diagnosis and treatment of cancer, which in his opinion would reduce by 20 per cent the deaths from this disease.
4. To reduce the "disgracefully high" death rate of mothers in child birth and of babies in their first month of life.
5. To correct conditions resulting from improper diet.
6. To restore crippled children to lives of usefulness.

These objectives require high degrees of governmental coordination and integration, changing concepts and methods in the attack on disease and expanding horizons of operation.

Voluntary Associations

Without reviewing in detail the contributions of different voluntary groups, reference should be made to the studies by the Milbank Foundation under the late Dr. Sydenstricker; the recent publication of the New York Tuberculosis and Health Association, *Hospital Care for the Tuberculous in Metropolitan New York; American Medicine*, issued by the American Foundation; and the report, *Public Health and Social Problems in the United States of America*, sponsored by the Health Organization of the League of Nations and the U.S. Public Health Service.

The last report is particularly striking in its reflections on consolidation of federal health agencies, and on the relation of federal to state and local governments. It comments particularly upon the fact that the last National Board of Health in the United States created in 1879 was repealed in 1882.

The concluding observations of this commission of foreign experts sponsored by the League of Nations is of more than special interest to students of public health practice in the United States.

It is useful to emphasize the impression made upon the visiting European hygienist by the impact of this world which is so new to him. In the first place, he is astounded by its size and its diversity, its considerable resources, the habits, methods of work, and aspirations of its people. He is even more bewildered by its constitution, its administrative machinery, its varying laws, and the special powers of the individual states. He is amazed by the multiplicity and diversity of its medical, public health, and social problems, requiring for their solution varying methods and formulae adapted to the manifold needs of regions which differ so widely as regards climate, population, and natural and acquired resources.

Daring reforms were born of the economic depression. They form part of a broad program capable of neutralizing the effects of the depression and of preventing its return. They are bringing about a social evolution and, in some instances, an actual transformation of living and working conditions. Here again is a profoundly interesting field of study, always provided that the underlying causes of the action taken or proposed are understood. For, as in many countries, including those of Europe, new methods are being sought to insure to the economically weaker classes of the population a greater measure of health and security by the improvement and more perfect adaptation of public health and social organization—including facilities as well as legislation—to the actual needs.

Here it is important to emphasize the efforts that are now being put forth, or which have already borne fruit, to promote the coordination of all the activities exerted on behalf of hygiene and health protection. Attempts to promote such coordination have been made in all countries; its value has been emphasized by commissions convened by the League of Nations, which have set out the ways and means of bringing it about. In the United States, such coordination is attempted at every level of government—federal, state, municipal, and rural. Its realization is all the more important, and even more difficult because it is opposed by obstacles inherent in the national and state constitutions, which gives the states and cities powers and privileges which they ardently desire to retain.

Strangely enough one of the important summaries of the changing aspects of public health activity during the past 10 years may be found in *Middletown in Transition*. In this volume the Lynds find "As in certain other phases of its life, Middletown's chief innovations in caring for health during this decade have come at the two ends of the economic scale: the important addition of the new hospital . . . during the boom years, and the extension of free health service to the needy under the impact of the depression."

They also sense one of the important disabilities which are beginning to arise in public health and other social activities from the fact that "The great majority of local social changes . . . are not locally generated but are diffused to Middletown, against the pressure of local inertia and resistance, from outside agencies." This tendency of human beings to resist change from external sources is emphasized by these two sociologists, who point out that people make small minimum adaptations by a process of "inching along" and not by heroic turnovers.

Conclusions

The investigations herein briefly reviewed may lead to generalizations which may be helpful in delineating the future programs of public health. Even at the risk of undue simplification, a statement of such generalizations should be provocative in discussion. They are as follows:

1. The field of public health activity is expanding. It may no longer be restricted to the simple list of communicable diseases prevented and of community sanitation.

2. The more familiar and older activities must continue with equal force to hold the gains which have already been made.

3. Causes of death less important a quarter of a century ago have now assumed the place of greatest prominence. They are the diseases of adult life, and represent the results of the impact of heredity, environment, and early experience, biological and otherwise, upon the individual. They require for control new technics, a wider base, more money, and more intensive activity on all fronts.

4. The maintenance and elevation of physical and mental efficiency must assume new importance in the public health field. The vast disability created by illness in the industrial and in the general population offers a tremendous field for future combined public and private service.

5. Increased facilities for hospitalization, dispensary service, nursing facilities, and medical care of all types are obvious requirements for the future.

6. These activities presuppose the development of professional services of an amount and of a quality not yet available. Facilities for training of personnel must be improved, extended, and maintained.

7. All these enterprises will require more money and hence a gradual extension of state and federal intrusion into the local public health field. With such intrusion the obvious advantages of higher levels of performance, of increasing standards of action, and of expanding research will ensue. Jointly with these advantages, however, the ever present problems of integration with lower levels of government and of coordination of all levels of government will emerge with

greater intensity. To these problems, all students of government must give serious and continuing thought. To steer between the Scylla of declining efficiency of and interest in local government operation and the Charybdis of throttling centralization offers the real challenge in the public health movement in the next 10 years. To meet the demands of an ever-expanding horizon an ever-expanding budget will be necessary. To obtain and use it successfully, will require a strict adherence to the age old axiom that government without understanding on the part of the people will fall of its own weight.

Local and central governments may be depended upon, with the continuing support and advice of voluntary groups, to develop the objectives of public health and the methodology of attaining these objectives, but their success must depend, particularly in the shifting and expanding zones of public health activity, upon public understanding and sympathy in the most remote hamlet as well as in the state and federal capitals. The practitioner in public health must add to his armamentarium of medical and public health science a new concept of governmental relations, in which local autonomy and interest are revived under the stimuli of intelligent state and federal agencies.

On this occasion and in New York State it may be particularly appropriate to close by referring to two paragraphs by a former Governor of New York, in his Foreword to *The Report on Public Health in New York State by the State Health Commission of 1931.* In them President (then Governor) Roosevelt summarized the future issues before the public health profession in the following terms:

> The first public health advances were made by doing things for people. Purify the city water supply and during the next few years the Albany typhoid rate drops from 90 to 9; pasteurize milk supplies and there is immediate decrease in infant mortality. In these typical details of mass public health, the work of our state and local administrations ranks high. The report of the Commission of 1931, however, may be contrasted with that of the Commission of 1913 not only by virtue of its greater emphasis upon better local health administration and the decentralizing of state health functions, but also by its clearly drawn picture of the transition of the public health movement from the single problem of attaining mass health to the double task of maintaining mass health and controlling preventable disease in the individual.

> This is a more difficult task than that of establishing wholesale preventive measures in which the people themselves are not required to take an initiative. It involves the fullest use of public health education, so that citizens may understand and cooperate with activities necessary for their own welfare. Important as are the laws which the Commission has recommended, of far greater importance is intelligent action on the part of the individual and of the community.

The National Health Program—
Present Status*

A year ago your speaker in his Presidential address, "A Century in Arrears," made the error of indulging in quantitative analysis of certain matters concerning the public health. A lapse of 100 years in recognition of important undertakings in the public health field was emphasized. The penalty for such an analysis was not long in coming, for today the program committee suggests that the estimates of progress or of delay be brought up to date for the past year.

The evaluation of accomplishment in a century is a far simpler assignment than the determination of the particular fronts on which real changes have occurred in a period of 12 months. Much has happened since October, 1938, but the task of assigning permanent values thereto is difficult. All that can be done today is to rehearse in as brief compass as possible what appear to be the important steps forward in discussion, legislation, or administrative accomplishment. In all these sectors the past year has been surprisingly fruitful.

* Reprinted from *American Journal of Public Health and the Nation's Health*, Vol. 30, No. 1 (January, 1940), 1–8. Copyright by the American Public Health Association, Inc. Read at a General Session on Medical Care and the National Health Program of the American Public Health Association at the Sixty-Eighth Annual Meeting in Pittsburgh, Pa., Oct. 18, 1939.

Activities of the American
Public Health Association

The executive board of A.P.H.A., following the Kansas City mandate of the membership, appointed a committee of Fellows of the Association to cooperate with the Interdepartmental Committee of the U. S. Government, the American Medical Association, the American Dental Association, the National Organization for Public Health Nursing, the Conference of State and Territorial Health Officers, and other agencies, for the purpose of translating certain accepted principles of the Association in the national health program, into effective action, whether of an administrative or legislative character.

This committee met in Washington on November 19, 1938, at the request of Miss Josephine Roche, Chairman of the Interdepartmental Committee, for extended conference. All members of the committee were present. For purposes of the record these included: Abel Wolman, Dr.Eng., Chairman, J. N. Baker, M.D., Louis I. Dublin, Ph.D., A. T. McCormack, M.D., H. S. Mustard, M.D., John L. Rice, M.D., F. J. Underwood, M.D., and, ex-officio, E. S. Godfrey, Jr., M.D., and Reginald M. Atwater, M.D.

Following these and other conferences, the recommendations were presented to the Executive Board of the A.P.H.A. for acceptance. Such acceptance has since been granted. The recommendations are here repeated without the supporting data which the committee presented, but which may be found in the official records of the Association.

    1. It is certainly theoretically desirable that a single state agency should be made administratively responsible for carrying out all the provisions of the National Health Program which may be enacted into law.

    2. In the initiation and development of the program, wide latitude should be given to the states in the definition of the population to be served, in the selection of the method of providing medical service, and in other important phases of the proposed program. We believe that similar latitude should be provided with regard to the method of raising funds in the states to accomplish approved objectives.

    3. The fundamental objectives involved are, first, conservation of health and vitality and, second, reduction of the role of sickness as a cause of poverty and dependency. With this in mind, it supports the concept that Recommendations 1, 2, and 3 of the Interdepartmental Committee (the expansion of public health and maternal and child health services, the expansion of hospital, clinic, and other institutional facilities, and the provision of medical care for the medically needy) should have priority in initiation.

4. Recent experience demonstrates that the Social Security Act provisions for aid to the states for health work provide a suitable framework for the expansion of preventive health services.

5. Any state program to be approved for federal aid should contain adequate provisions for the maintenance of high personnel standards and that payment of such federal aid to state agencies should be withheld when it is found that substandard services are being furnished. Similar policy should obtain with respect to state aid to local areas within a state. The appropriate federal administrative authorities should have power to establish minimum standards through rule and regulation after consultation with competent advisory professional bodies.

6. Careful study will be necessary to perfect administrative regulations to cover the details concerned with the provision of medical services, so as to assure a high level of quality. We believe that standards of medical practice should not be written into basic law. Federal aid should be conditioned on inclusion with the state plans of adequate safeguards for maintaining appropriate standards.

7. The extension and improvement of public health services in general throughout the country requires complete integration of health services of the federal government under one cabinet officer, preferably a Secretary of Health.

During 1939, the Association continued sessions with key representatives of a number of the federal and state agencies interested in the development of the National Health Program. These culminated in the appearance of your President before the Senate Committee on Education and Labor on May 4, 1939, to present a statement of the position of the American Public Health Association with reference to the National Health Bill of 1939, S. 1620. A summary of that statement appears in the JOURNAL of the Association for June, 1939, pages 686 to 688, inclusive.

The Association approved in principle the major aspects of the National Health Program. It pointed out, however, important details or principles in which the proposed legislation differed from the principles accepted and already enunciated by the Association. The essential agreements and exceptions noted in this statement are not again recorded here, for they may be read in detail in the JOURNAL already referred to and in amplification in the testimony before the Senate Committee, now available in printed form.

Congressional Action

Although several acts affecting the program for improvement of the public health of the nation were introduced into the Congress during 1939, the most significant and comprehensive of these is Senate Bill 1620, providing for the general welfare by enabling the several states to make more adequate provision for public health, prevention and control of disease, maternal and child health services, construction and maintenance of needed hospitals and health centers, care of the sick, disability insurance, and training of personnel. The bill was introduced in the Senate by Senator Robert F. Wagner of New York on February 28, 1939.

The National Health Bill translated into concrete legislation the recommendations for action which had been developed from some years of inquiry. It extends the procedure of grants-in-aid developed in various titles of the Social Security Act, on the assumption that this procedure permitted the widest latitude to the states in the development of their own plans consistent with the needs of their own people. The bill further provided grants to establish, expand, and improve state programs for

    a. Child and maternal health
    b. General public health services and investigations
    c. Construction of needed hospitals and health centers
    d. General programs of medical care
    e. Insurance against loss of wages during periods of temporary disability.

The administration of the purposes of the Act is vested in the existing federal agencies: The Children's Bureau, the Public Health Service, and the Social Security Board.

The bill does not establish a system of health insurance, or require the states to do so. Although the bill does not include such a program, common assumption that it does still persists.

The financial implications of the proposed act are briefly set forth in Table 1. A review of this table indicates that the present 1938 authorizations for health purposes under the Social Security Act are approximately $17,000,000. The proposed authorization under S. 1620 for the fiscal year 1940, was $98,250,000. An authorization should be distinguished from an appropriation, since the former is an indication of Congressional intent, while the latter is a statement of budgetary allotment. In other words, the authorizations suggested in S. 1620, even if this bill had been passed, would have to be translated into appropriations by subsequent Congressional and budgetary action. The authorized and the appropriated amounts are rarely the same.

The proposed legislation rests upon an agreed need for a national health program in which the following assumptions were dominant:

    1. The health of the people is a matter of public concern.
    2. Ill health is a major cause of suffering, economic loss, and dependency.
    3. Good health is essential to the security and progress of the nation.

Table 1

Present Appropriations for Health Purposes under the Social Security Act and Appropriations Proposed to Be Authorized by S. 1620

Purpose	Present Authorization under the Social Security Act	Proposed Authorization under S. 1620[1] Fiscal Year 1940
Title V:		
Part 1: Maternal and child health services	$3,800,000	$ 8,000,000
Part 2: Medical services for children,		
including crippled children	2,850,000	13,000,000[3]
Part 5: Administration, investigations, and		
demonstrations, etc.	425,000	2,500,000
Title VI—Public Health work and investigations:		
Part 1:		
Payments to States	8,000,000	15,000,000
Administration, studies, demonstrations, etc.		1,500,000
Part 2: Investigations	2,000,000	3,000,000
Title XII:		
Grants for general hospitals		8,000,000
Grants for mental and tuberculosis hospitals		(2)
Administration, etc.		
Public Health Service		1,000,000
Public Works Administration (etc.)		(2)
Title XIII:		
Grants for medical care		35,000,000
Administration		1,000,000
Title XIV:		
Grants for temporary disability compensation		10,000,000
Administration		250,000
Total	$17,075,000	$98,250,000[4]

1—These amounts replace, and are not additional to, the amounts authorized by the Social Security Act.
2—A sum sufficient to carry out the purposes of (this part of) this title.
3—Of which $4,000,000 in the fiscal year 1940, $5,000,000 in the fiscal year 1941, and so much as the Chief of the Children's Bureau deems necessary in succeeding years, are to be allotted "for service to crippled children and other physically handicapped children in need of special care."
4—Total of limited expenditures authorized.

Preliminary Report from the Committee on Education and Labor

The Committee on Education and Labor of the Senate appointed a sub-committee to study the bill. The sub-committee held numerous public hearings in which a large volume of testimony and supplementary information was acquired. The committee on August 4, 1939, reported that it is in agreement with the general purposes and objectives of S. 1620. It wished to give this legislation, however, additional study and to consult further with representatives of lay organizations and of the professions concerned. The sub-committee intends to report out an amended bill at the next session of Congress convening in January, 1940.

The report of the sub-committee released in August, 1939, as Report No. 1139, is replete with important observations on many of the accepted and controversial features of the National Health Program. The document deserves careful review and analysis by every individual interested in public health progress in the United States.

Even a brief summary of all of the features of the report would be impracticable of presentation today. One cannot escape, however, the temptation to record some of the outstanding observations in the report. The speaker takes the liberty of quoting some of the more striking comments below:

1. The evidence on needs, in urban and in rural areas, is overwhelming, as may be evident to anyone who will examine the record.

2. There are various factors which explain why large proportions of the population fail to receive the medical and health services they need. So far as community services are concerned, there is often a lack of understanding or experience as to the benefits to be derived from public health and related services and, perhaps more important, there is lack of financial resources. So far as services for individuals are concerned, there is, among other factors, ignorance as to the benefits of modern medical care, reliance upon unsuitable methods of care, distance from practitioners and facilities, etc. But while these particular factors play a part in the case of services for individuals, we are convinced from the evidence placed before us that the major reason is lack of financial ability on the part of large proportions of the population—as individuals, as groups, or as members of committees—to meet the cost of needed services.

3. The fact that a considerable proportion of general hospitals are being used to far less than their capacity in some places does not alter the basic need for additional facilities, or for facilities within the financial resources of particular groups of people, in other communities.

4. The irregular and unpredictable occurrence of sickness, and consequently of expenses for medical treatment, tends to create a new class of dependent or needy persons, so that, in addition to the indigent, people everywhere are beginning to characterize a large proportion of our population as the "medically indigent" or the "medically needy." These are persons who are self-supporting in every respect except as regards need for elaborate or expensive medical care; they include tens of millions of people, on farms and in cities, above the relief level. Yet, though these are people who need no public assistance for their ordinary support, their health and medical needs are as much the concern of government as are the needs of the indigent.

5. The long history of this subject shows that these problems do not solve themselves by being ignored; neither do they cease to exist

by being either ignored or denied. Nor, as a long history of special studies makes plain, are these problems new or the result of an economic depression. They were with us in the 1920's, as Dr. Wilbur's Committee on the Cost of Medical Care fully recognized, and they are still with us today. These problems must be faced squarely and solved on a basis which not only safeguards the quality of medical care but also preserves the dignity and self-respect of the people who are to be served.

6. There is no escaping the fact that the costs of sickness are a heavy burden on large portions of our population, that modern medical care is of necessity elaborate and expensive in many cases of serious illness, that the costs may be out of reach for people with small incomes, and that the burden should not be left so largely on the practitioners, hospitals, and voluntary organizations as it is today. We must provide substantial solutions, as we believe we can, which will be beneficial alike to patients, to the entire public, to practitioners, to the hospitals, and to the related institutions and organizations.

7. This bill does not propose a new departure or a new type of activity for the federal government. Participation in health services by the federal government is as old as the nation itself. Federal cooperation with the states in safeguarding health and strengthening state and local health services has an unbroken history of 150 years. The bill before us proposes only to lay out a long-range and systematic program on a basis for carrying on old and traditional activities in a sound and efficient manner.

8. It is our opinion that the administration and operation of health services should be left to the local communities and to the states, and that the federal government should not control or dictate to the local communities or states in the management of these functions. But the federal government cannot be indifferent to remediable deficiencies or inadequacies in the provision of services that are necessary to health. It should take steps to aid the states and, through them, the local communities, in the provision of necessary health services to their inhabitants. The primary opportunity for the federal government is to give financial and technical aid to the states.

9. Disease germs and the economic effects of sickness do not respect state lines. The opportunities for the spread of disease are increased by modern methods of transportation and by the mobility of of population. The citizens of one state cannot be safe from communicable disease so long as such disease prevails among the citizens of other states. One state cannot stamp out tuberculosis among its people unless the disease is also stamped out in neighboring states. One state cannot meet all the costs of improved health services and cannot protect itself against the burdens of dependency caused by sickness, disability, or premature death unless other states also participate in a common effort against disease. But together, and with the aid of the federal government, an effective and concerted war can be waged against disease.

10. A long-range health program offers a challenge not only to our humanitarian impulses but to our economic judgment; it offers an opportunity to balance the health budget of the nation.

11. Cooperative federal-state health and assistance programs now in operation only emphasize the need for a carefully planned, well coordinated, long-range health program, adequately financed, so as to assure that we will make those efforts and expenditures that will bring the maximum return, especially in the prevention of disease and disability. It is to such a balancing of the health budget that the National Health Program and the present legislation is directed.

In addition to this brief summary of some of the committee's findings, reference should also be made to the careful discussions which the committee devotes to such special problems as the general principle of federal aid to states, the problem of variable grants and matching proportions, the income limit of populations to be aided, the importance of medical education and research, the significance of health education of the public, the administrative provisions and difficulties with multiple federal agencies, the protection of minority population groups, the clarification of the scope of services under state plans, the eligibility of practitioners under state plans, cooperation with representative groups, clarification of the implication of the construction of needed hospitals, and the important question of payment for services furnished by nongovernmental hospitals and other agencies.

The general conclusions of the committee are sufficiently brief and clear to warrant repeating at this point. They are as follows:

S. 1620 has received wide support from large and representative organizations. Its objectives are noncontroversial. Our government is dedicated to promoting the welfare of the people and the protection and improvement of health and well-being. Making available to all of the people the great life saving services which modern medicine has to offer is an objective which every right thinking citizen supports.

The committee is convinced that federal legislation along the general lines followed by S. 1620, based upon federal-state cooperative programs, is necessary to strengthen the health services of the nation and to make provision for the progressive and effective improvement of health conditions in all parts of the country and among all groups of people. The needs are large, and an adequate program to put knowledge and skill more effectively to work will involve considerable expenditures of funds. The program must therefore be worked out with great care. We are confident that such a program can be worked out and that the expenditures will be sound national investments which will bring large returns. The role of the federal government should be primarily to give technical and financial aid to the states.

A critical analysis of the present provisions of S. 1620 shows a number of points at which its specific purposes can be more clearly stated and its provisions improved. The committee has not yet reached any conclusions concerning the precise rate at which federal appropriations should be increased, but the committee is agreed on the general principle that the proportion of federal assistance should be greater to those states in which there is the greatest need for the services contemplated under the bill. The committee is prepared to augment the provisions of the bill—if additional provisions are needed —to assure that the amount of federal assistance would in no instance be in excess of clearly demonstrated need.

Some misunderstandings seem to have arisen, and criticisms have been expressed concerning parts of the bill. Some witnesses have assumed that it would bring about revolutionary or dangerous changes in medical care. We think these fears are unwarranted, but we will welcome further suggestions as to specific amendments which may safeguard the objectives of the bill. Medical science has reached a commendable status in this country. The bill should encourage the further evolutionary development of medical science, teaching, and practice.

Additional Steps Forward

In reviewing the present status of the National Health Program, it is surprising to discover the number and variety of steps which have been taken during the past year to extend and to facilitate public health and medical care practices by official and nonofficial agencies.

A number of the states have developed administrative procedures in the fields of public health, medical care, and hospitalization, particularly for the medically needy, which represent advances in a single year comparable with those made in several decades preceding. It is impracticable to record each of the areas in which these activities are rapidly moving forward, but they extend from the Atlantic to the Pacific coast. Many of them have no doubt been stimulated by discussions before the American Public Welfare Association, the American Public Health Association, the American Medical Association, the American Hospital Association, and other groups interested in the subject.

The provisional drafts of material on "The Administration of Tax Supported Medical Care" informally discussed by the American Public Welfare Association, have given great impetus to the adoption of sound principles and practices throughout the country, particularly in the field of providing medical service for the indigent.

In those states where actual extensions and improvements in practice have not materialized, serious consideration is being given by public health, medical, and lay groups to the entire problem. In the State of Maryland, for example, during this past summer the Medical and Chirurgical Faculty has suggested to the State Planning Commission the creation of a continuing committee to concern itself with the problems of medical care and to formulate from time to time recommendations for better utilization and for extension of existing medical facilities, and for the institution of new facilities as they are required. The Faculty emphasizes its use of the term "Medical Care" in an inclusive sense to cover all the agencies available in safeguarding and improving the health of the people and in the treatment of disease.

The Faculty, in its proposal, recognized that—

> Although Maryland is fortunate . . . in her wealth of medical facilities and in the average high level of medical care which her citizens receive, yet this committee will quickly become aware of many urgent needs for improvement.
>
> Among the deficiencies in the present system of medical care in Maryland the following may be cited as outstanding examples:
>
> 1. The lack of facilities for hospital care for Negro patients in the counties.
>
> 2. The lack of adequate support for the out-patient departments of city and county hospitals.
>
> 3. The lack of funds or organization for the medical care in their homes of those upon relief and for other classes of indigent patients.
>
> 4. The lack of facilities for postgraduate education for practising physicians.
>
> 5. The inadequate buildings, equipment, and budget of certain county hospitals.
>
> 6. The lack of beds in the counties for the care of chronically disabled patients.
>
> 7. The lack of adequate accommodations for existing institutions for the feebleminded, especially among the colored race.
>
> These urgent needs are cited merely as instances of some of the problems which demand solution.

The State Planning Commission of Maryland has agreed to the formation of such a committee on medical care, has recommended such a committee to the Governor, and steps are now under way toward its organization.

The method of approach used in Maryland is presented only as an example of the great interest which has been aroused in health as an element in social security. It is gratifying that in these efforts during the past year, the members of the medical profession have taken a leading and cooperative part, although the American Medical Association in its 22 objections to the Wagner Act still bases its militant contribution to the development of a sound national program upon the negative thesis of "all is well in the public health and medical field."

Stock Taking

Even this necessarily cursory review of the present situation in the public health field discloses that the national health program has advanced far and fast in the characteristically democratic experimental fashion with which we are familiar in this country. Innumerable approaches to the problem and to its solution have been developed at the various levels of government, with the earnest and helpful support of lay and professional groups. All of the undertakings, prospective, potential, and actual, augur well for the future.

In March, 1939, your present speaker ventured a prophecy before the New York Tuberculosis and Health Association. Of the four elements implicit in that prophecy all have moved forward in an unexpectedly rapid though uneven formation during less than seven months.

That prophecy rested upon the concept, paraphrased aptly by Surgeon General Parran in his testimony before the Senate Committee on Education and Labor:

> In connection with balancing the budget, Mr. Chairman, I hope this Congress will give more attention to balancing our health budget. It is cheaper to keep a woman from dying in childbirth than to take care of the orphans in an orphan asylum or to give aid to the dependent children. It is cheaper to aid in building tuberculosis sanatoriums than it is to pay for the death from tuberculosis and the widows and children who are left. The State Health Officer of Tennessee estimates that it costs on the average of $150 to bury a person in Tennessee, and on that basis it is costing that state more to bury people dying from tuberculosis than for its entire health program, including tuberculosis and all the other diseases.

The past year gives evidence of a number of adjustments of the American people to a changing environment, in which political, social, and economic forces, of historical and international scope, have been at play. It is not surprising that in these adjustments, public health and medical care problems, as important phenomena of this environment should come in for their share of discussion and experiment. People have long accepted the principle that in respect to public health no distinction should be made between the rich and the poor. Now they really want to put it into effect. Can we meet the challenge of economics, as we have always tried to meet the humanitarian one? The next ten years will give the answer. I, for one, feel it will be met!

Trends and Challenges
in Public Health*

It is rare that one is challenged to look into the future under the critical eye of an audience of scientists. In a rash moment I agreed to the role of seer and prophet on the occasion of the dedication of the new building for the School of Public Health. It is safe to do so only because memories are short and the future I behold will be dimmed in the realities I have not foreseen.

There is some intellectual sport and satisfaction in playing the role of a public health nabob and designing the kind of educational effort he might be willing to defend and to pay for. Such a design should stem from the kind of world we live in, the shape of things to come, the anxieties and demands of society, the strengths and weaknesses of our scientific underpinnings, and the willfulness and resistances of professional leaders. All of these forces guide and regulate the decisions one should or could make for any new or revised objectives in a school of public health.

In these considerations one fundamental assumption is tacitly accepted, even though this assumption has by no means universal assent. The central thesis upon which this paper rests is that a school of public health has a primary place in our society, distinct from a school of medi-

* Presented before the School of Public Health, University of North Carolina, Chapel Hill, N.C., Apr. 6, 1963.

cine, of engineering sciences, of biology or of other recognized disciplines. This is not the time to labor this point, except to emphasize that, in the past and in prospect, accomplishment in the prevention of disease and in the preservation of health has had and must continue to have a broader base than that afforded by the traditional medical disciplines alone.

The World in Ferment

The last twenty-five years have been characterized as the years of crisis—whether in politics, science, technology or education. Hardly a day passes without real or pseudo issues making the headlines. So familiar has this become that not so long ago one newspaper found itself impelled to issue a two-inch headline: "No Sensational Event Has Occurred Today!"

Public health practices are no exception to this ferment. Last fall William H. Stewart discussed these changes,[1] before the Academy of Preventive Medicine in Raleigh, North Carolina. He once more noted the shift in emphasis in public health practice from the concern with infectious diseases to a marriage of preventive and curative medicines. This view of public health endeavor as a massive social force is a thread, of course, which has linked the public health crusaders of the nineteenth century with the emerging, but limited, pioneer public health–social reformers of today.

In our complex society a number of conflicting phenomena prevail. From their listing, one may obtain a cue to the obligations of the school of tomorrow. The enumeration which follows is significant, although not complete:

(a) Of the twenty leading causes of disability and death in the United States, perhaps only two or three are sufficiently well understood in etiology and therapy to be prudently mass attacked. These would appear to be tuberculosis, some respiratory diseases and some cancers.

(b) Although there are limitations in scientific and technologic information, the knowledge we have is inadequately applied.

(c) The development of political and social structure to implement intelligent action is almost universally absent.

(d) The imaginative initiation of new financial processes for providing services is almost negligible.

(e) The research required for the determination of the subtle, long term effects of the insults of industrialization and urbanization is meager.

(f) The recognition of the necessity of developing auxiliary personnel to carry out many duties hitherto assigned to medical doctors and nurses is shunned. Yet, in New York City with its abundant resources, such substitution is taking place successfully.

(g) Increases in the gross national product and in the standard of living, in our own country, help to alleviate the stresses of diseases, but do not dispose of them automatically. In fact demands for services increase as standard of living rises.

(h) With limited resources, selection and priority of program assume increasing importance, although rarely practiced.

Modern public health literature, reflecting the above milieus, is replete with delineation of needs, of desires, of probabilities, of threats of doom and of unverified epidemiologic consequences. The same publications are correspondingly devoid of institutional and fiscal solutions and of scientific and technologic supports.

In this world of turmoil, of fact and fancy, of desires, needs and methodologies of accomplishment lies the opportunity of the school of public health. To say that the fragmentation of this opportunity and its conversion into curriculum is difficult and baffling, is merely to acknowledge reality. Perfectionism and wholeness are not the aim. Judicious isolation of the most important areas of effort, with a fair sprinkling of even the less significant, are reasonable objectives for the faculty.

With the recognition that man essentially lives in a world of his own making, how may the school diagnose the ills thus created and determine their cause? How may this rediscovered environment be adjusted to the benefit of man? The matter has been well stated in the recent Summary Report[2] to the President of the United States by the National Academy of Sciences, in the following terms:

> It is apparent that man must concern himself with a variety of changes in the environment, both those caused by human beings and those reflecting man's responses. Some are good; some may be very harmful. That we often do not have any clear-cut idea of their impact on man, or of man's response is cause for concern. It would seem unwise to continue to tamper with environment without, concurrently, striving to determine the real and lasting effects of our actions.

There is nothing in the history of man's behavior to suggest that he is likely to discontinue "tampering" with his environment. It is all the more essential that the scientist and technologist speed up their inquires into the effects of such activities upon biological function, in general, and disease in particular.

The School's Opportunities

Twenty years ago, Sir Arthur S. MacNalty spelled out[3] what appears to me still to be the bases of a school of public health. It is true that the institute he was then describing was the new chair of Social Medicine at Oxford, for which hopes were then high and which has since fallen by the way side because of University disinterest.

The principles then outlined, however, have present-day force. They are briefly paraphrased as follows:

(a) The investigation of the influence of social, genetic, environmental and domestic factors on the incidence of human disease and disability.

(b) The search for and promotion of measures, other than those usually employed in the practice of remedial medicine, for the protection of the individual and of the community against such forces as interfere with the full development and maintenance of man's mental and physical capacity.

(c) The provision of instruction of students and practitioners of medicine, if required by the University to do so.

These desiderata and hopes parallel the central assumption of my paper today that "the science of public health is a compendium of specialized knowledge to which not only medicine in all its branches, but many other professions contribute."[3] Over the years, the disease entities have changed materially and hence methods in prevention have changed or should be adjusted to newer challenges. This does not imply that all the implements successfully used in 1910 need to be discarded. It does mean, for example, that the environmental controls required in 1910 to prevent 1,891 cases and 235 deaths from typhoid fever in Baltimore City might be appropriately modified to meet the newer challenges of the environment of 1963. Past achievements in reduction of disease still hold some lessons for the far more complicated control problems of the present.

All of these significant changes in disease prevention and amelioration wait upon advances on the following fronts. They come within the purview of a school of public health.

(a) *Research in the Causes and Behavior of Disease*

The laboratories, bench and field, have a difficult and long term responsibility ahead. Incidentally, it is one which is often avoided, because the disease complexes which confront the public health worker today appear far more subtle in origin and long term in time than were the presumed simpler infectious diseases of past eras. Yet, intelligent management of the diseases now at the top of the list waits upon scientific disclosures of causes and effects. These latter in turn rest upon the combined efforts of biologists, physiologists, biochemists and collateral disciplines. Most of them are reluctant to desert their present lasts for the baffling labyrinths of chronic diseases, cardio-vascular disasters, mysteries of aging and the impacts of urbanization, industrialization and outer space.

Answers must be provided as rapidly as possible, however, to such significant questions as:

Does industrialization and urbanization engender disease? If so, what kind and why?

Are climate, temperature and altitude causal agents or at least stimulants to disease?

Should we worry about the increased CO_2 in the atmosphere?

Are the chemical insults periodically impinging upon man, via air, water and food, truly productive of disease entities?

Is modern life conducive to objectionable stresses or is the future boredom of the promised land of leisure more hazardous to health than the present ulcers?

The health officer, eternally pressed for action, for advice, for handsome posters, for parent-teachers meetings, for legislative hearings, really needs authoritative help rather than propaganda.

(b) *Intensification in Epidemiologic Evaluation of Modern Diseases*

While waiting upon the laboratories of the biologist, virologist and biochemist, much light may be shed upon disease causation by extending the horizon of the epidemiologist. Here, too, resistance is high, to a shift from the infectious diseases to the more complex public health issues of present decades. One of the greatest causes of death and disability today lies in accidents. Detailed and objective inquiry into these causes is singularly limited. It is sadly in contrast with the epidemiology of poliomyelitis, scarlet fever, typhoid, etc. Yet, its toll is thousands of times greater than from these familiar diseases.

The accident rates are perhaps excellent examples of the real challenges to public health of the future, because inherent in them, are the intertwined practices and mores of the entire way of life of the present century. Does the health officer have the courage to tangle with the auto manufacturer, the highway designer, the traffic engineer, the police, the planner, the architect and builder of houses and the airplane designer? All these forces and more determine the accidents he wants to conquer. Or should these deaths be treated as we once regarded leprosy, tuberculosis and syphilis, to be concealed and consigned only to statistical tables and undertakers' certificates?

(c) *Research in Public Health Practice*

The demands and requirements of society most often run ahead of the development of institutions and of administrative procedures. In public health, the lag between the two appears to be unnecessarily wide and long-sustained. Part of the reason for the lag lies in the inadequate interrelationship between preventive and curative medicine, between health officer and physician, between hospital and patient and among political structure, money and other public and private agencies. In each of these areas a school of public health finds rich ground for tillage in administrative practice, provided it adds to the exposition of historical experience, the experimentation with new administrative and fiscal tools and the continuing evaluation of old practices. Only a few areas for such exploration are listed here as examples of the need and opportunities for administrative research.

The decentralization of activities has always had a high degree of lip service, unmatched by actual practice. But approaches to such localization, now coupled with the desire to use the hospital, if possible, as a central core for preventive medicine, still need to be tried and assessed.

In such efforts, more and more attention is being devoted to the family complex, particularly where mental problems arise or the elderly chronic disease issues are pressing. The detailed operation drives the health officer into far closer relationships with the doctor, the voluntary agency and other governmental agencies than ever before. These requirements have already resulted in new institutional relationships, such as the health and welfare departments interchanging and making joint key staff appointments. In New York City, for example, the health department places and pays for a top staff medical officer in the department of welfare.

Much still remains to be ironed out in public health practice in the elimination of the fragmentation of the individual. The continuing separation of the mind from the body and the child from the adult in much of the present day health administration has, of course, the sanction of history, but not of wisdom or logic. Inappropriate vested interests in public health are no less difficult to obliterate than they are in any other human endeavor.

A similar fragmentation of control is increasingly evident in the whole field of housing and urban renewal. The impact of housing shifts in the great urban areas throughout the country has had only desultory interest to the health officer. These changes, however, are perhaps subjecting millions of people to mental, physical and economic stresses still waiting to be identified. Their lot, in our fragmented inspection systems, is not a happy one.

The community health center promised great returns for teaching purposes, if and when attached to a school. How completely have these promises been fulfilled? Of even greater importance, perhaps, is a determination of how significant has been the contagion from such a center to the community as a whole. One has the uncomfortable feeling that neither of these objectives has been universally attained.

Coupled with these aspects of our society and its rapid urbanization are the twin issues of what part the school may play in gearing medical and health services more efficiently into the amorphous metropolis and in facilitating the planning of such services for maximum coverage and minimum cost. Is the school of public health generating new fiscal systems for meeting health and medical demands? Undoubtedly, such inquiries will force joint participation of medical school, socio-economic and engineering departments. Although one should not under-estimate the difficulties in harnessing multi-disciplines—and they are great—it is doubtful whether these problems of society will be resolved without such marriages.

Unfortunately, one of such efforts has so far been distinguished by only meager success. It is said that preventive medicine is being well transfused into medical students at one or two schools. But no one brags about universal success. No school of public health or medicine can remain permanently complacent about turning out doctors or health officers unaware of their potential impact upon society as a whole. Experimental approaches to closing this gap are still required. How rapidly may we expect to reach the concept of Dubos of a "hospital without walls that would help physicians to become aware of the whole range of community problems and broaden the scope of medical help"?[4]

The Other Worlds

So far we have been talking almost exclusively about the problems, the political structure, the economy and the mores of essentially a Western world. This school, however, deals and will continue to deal with additional worlds. A second world encompasses some three-quarters of the population of the globe—half-starved, half-housed and beset by most of the diseases in the book. Their catastrophes wait for solution upon economic development and the telescoping of time in the adaptation of public health and medical practice. Stacy May has put it well in the words: "tropical medicine is the midwife of economic progress in the less developed areas of the world."

The students from these countries, with meager professional manpower and even less money resources, pose real challenges to teaching and research staffs. Efforts, simply to transplant Western practices to these countries, are unlikely to succeed. They have much in common with the difficulties of all biologic transplants. This is not to say that imagination and initiative will not disclose adaptations of American practice which will flourish in another soil. If our experience means anything at all to the rest of the world, it is because many methods may be culled from it which have appropriateness in Asia, Africa or South America.

Can the school identify the part which public health may play in the economic development of a country? Can it dramatize the importance of joint action of public health with that of agriculture, industry and commerce? Can it provide criteria for priority selections of public health activity, without falling into the trap of frozen plans? Or as the late Will Rogers once so succinctly put it: "Plans get you into things, but you got to work your way out."

In this second world science and technology have already provided far more answers to disease causation and prevention than we have the resources or the wit to translate into effective social action. This transfer waits upon the skill and the ingenuity of the schools of public health. Malnutrition, that great stalemate of progress throughout this second world, waits upon such a series of transfers in agricultural practices, cultural food habits, industrial production of cheap proteins and public health demonstrations of disease effects and reductions.

One of the great values of this arena of effort to the school is that it offers perhaps the greatest laboratory for ecological approach to disease prevention that we have ever had. Are we sufficiently astute to develop a logical protocol for best use of this laboratory?

The delineation of a third world—that of outer space—would require another speech in itself. Its challenges to a school of public health, however, must be recorded, for outer space and man's behavior therein may provide also a widely extended laboratory for detailed recording of biologic behavior under the impact of a belligerent environment. Many of its ecological lessons will undoubtedly find their way into these corridors—carrying with them new public health problems and weapons.

Summary

The outline of opportunity in a school of public health here presented rests upon the assumption that such an institution is not synonymous with a medical school. Its obligations and underpinnings are broader in their emphases upon the mass handling of disease causation and prevention. These objectives require the multi-discipline attacks and perspectives of the doctor, engineer, nurse, economist and social scientist.

The Western world has changed in the incidence of major diseases. This change may be characterized as a shift from the simpler and short term diseases to subtler, long term difficulties associated with aging populations, adjustments in social behavior, urbanization and industrialization. With these modifications have come the challenges and opportunities for a school of public health.

The necessities for laboratory bench and field research in disease causation and therapy have been intensified. Epidemiologic inquiry of more complexity waits for elaboration. Public health practices adjusted to a newer society, to a second industrial revolution and to a new array of diseases are in need of exploration and appraisal. On all three fronts, teaching methods and criteria will require parallel adjustments.

Besides the Western world, two additional worlds need to be diagnosed and benefited. One of these encompasses some three quarters of the people of the world. The diseases which have been largely defeated in the Western world are still dominant in their world today. In this world, new practices must be developed out of the rich experience so successful in the more fortunate West.

The third world, offering both challenges and response in biologic equilibrium, is in outer space. What it offers to the school is the subject for another speech at some other time.

REFERENCES

1. William H. Stewart, M.D., "Community Medicine—An American Concept of Comprehensive Care," *Public Health Reports*, U.S. Department of Health, Education and Welfare, February 1963, 78:2.

2. Committee on Natural Resources, National Academy of Sciences. *Natural Resources: A Summary Report to the President of the United States*, N.A.S. Publication No. 1,000. 1962.

3. Arthur S. MacNalty, "The New Chair of Social Medicine at Oxford," *The Oxford Magazine*, October 29, 1942, 61:3.

4. Rene Dubos, M.D., "Man Meets His Environment," *Health and Nutrition*, U.S. Papers for the United Nations Conference on the Application of Science and Technology for the Benefit of the Less Developed Areas, Vol. VI, 1963.

THE ROLE
OF
THE ENGINEER

The Small Plant Operator
as Scientist*

To many small plant operators the title of my present paper may appear objectionable, for there still exists a vague distrust of the term "science." In most cases, a scientific worker or a scientific paper is synonymous with long words, difficult concepts, impractical ideas, and a certain aloofness of attitude. On the other hand, the so-called practical man stands with both feet on earth, talks American English, and presents facts that are workable and intelligible to the man who operates the pumps or fires the boiler. Is it not rather impertinent, therefore, to link these two conflicting spirits in the title I have chosen?

I have set before myself the task of indicating that the absurdity of the contrast between "practical" and "scientific" is more apparent than real. This task has been chosen advisedly, since, by eliminating a certain amount of antagonism engendered by terms, it may be possible to bring about in the water works field a more fruitful use of the vast array of facts which the small plant operator has accumulated and will continue to collect.

* Reprinted from *Journal of the American Water Works Association*, Vol. 8, 1921. Copyright 1921 American Water Works Association, Inc. Excerpts from paper read before the Association convention at Cleveland, Ohio.

Science Is Observation and Interpretation of Facts

Karl Pearson in *The Grammar of Science*[1] defines the function of science as "the classification of facts, the recognition of their sequence and relative significance." Stripped of its classical verbiage, the function of science is no more than the function of every technical practical operator, namely, the observation and interpretation of facts. It is important to emphasize that a "a scientific frame of mind is not a peculiarity of the professional scientist."[1] And it is just as important to point out that, because scientific reports are often couched in English too elegant to be clear, it is not therefore true that science is a mere matter of language. It follows then that, if an operator sees facts and reasons as to their cause and effect, he becomes a scientific observer. I am sorry to destroy, in this way, the illusion of many of my listeners that they, thank Heaven, are practical men and not theorists. I make the charge that each man in this audience is a scientific worker, provided he is in possession of all his mental faculties. We must establish for ourselves, therefore, the axiom that practice and theory are not antithetical, but complementary.

Plant Operators in Three Classes

A little thought will make clear that all plant operators may be divided into three classes, the first, who feel that they are scientific but hesitate to present their observations because of inherent modesty; the second, the practical, who observe but do not report because of a supposed lack of scientific language; and the third, who neither observe nor report. This last class is, I hope, numerically small and need not concern us. The first two classes have much in common both as to method and result. It is to these two classes one must look for real development in water treatment, since they are the first to encounter new problems and the first to try out new solutions. A scientific hypothesis is useless if it is not in accord with the facts everywhere. A scientific solution is worthless if it does not solve our problems. Both the hypothesis and the solution must be tested by the plant operator. He is an important factor in real scientific progress. How important, he has evidently failed to realize, if we judge from the infrequency with which he takes part in discussions of theory and hypothesis.

When we speak of a problem in water treatment, we are prone to emphasize its simplicity rather than its complexity. We find it easy to fall into the error of considering "water" as a definite thing, a simple compound, instead of regarding it always as a most variable substance, delicately fluctuating with atmospheric, geographic, and geologic influences. When water is considered in this sense, each water filtration plant becomes a laboratory, a scientific structure, a research bureau, where facts and opinions may and should be tested out upon the peculiar and rare fluid there being handled. When a new hypothesis is announced, each plant operator has the opportunity to make a real contribution to science and to practice by determining if it tallies with the phenomena experienced with his own rarity, the little stream used in his plant. Likewise, he has the continual advantage of learning whether older theories account for the present observations and whether older methods are adequate. Each small plant stands, therefore, in the position of a special research laboratory upon the director of which there has been placed the duty of watching and interpreting a continuous series of experiments performed under conditions common to no other laboratory. I emphasize the distinctiveness of each plant, since on the same stream, a few miles apart, the water has undergone profound change which converts it into a new substance, with new, though possibly slightly varied, attributes.

Each Operator an Investigator

If we accept the concept of each plant as a true specialized investigative bureau and of water as a variable and not a constant substance, what operator has the right to say that he is not or should not be a scientific observer? His duty, whether he likes it or not, has been enlarged from that of a valve-operator to an investigator. His responsibility is greater than to his immediate community, it is national and even international. For the plant operator is now research worker, and the fruits of research are limited only by the infinite.

It is clear from the above discussion that in each plant, no matter how small, no matter how crude, phenomena of great importance and of peculiar significance are occurring and recurring. They are not always observed and still less often are they reported. It is the special plea of this paper today that this condition be remedied, for with its remedy, perhaps, many of both scientists and practical men will avoid voyages "bound nowhere, under full sail." In concluding my remarks, I have recourse once more to a quotation from *The Grammar of Science*, which presents so much better than I the argument for the reporting of facts and opinions by the small plant operator.

Symmetry and Unity of Scientific Method

It is as if individual workers in both Europe and America were bringing their stones to one great building and piling them on and cementing them together without regard to any general plan or to their individual neighbor's work; only where someone has placed a great cornerstone is it regarded, and the building then rises on this firmer foundation more rapidly than at other points, till it reaches a height at which it is stopped for want of a side support. Yet this great structure, the proportions of which are beyond the ken of any individual man, possesses a symmetry and unity of its own, notwithstanding its haphazard mode of construction. This symmetry and unity lie in scientific method. The smallest group of facts, if properly classified and logically dealt with, will form a stone which has its proper place in the great building of knowledge, wholly independent of the individual workman who has shaped it. Even when two men work unwittingly at the same stone they will but modify and correct each other's angles.

REFERENCE

1. Pearson, Karl, *The Grammar of Science*, Part 1, Physical, London, Adam and Charles Black, 1911, p. 13.

The Trend of Civil Engineering
Since Franklin*

A man who is less concerned with the golden pavements of the City of God than that the cobblestones on Chestnut Street in Philadelphia should be well and evenly laid, who troubles less to save his soul from burning hereafter than to protect his neighbors' houses by organizing an efficient fire-company, who is less regardful of the light that never was on sea or land than of a new-model street lamp to light the steps of the belated wayfarer—such a man, obviously, does not reveal the full measure of human aspiration. Franklin ended as he began, the child of a century marked by sharp spiritual limitations. What was best in that century he made his own. In his modesty, his willingness to compromise, his open-mindedness, his clear and luminous understanding, his charity—above all, in his desire to subdue the ugly facts of society to some more rational scheme of things—he proved himself a great and useful man, one of the greatest and most useful whom America has produced.

In these words Vernon L. Parrington in his analysis of "The Colonial Mind" described Benjamin Franklin, America's first social philosopher.

To Franklin, the municipal housekeeper, therefore, the present speaker will devote the major part of his remarks, for since the dawn of history the civil engineer has devoted his efforts to directing the great

* Reprinted from the *Journal of the Franklin Institute*, Vol. 226, No. 3 (September, 1938), pp. 413–28.

sources of power in nature for the use and convenience of man. His activities have been to a large extent in the field of works of permanent public value. In this field of applied science for the improvement of public welfare, comfort and safety, Franklin was a distinguished pioneer.

Advocates of mechanical, electrical and chemical engineering will no doubt discover in his activities ample support for their claims that he initiated undertakings in their fields which should result in labelling him a mechanical, electrical or chemical engineer. His facets were many, but in all of his enterprises, the motive of social improvement through scientific works was foremost, and in these no small part of his energy was devoted to the civil engineering field. Most of his activities fit into a general plan, although they range from the founding of the first public library in 1732, the institution of plans in 1743, which ultimately resulted in the present University of Pennsylvania, the writings which bore fruit in the establishment of a Pennsylvania Militia, the program for the development in Philadelphia of paved streets, street lighting and improved police and fire protection and his interest in agriculture, the land problem, the organization of the colonies and the expansion of the colonial frontier.

Even in founding the Philosophical Society he pointed out that its energy should not be devoted solely to abstractions, but to the spread of new discoveries and useful knowledge in practical affairs.

What kind of world was the United States in Franklin's day? One hundred and fifty years ago the inhabited part of the United States consisted principally of the area east of the Allegheny Mountains and between the St. Lawrence River and the Spanish Province of Florida. The first census of 1790 of the New Republic showed a population slightly less than 4 million. The living conditions of the great mass of the people were simple, with open fires or brick ovens, lighting with tallow candles or the sperm oil lamp, clothing of homespun, few public water supplies, no public sewerage systems, plumbing practically unknown, with primitive methods for the removal and disposal of household and industrial wastes.

At the time of this first census only four municipalities in the United States had populations in excess of 10,000—New York was a metropolis of 33,131; Philadelphia of 28,522; Boston, 18,320 and Baltimore, 13,503. The remaining population lived under rural or semi-rural conditions.

In the intervening 150 years this meager society of men grew to 130,000,000 souls. To make this possible an unprecedented extension and utilization of science and engineering to ameliorate and control the environment of man was an absolute necessity. In that extension Benjamin Franklin pointed the way. The Philadelphia of his day was small, filthy, unprotected against fire, against thievery and against disease. The streets were muddy, frequently impassable, dark and dangerous.

An Englishman visiting the city in the 1790's described its harbor as putrid and dangerous to health.

Water Street, in 1793, was the hub of the spread of yellow fever throughout the City. In the yellow fever epidemic of the summer of 1793,

> . . . the poor of the congested quarters near the water front fell like flies in the winter. Soon it spread to the best residential sections. Soon all the great houses were closed, and everyone who could afford it, abandoned his business and fled from the stricken city.—Day and night the death carts rumbled through the town.—The streets were as those of a dead city—Life-long friends evaded one another like guilty creatures. Even the families of the stricken fled, leaving the suffering to die in barbarous neglect.—Only the negroes seemed immune and much to their honor they zealously contributed all in their power . . . .
>
> When the death toll mounted from scores to hundreds, from hundreds to thousands, the neighboring villages and towns met to devise plans for keeping the Philadelphians away. . . . The death rate increased frightfully. It was impossible to keep a record. On October 20, Wolcott wrote Washington that more than 4000 persons had died.

With the approach of winter the disease died out having taken a toll of almost one-sixth of the total population of Philadelphia. This attack of yellow fever was typical of the impact of disease upon most of the cities of the United States of that day. Their number and their kind, multiplied ten fold, dominated the program of the succeeding century and a half, a program directed primarily to the conquest of the material environment of our people.

Restrictions of time alone make it impossible to multiply the descriptions of American communities of Franklin's day. They were universally characterized, however, by the absence of public interest in or control of the deficiencies or dangers of environment and by the inadequacies of private and public funds for protecting and safeguarding the lives of citizens. Franklin's insistence upon extending public responsibility for streets, for public lighting, for police and fire protection marked the first recognition in this country of the responsibilities which growing populations place upon the civil engineer and simultaneously upon organized society at large. He was the first to emphasize that the people walked this earth upon a thin crust of civilization.

It is peculiarly appropriate, therefore, for a member of the civil engineering profession to review the progress in that field since the day of Franklin. A detailed statistical summary of the advance in the various fields of civil engineering during 150 years would be possible, but no doubt appalling to any audience. The speaker will select from that history, therefore, only three or four phases of civil engineering in which the progress has paralleled that of other sub-divisions. Again only the significant trends in these limited fields and their import to society will be discussed.

Roads

If Franklin were to return to this earth in 1938, perhaps the most impressive physical change in his favorite American city would be in the highways and streets. He himself described Philadelphia of his day as "filthy-dirty," because of the unpaved streets, the quagmires in winter and the stifling stretches of dust in summer. With true, but rare, municipal conscience, he introduced the first bill in the legislative assembly of Pennsylvania providing for paving the entire city and establishing, incidentally, for the first time, public financial responsibility through the assessment method.

An exposition of the development of the highway since that time would require a volume in itself, if ample discussion and speculation on the effect of highway development in shaping America's destiny as a nation were to be considered. For our purposes, it is important to point out one impressive change which that development has brought in its wake, namely, the tremendous reduction in time and space relationships over that of a century and a half ago. Even our form of government, as originally established, may have been somewhat regulated by the inadequate facilities of communication between the colonies.

When Washington came from New York to Annapolis to attend the ball in his honor after the Peace, the trip required 13 days, a distance which may now be covered in less than one-third of one day. In that same period it took a day of almost 24 hours to ride from Elkridge Landing in Maryland to Annapolis, a distance of less than 30 miles.

From 1743 to 1775, additional highways were opened to the west. In 1775 Daniel Boone marked out the wilderness road through the Cumberland gap to Kentucky. The location of the road was a monument to the skill of Boone as a civil engineer and surveyor, for he laid out 200 miles of road through a mountain wilderness which, for a hundred years, remained practically unchanged. These developments were followed in the 1780's by the construction of many turnpikes operated for the most part by turnpike companies, many of which continued in operation for 100 years thereafter.

The construction of the National Pike was initiated by an Act of Congress in 1802 and in 1805 the building of the road from Cumberland, Md., to the Ohio River was authorized. The first contract for its construction was let on April 11, 1811, and the road was completed from Cumberland to Wheeling, W.Va., about ten years later. The total length of this section was 131 miles and the total cost of construction was

$1,706,845 or an average of $13,029 per mile. Today it would probably cost us $10,000,000.

This period was followed by an epidemic of plank road construction begun in Syracuse, New York, about 1846. Within 4 years more than 2,000 miles had been constructed in New York State alone. By the third quarter of the 19th century modern types of pavement were introduced in this country, with brick pavements in Charleston, W. Va., in 1872, sheet asphalt surface on Pennsylvania Avenue in Washington in 1879 and rock asphalt surface in Newark, New Jersey, in 1870.

To New Jersey belongs the credit for the first practical step taken anywhere in the United States, in 1891, to participate directly in the construction of roads, although Kentucky for many years prior thereto had established a well defined State road policy with a State Highway Department from 1821 to 1837.

After a lapse of almost 55 years the Federal Government assumed once more participation in the highway program of the country by an Act of Congress in 1893 establishing a Department of Road Inquiry. Up to 1904 there had been no important change in the methods of road construction that had been used for a century or more. In 1904 the United States Office of Public Roads, the successor to the United States Department of Road Inquiry, took the first census of American roads. In that year there were 2,151,570 miles of rural highways, of which 153,662 miles had been surfaced with various materials.

The decade following 1904 was marked not only by the development of new types of road, but by two other changes of much greater significance. A general increase in the radius of travel by highway was occasioned by the use of the automobile and secondly, a complete change occurred in the character of the public demand for highway improvement. These major changes in turn resulted in the initiation and extension of Federal aid through a series of Federal aid road acts, with accompanying grants-in-aid by the Federal Government of increasing total amounts since 1916.

At the end of 1924, over three million miles of highways had been constructed in the United States, of which somewhat over seven hundred thousand miles had been improved in some degree.

In the State of Pennsylvania alone the total surfaced and improved roads in 1937 amounted to 27,935 miles. The unimproved roads totalled 10,099 miles and approximately 46,500 miles of second class township roads of lesser importance. This is a far cry from the first struggle which Franklin had to obtain a legislative act for the paving of the streets of Philadelphia. During the period from 1917 to 1938 inclusive, the Federal aid grants to Pennsylvania alone totalled approximately $139,000,000.

It is of passing interest, however, to remind Pennsylvanians that history repeats itself, for in 1937, its Legislative Assembly reverted for one reason or another, to the turnpike days of 1785 by the passage of an act creating the Pennsylvania Turnpike Commission, with authority to construct and finance a turnpike from Middlesex, Cumberland County, to Irwin, Westmoreland County. The construction is to be financed wholly from funds derived from bonds to be issued by the Commission, and these bonds will be secured solely from revenues from the turnpike. The officials of the Lancaster Turnpike Company incorporated by the Governor on April 9, 1792, may well turn over in their graves.

In 1938, the Federal aid contribution to highway construction will probably exceed $238,000,000 indicating a 1938 highway program in the United States exceeding $1,000,000,000. When Cyrus, the Elder, during his reign in the Persian Empire, constructed roads in 559 B.C., he opened the way for that continuing demand for trade relations between the people of a country. Franklin extended that program at the end of the eighteenth century and the end is not yet in sight.

Water Supply

At the close of 1800 there were only 17 waterworks in the United States. All but one of these was privately owned. For the most part the water works of the colonies were simple, with most of the community works consisting of large wells from which the householders carried water. New York, Philadelphia and Boston had water supply systems prior to 1800, but they were inadequate for either domestic or public purposes. As a matter of fact, a water works owned by Aaron Burr's Manhattan Company, created under an act of the legislature in 1799 for New York City, consisted of a large well and two pumps. Since the real objecet of the company apparently was to conduct a bank under a clause concealed in its water company charter, it made no strenuous effort to furnish water for general municipal purposes.

By 1832 the supply furnished in the City of New York by the Manhattan Company and by the public and private wells was so offensive that all who could do so purchased water from unpolluted wells in the northern part of the island. The water sold for $1.25 a barrel. With a serious outbreak of cholera in 1832, discussion for a more permanent and safe water supply crystallized in an election in 1835 when the Croton project was approved by the citizens. Croton water was delivered to the city in 1842, when the city had attained a population of more than 300,000.

After the great fires in Chicago and Boston, the number of water plants in the United States increased from 243 in 1870 to 598 in 1880. By 1900 this number had increased to over 3,000 and today there are well in excess of 10,000 public water works in the United States supplying over 80,000,000 people. While in 1800 the percentage of water works owned by private companies exceeded 90, the reverse is probably the case at this time, showing a continuing trend toward public assumption of responsibility for supplying safe and adequate water supply to the people.

Important technical changes in the materials and equipment for water works systems naturally paralleled the development in extension and ownership of these facilities. The change from bored logs in the early 18th century to cast-iron pipe, first laid in Philadelphia in 1807, marked the first important improvement in materials in distributing systems. Wrought iron pipe appeared in the 1840's as a competitor and with the advent of hydraulic mining in California in the 1850's, wrought iron and steel came into wider use because cast-iron was too expensive in the western territory. It was in this fashion that wrought iron and steel water pipe gained a foothold on the Pacific Coast for distribution systems from which they have never been dislodged.

The first important riveted wrought iron water pipe in the east was laid in Rochester in 1875. Into this active competition between materials, reinforced concrete pipe later entered, so that today we have an ever increasing variety of materials for this important part of our public necessities.

The construction of dams and reservoirs has increased in numbers and in complexity, with a variety of structures available for every purpose under the sun. The theoretical bases and the practical controls have been steadily amplified for hydraulic fill dams, for rock fill dams, for arched dams, hollow dams, steel dams, with increasing volumes, heights and strengths, culminating in such structural wonders of the engineering world as the Boulder and Grand Coulee Dams.

It is particularly appropriate to point out that Pennsylvania not only holds the record for the first water supply, but also for the first public supply furnished by pumping. The pump was installed for the City of Bethlehem in 1754.

The first steam pumping plant in Pennsylvania was put in operation in 1801 in Philadelphia on the Schuylkill River at the foot of Chestnut Street. The steam pump held practical sway over the water pumping field from 1800 until about 1900 when the centrifugal pump became a strong competitor for favor.

Paralleling these changes in pumping were the equally important changes in the improvement of the quality of public water supplies by the introduction of filters in the early 1870's for Poughkeepsie and Hudson, New York. Although such filters had been constructed in London as early as 1829, their application in this country did not begin until the early 1870's. It is difficult for most of us to realize the extent to which the United States suffered from the scourge of sewage polluted waters, which caused epidemics and almost continuous typhoid fever in most cities. These scourges were particularly severe in the manufacturing cities of Massachusetts and in the steel districts of western Pennsylvania. Most of us have forgotten that a number of visiting engineers at the Columbian Exposition at Chicago in 1893 contracted typhoid fever while there.

In 1892, Asiatic Cholera appeared on vessels quarantined in New York harbor and in 1895 detailed investigations began in Louisville on rapid or mechanical filtration.

The first reinforced concrete units for filters were adopted at Little Falls, N.J., in 1901. By 1938, filtered water was being supplied to over 30,000,000 people with a daily capacity exceeding approximately 5,000,000,000 gallons. In the interval of approximately 150 years, the typhoid fever death rate per 100,000 population has declined in this country from approximately 75 to less than 2. If the death rate of 1800 prevailed today for this disease, 13,000 more people would have died in the United States in 1937 than did. In Philadelphia, the death rate for this same disease per 100,000 population varied from 60 to 78 in the period from 1880 to 1890 while in Pittsburgh, for this same decade, the rate climbed as high as 158 per 100,000. In both cities, fortunately, this disease has dropped to a death rate of less than 2 in 1937. In the field of water supply improvement, progress in applied science has far outstripped even the highly imaginative hopes of a Franklin. Many of the devices were still unknown to him and certainly their widespread availability was hardly to be anticipated.

The effects of epidemics in the early days of the Republic on pushing forward installation of public water supply and sewerage facilities can hardly be overestimated. Yellow fever and cholera between them created havoc decade after decade with important results so far as municipal housekeeping was concerned. In New York City, yellow fever epidemics occurred in 1791, 1795, 1798, 1799, 1805, 1819 and 1822. The epidemic of 1798, when the population of that City was only about 80,000, resulted in more than 2,000 deaths. In the southern cities, of course, yellow fever persisted until almost the 20th century.

It was extremely fortunate, however, that the "building out" of yellow fever in the United States did not have to wait upon the discovery of the part which the mosquito played in the transmission of that disease. The increasing public demand for sewering and draining cities to avoid nuisance and to gain convenience diminished remarkably the incidence of yellow fever, due primarily to the elimination of the breeding places for mosquitoes. In similar fashion the epidemics of cholera in 1832, 1834, 1849, 1854, 1865 and 1873 brought about a certain amount of recognition of the probable relationship between this disease and the inadequate and unsafe methods of the disposal of household wastes, and undoubtedly stimulated the establishment of drainage and sewerage systems in the larger communities.

Sewerage

Perhaps the first application of engineering skill to the design of sewers was for Brooklyn, New York, in 1857, followed by similar developments for Chicago, Ill., in 1858. Some 15 years later installations were designed for Providence, R.I., and Boston, Mass. The first systems of separate sewers in America were built in 1880 at Memphis, Tennessee, and at Pullman, Illinois. After three-quarters of a century no large municipality remains in this country without a water-carriage sewerage system.

The progress in sewage treatment and the consequent correction of resulting stream pollution has not been as favorable. Much remains to be done in this last step of handling the sewerage problems of metropolitan areas by adequate control of the discharge of raw sewage, although at this time the sewage from more than half the total urban population of the United States is subjected to some form of treatment. One of the important problems still demanding more adequate solution deals with the discharge of untreated industrial wastes. Industry by and large is one of the principal offenders in the pollution of our streams, either through difficulties in finding technical methods of treatment or through inertia or through lack of funds. The problem offers one of the pressing challenges in modern stream control.

In 1875, of the 67 cities having a population of 100,000 or more, according to the 1920 census, not one was treating its wastes. By 1900 only two of these same cities had built treatment plants for approximately an aggregate population of 197,000. Today of a total population of 72,000,000 supplied with sewers 37,000,000 have made provision for sewage treatment.

Refuse Disposal

Progress in the collection and disposal of refuse has followed that in the fields of water supply and sewerage. As early as May, 1701, discussion of public procedures and of public payment for cleaning the streets was under way, but it was not until the third quarter of the 19th century that any real progress in this additional phase of municipal work was made. In statistics on about 70 cities in the United States in 1876, only 25 were removing house refuse in carts. In the remaining 45 places it was either thrown into adjacent cesspools, fed to hogs, thrown into the nearest river, dumped in nearby valleys or used for fertilizer. In less than half of these cities was there anything approaching a regular collection service.

For the most part the refuse was frequently dumped on the streets, from which it was gradually removed by hogs, scavengers or disintegration by traffic. Special methods of disposal began late in the 19th century. Today refuse collection and disposal is provided by virtually every large municipality in this country. Considerable room for improvement and extension of facilities remains, but the last century and a half has provided a record of increasing efficiency and availability of processes and equipments. Future progress will depend upon the character and training provided in muncipal governments.

General Progress in Civil Engineering

The examples presented may be multiplied in virtually all the fields of civil engineering practice. Adequate review and discussion of the advances in waterways engineering, in the design and construction of bridges and tunnels, in the development of power, in the vast programs of river regulation for flood control and reclamation, in railway transportation, in building construction, in the science and art of ventilation and in many other branches, would require volumes. They all tell the same story of major use and application of the fruits of science, by orderly processes, to the service and benefit of men. The beginnings of civil engineering certainly date back at least as far as 3000 B.C., but in number, complexity and wide spread application the works of civil engineers have shown their greatest advance since 1750. Perhaps the most significant phase of that advance is in the recognition by Franklin and his successors of the major responsibility which rests upon government for the continued extension of engineering works for the benefit of society in general. It was only after the middle of the 18th century that the profession of engineering began to receive public recognition. As a matter of fact, it was just after 1750 that John Smeaton, James Watt and Henry Cort, all contemporaries of George Washington and George III, began true engineering experimentation and led the way to the solution of problems in engineering on a scientific rather than upon an empirical basis.

There then followed the great eras in the United States of bridge building, of canal building and of railroad extension. The development of steel in the middle of the 19th century, followed by pioneer tunnelling methods and the universal application of nitro-glycerin, added to the equipment of the civil engineer. Throughout this whole period of a century and a half, structures of every sort were pushed forward with increasing research, with new tools and with ever increasing use of public funds.

Some index to this remarkable growth of civil engineering works is afforded, of course, by the increase in numbers of individuals associated professionally with these activities. The American Society of Civil Engineers had a membership at the time of its founding in 1852 of less than 100. By 1936 its membership had exceeded 15,500, a figure which, of course, does not include by any means all of the professional civil engineers of the United States. The trend of membership increase, however, again parallels the increased demand in this field of activity.

Retrospect and Prospect

Since the days of Benjamin Franklin time-space relations have changed, population has multiplied almost fifty fold, the area of the country has been tripled and the fruits of science have been generously applied for the benefits of man. It is a far cry from the engineering day of the land surveyor with "the nice combination of technical skill, and woodsman's instinct," who combined the functions of surveyor, historian, arbitrator and magistrate, to the skillful mathematician with tools of precision, the civil engineer of today.

How far Franklin's interest in the problems of the atmosphere, in his experiments with balloons and kites, and in ventilation, has been extended in daily application would have both intrigued and astounded that inquisitive philosopher. This one field of the ordinary "bookkeeping" of society exemplifies the profound changes from the past. It is interesting to speculate upon what his reactions would have been to the development of meteorological observation stations over this entire country and extending to Alaska, the West Indies, Canada and Mexico, with first steps taken for even international exchange of reports for similar stations throughout the world. He was so greatly interested in all matters of weather on every one of his ocean trips that he no doubt would have been pleased with the meteorological reports from ships at sea by the use of radio, one of the most important developments in the entire history of our Weather Service. One can imagine the excitement which would have been aroused at a meeting of the Junta on reporting on the use of the radio-meteorograph, an instrument attached to a balloon which sends back signals of pressure, temperature and humidity from the upper air at heights well above those attainable by airplanes.

It is perhaps fitting that in the Commonwealth of Pennsylvania the first widespread service for river forecasting should have been established in 1937, with the location of 130 recording rainfall stations on the watersheds of the Allegheny, Monongahela, Susquehanna and Delaware Rivers. The developments in this particular field are mentioned not only because they were so close to the heart and mind of Franklin, but more important because they are excellent examples of an increasing complexity of a universe which demands from science applications which make for safety, health and comfort of society.

The primary interest of Franklin in public service makes it important to emphasize and reemphasize that in our pride in the performances of the past 150 years we should find increasing challenges for the future. It is unfortunately true that the accomplishments of the past so frequently create both the complexities and the opportunities of the future. This is particularly true in the field of which we speak today, because parallel with the engineering development herein broadly delineated, has evolved the social and economic life of the nation. By virtue of this parallel growth it is true for the American as for the average English citizen, as Graham Wallas has recently pointed out, that the "possibility of health, of happiness, of progress, towards the old Greek ideal of 'beautiful goodness' depends on his local government more than on any other factor in his environment." So smoothly has this system worked in its essentials since the day of Franklin and since his inspiration to its creation, and so accustomed are we to its existence, that we not only overlook the vast amount of activity which led to its creation, but we may ignore the problems involved in the efficient maintenance and extension of its benefits.

The recognition by Franklin that government has responsibilities for applying the fruits of science to the needs of man marks him as perhaps one of the most important civil engineers of his day. He was one of the first master planners of our country, performing the most useful function of the engineer as the guardian of nature's resources. That he builded well in his introduction of government into the affairs of men can no longer be doubted, for since his day government has virtually halved the death rate and reduced the infant mortality rate by three-quarters. It has relegated cholera, smallpox and enteric fever to the archives of history. It has reduced tuberculosis to proportions regarded a century ago as impossible. In similar fashion, comfort and convenience of the people, not so easily statistically demonstrable, have enormously increased as other services have moved forward.

This discussion, however, should not be closed upon the note of celebration of the triumphs of the past, without reflecting upon the emerging needs of the future. The progress in engineering during the past century and a half brings into sharp focus some of the probable difficulties of the future. Perhaps the first and most pressing of these lies in the structure of our local and central governmental systems. Civil engineering activities of the last quarter of a century have become increasingly dependent upon and intimately related to the operations of government. It is unlikely that the next 25 years will see any relaxation of this relationship. If progress in civil engineering is to continue it must carry with it improvements in governmental functioning, particularly in the structure of local government. This is especially true in that vast field of engineering enterprise dealing with the control, development and regulation of the water resources of the country. As these problems impinge upon associated problems of land, minerals and industrial development, it becomes apparent that the present areas of local government operation will require moving integration with the higher levels of government.

A vast expansion in scale and scope is probable in the fields of public health, education and housing, in two of which at least, civil engineering is likely to play a signficant part. In the century and a half which has passed, the energies of authorities have been directed primarily to the conquest of the material environment, which some authors have perhaps too aptly described as a municipal administration with a "pedestrian and unimaginative flavor." Perhaps the future may demand an extension of the municipal horizon to the cultural aspects of civic life.

All of this will demand an increase in size and in professional quality of the engineering expert to whom new responsibilities and new leaderships will be entrusted, for in spite of all of our fears government will continue to assume new responsibilities and with it civil engineering must proceed. The future holds new hopes for a new kind of pioneer. A new frontier, technological rather than geographical, remains to be crossed with the same courage and with the same promise as Franklin foretold that "perhaps in less than another century the Ohio Valley might become a populous and powerful dominion." In the same vein the civil engineer of today views the next hundred years of his country as a territory virgin and rich in its promise of new returns to our people. He must continue Franklin's task of "subduing the ugly facts of society to some more rational scheme of things."

Contributions of Engineering
to Health Advancement*

Synopsis

The engineering profession has been instrumental in the successful fight against disease in the United States. Virtual elimination of the intestinal and insect-borne diseases proved the true value of engineering accomplishment. This paper reviews the unbelievable sanitary conditions that existed in former years and traces the work of the sanitary engineer in curbing the disease rate. Progress to date is evaluated, and a program for future development is suggested. The paper touches on many related problems that await solution by the sanitary engineer.

Introduction

Suppose the daily newspapers announced this morning that last year New York (N.Y.) had 95,000 cases of typhoid fever; Chicago (Ill.), 43,000; Philadelphia (Pa.), 24,000; Los Angeles (Calif.), 24,000; and Detroit (Mich.), 22,000. In 1952, this newspaper account would have somewhat the same effect as the dropping of an atomic bomb on the five largest cities in the United States. Times have changed. Nevertheless,

* Paper No. 2611, *Transactions of the American Society of Civil Engineers, Centennial Transactions*, Vol. CT, 1953, 579–87.

that is exactly what would have happened to these five major cities if the 1850 death rates had prevailed.

The intestinal diseases were the chief concern of the public health officer 100 years ago. These were the diseases of fundamental importance in environmental sanitation, and were, therefore, those offering the engineer the opportunity to make his greatest contribution toward preserving the health of mankind.

Early Progress

The intestinal and the insect-borne diseases provided the great proving ground for engineering accomplishment. Geddes Smith has aptly described these opportunities in the following terms:

> The bacteria that survive a Rhine-journey down the water courses from one man's intestine to another's gullet—typhoid, bacillary dysentery, cholera—are vulnerable at any point of their extra-corporeal travel, but most accessible where they pass through the channels of a city water supply.[1]

Recall what kind of water the citizen used 100 years ago in the average American city. It was described by a professional in the following terms:

> The appearance and quality of the public water supply were such that the poor used it for soup, the middle class dyed their clothes in it, and the very rich used it for top-dressing their lawns. Those who drank it, filtered it through a ladder, disinfected it with chloride of lime, then lifted out the dangerous germs which survived and killed them with a club in the back yard.[2]

—an exaggeration perhaps, but those who remember the river water supplies on the Ohio as late as 1912 submit that the exaggeration is not too overdrawn. Where water was available, it was too frequently a carrier of silt and disease, rather than a safe potable liquid. Not until 1835 could even New York City pride itself on a substantial water distribution system, even though its first limited source and distribution system date back to 1744. The great city of Chicago did not have even the elements of a public water supply system until 1840. Buffalo (N.Y.), Washington (D.C.), Cleveland (Ohio), Denver (Colo.), Indianapolis (Ind.), Milwaukee (Wis.), and Kansas City (Mo.) only translated this public responsibility into a physical system between the 1850's and the 1870's.

Public sewerage systems came even later. Baltimore (Md.) has the unenviable distinction of having replaced the bulk of its individual cesspools by a comprehensive public sewerage system as late as the beginning of the twentieth century.

Not a city in the United States from 1850 to 1900 escaped the ravages of the intestinal diseases. Typhoid fever death rates ranged from 50 to 175 per 100,000 in the great cities of the New World. The death rates from cholera at times reached more than 300 per 100,000. The toll from environmental diseases of water-borne character was truly appalling.

From 1800 to about 1880 the insect-borne disease, yellow fever, visited the United States virtually every year. In the New Orleans (La.) epidemic more than 29,000 cases with 8,100 deaths occurred. In Memphis (Tenn.) a single epidemic accounted for 17,600 cases and 5,150 deaths.

Malaria covered almost every part of the United States, as far north as the Great Lakes and including the great state of Illinois. Insect-borne disease literally roamed the continent, and people either accepted the scourges or turned to quarantine, evacuation, and witchcraft to contain the epidemics.

New York City during the summer of 1798 was visited by one of the most virulent of yellow fever epidemics. It treated the situation as its neighboring city Philadelphia and others had met it, by:

> . . . burning nitre in the streets, firing horse pistols at the bedsides of sufferers and carrying garlic in their shoes and bags of camphor around their necks, and dousing themselves with Haarlem Oil, essence of aloes and Vinegar of the Four Thieves.[3]

In Philadelphia, the entire population:

> . . . had been driven into camps along the banks of the Schuylkill. Government had retired, entire streets had been barricaded, pest houses organized which surpassed all conceivable horrors.[3]

The elements of emergency civil organization were completely lacking. These events give perhaps a preview of the latter day community of 1953, struck by an enemy and ill equipped with a civil defense organization.

These vivid examples of a country ridden with environmental disease could be multiplied indefinitely. Sanitary literature and public health literature are filled with detailed accounts of tragedies resulting from failures to interpose a barrier between the sick and the well. The record appears in dramatic detail in the papers of Stephen Smith, Lemuel Shattuck, Edwin Chadwick, C-E. A. Winslow, William T. Sedgwick, Gordon M. Fair, M. ASCE, M. P. Horwood, the writer, and others. The further repetition here of vital statistics and of lurid description would serve no useful purpose beyond that already achieved by the few examples noted. In the United States, in England, and in continental Europe, the sanitary conditions a century ago were the same. No country in the world then escaped the ravages of environmental disease. It was on this stage that the public health team of engineer, physician, and nurse created the miracles of the modern world in the control of these diseases.

The Scene Today

In the United States today typhoid fever, malaria, yellow fever, and cholera are vanishing or vanished diseases. The death rate from typhoid fever in the country as a whole is less than 0.1 per 100,000 population. Malaria is nonexistent in the greatest part of the nation and is rapidly declining even in those parts where it may still be found by the physician. Cholera has not been seen in the United States for more than a half century.

Each of these diseases remains a constant threat. Their disappearance for the most part is man made. The world has not been rid entirely of any single infection known to man. In the United States and in a handful of European countries, the elimination is largely the result of protective measures interposed by man between the diseased and the well. In practically no other nation in the world is it possible to drink water or milk with safety.

In England and in continental Europe, too, man has been well protected, but some phases of control still leave much to be desired. In the rest of the world, perhaps 75% of the total population of the globe, the intestinal diseases, the dysenteries, and the insect-borne diseases still demand the same toll of lives as prevailed on this continent 100 years ago. Typhoid death rates still run from 20 to 80 per 100,000; cholera epidemics periodically visit the unfortunate populations; malaria cases are measured in hundreds of millions per year; bubonic plague ravages unfortunate areas; and infant mortality in the first year of life at times rises to as much as 800 deaths per year out of every 1,000 births.

Disease Reduction Methods

Long before the specific organisms that cause many of the environmental diseases were identified, progress in their reduction began to take place on an empirical basis. The incentive in many instances was to make water supplies more palatable to the taste and more attractive to the eye. When the earliest filtration plants were built in England in the first third of the nineteenth century, they were demanded primarily to provide a physically more attractive liquid. Regardless of the empirical basis for these improvements, they brought immediate returns from the standpoint of reducing water-borne disease. Effective control of water supply, disposal of excreta, the control and pasteurization of milk, the elimination of insect breeding areas, the disposal of community refuse, the adoption of rodent-proof building techniques, and the institution of general practices of cleanliness were singularly effective in the reduction of disease.

Sanitary Engineering Leaders

It is always rash to assign credit for major accomplishments in any field. The invidious selection of the names of individuals or of professional groups to share this credit invariably causes controversy. In the subject matter of this paper, however, both individuals and professional groups may be singled out, on whom rests at least a major part of the responsibility for the successes achieved.

Nonprofessional Laymen. A great contribution was made to the sanitary awakening of the nineteenth century by the nonprofessional layman, who, in the United States and in England, played so significant a part in arousing the public to the deficiencies of individual and communal living. These laymen were pressed toward their task by the visible suffering of so large a part of the population surrounding them. Their contributions to sanitary accomplishments should be recorded time and again, if for no other reason than to awaken similar interest in the lay readers of today. Chadwick in England and Shattuck in the United States will go down in history forever as shining bearers of new light in the protection of people. They cried for solutions to environmental problems that the professional first ignored and was then permitted to develop.

The Sanitary Engineer. In the United States, the engineer–medical officer–nurse combination carried the load. The peculiar contribution made by this nation, however, is in the development of that specialized individual, the sanitary engineer, who combined into a hybrid discipline and practice the fields of biology and engineering. To him may properly be attributed a major part of the success achieved in the virtual elimination of the intestinal and insect-borne diseases. He brought to the task an understanding of the biology of disease transmission and of the engineering techniques by which structures, devices, and physical adjustments in the environment could be provided so as to interrupt the hitherto successful link between the diseased and the healthy individual. Sanitary engineers, more than any other single professional group, provided the engineering tools with which to attack the physical environment so closely related to the transmission of the diseases of man. Sanitation programs have accomplished more to improve man's surroundings and reduce infectious disease than any other endeavor in the field of public health.[4]

Nowhere else in the world has this special discipline been developed to any high degree—not that accomplishments in environmental disease control are lacking in England and in continental Europe. In those countries engineers have to their credit similar accomplishments, but through more orthodox engineering channels. Some at least believe that these disciplines may in the course of time reach greater parallelisms with sanitary engineering functions in this country.

In the rest of the world these peculiar hybrid functions are virtually unknown. However, they are beginning to penetrate fairly rapidly into many areas, and they will gain force in numbers and in influence as the potentials for engineering accomplishment in public health are increasingly recognized.

What Remains to Be Done

One may never review the past with optimism only, although the long record of great accomplishments is certainly to its credit. Does this mean, however, that the engineer may rest on his laurels or does it mean that the past is only a prelude to the engineering necessities of the future? The work yet to be done is always as great as the work already completed.

The United States. In the United States, a static situation would be almost an index of stagnation. Fortunately, the realities run contrary to this assumption. More than 5,000 communities in the United States still have no public water works systems. More than 79,000,000 people need important improvements or extensions in existing systems. These water needs represent a future expenditure of something more than $2,000,000,000.

In water quality much remains to be done. Investigative activities to disclose the impact of new contaminants of industrial or other origin offer only one index of many of the opportunities ahead. In sewerage, the next 10 years will demand an expenditure of about $3,000,000,000. The great metropolitan areas of the United States will require increasing attention. In many, modern sanitary facilities are virtually absent. Engineering skill, fiscal ingenuity, and administrative imagination all require detailed application and elaboration.

Pollution of surface waters will constitute a daily problem, involving domestic water supply, industrial water supply, recreational use, and agricultural necessities. Although more than 90,000,000 people are served by sewer systems, sewage from approximately one third of the population using such systems is discharged into streams without treatment.

The control of milk and other food products demands increasing perspective and development. In the past 20 years the United States has undergone a major revolution in food production, handling, processing, and distribution. In every phase of this development technology has played a significant part.

In insect and rodent control there is much to be done. Rocky Mountain spotted fever, murine typhus, encephalomyelitis in horses, and encephalitis in man remain hazards of great human and economic significance in this country. The recent experience with encephalitis in the Central Valley of California was a dramatic reminder in death, economic loss, and community distress of how much still must be learned.

The World-Wide Picture. In the rest of the world, it is easy to visualize the picture, at least for the next 25 or 50 years. Progress there can almost duplicate the phase of development that the United States passed through from 1850 to 1930. Environmental deficiencies in the bulk of the population of the world are orthodox and simple in character. They revolve primarily around inadequate control of water, unsafe handling of human excreta, and almost complete absence of the control of milk and of other food products. Procedures for correction are elementary, and the promise of accomplishment by the simplest of expedients is tremendous. The new tools, such as insecticides, will certainly provide immediate reduction in insect-borne diseases, giving man time to undertake those major physical adjustments in the environment that would result in permanent eradication.

Rate of Progress. Although these problems are the same as those of a century ago, their correction need not take as long. With the great body of information and tools now at hand, the engineer and the medical health officer should be able to telescope the rate of accomplishment in the rest of the world by many decades—but not by merely transferring the machines of the new world to the old. A wise adjustment of modern equipment to the needs of vast populations should, however, facilitate correction. The expanding horizon for the engineer in the protection of health offers one of the greatest opportunities the world has ever seen. Technical precedent is available and convincing. Scientific understanding is great and generally accepted. No one underestimates the fiscal, the cultural, the economic, and the political obstacles to such accomplishments, but there are no better traveling ambassadors than those alleviators of human suffering—the engineer and the doctor.

The Future

Environmental Control. In the control of environment, the engineer has been perhaps least successful in the maximum adjustment of the air, the shelter, and the clothes of man to the vicissitudes of his surroundings. On a comparative basis, the successes in these fields are neither as obvious nor as great as in those with which this paper has so far been concerned.

The delays in accomplishment are probably caused by the fact that the effects of these features of the environment on man's health and well-being are more subtle, less susceptible to physiological measurement, and, of course, more difficult to adjust.

The engineer shares these deficiencies with other professional groups. The environmental physiologist has so far provided no sensitive measurements of the effect of the constituents of the air on physiological well-being.

The physiologist, the psychiatrist, and the sociologist have not provided the engineer with any accurate or comprehensive criteria of the effect of poor housing on man's physical and mental health. Scattered observations, many of them significant, in the field of housing are available, but are still meager in amount and scientific nature.

Advances, either in understanding of physiological reaction to climate or in the development of clothing best to meet such variations, have been significantly slow. Military pressures in recent years have forced science and art forward in important directions, but the field is still wide open for engineering scrutiny and contribution.

Atmospheric Pollution. Perhaps one of the most unsatisfactory fields of the three mentioned is the control of atmosphere. The reaction of human organisms to the day-by-day exposures to varying physical, chemical, and biological contents of air has not been explored to the point at which these subtle influences, if any, may be evaluated. Only when extraordinary circumstances arise in the atmosphere such as in the Meuse Valley in Belgium and in Donora, Pa., does the significance of the atmosphere in the well-being of exposed individuals become apparent. It is disturbing to realize how little is known of the effect on the population of meteorological conditions, coupled with unusual concentrations of foreign materials in the air.

An interesting example of such potential atmospheric effects is the experience in Japan, with what has been designated locally as "Yokohama asthma." This disease has been reported by the American military forces since 1946. It ranges from mild bronchial irritation to severe respiratory distress, requiring emergency treatment, and differs markedly from any of the more familiar allergic types. The incidence is associated primarily with the Yokohama area, from September or October through March or April. Some of its aspects suggest that it stems from air pollution. The high industrialization of Yokohama and its location on a bay enclosed by hills and bluffs offer ideal conditions for the formation and retention of smog. The situation is being studied by the United States Army, with particular reference to meteorological phenomena. The weather data so far collected appear to provide supporting evidence, although indirect, implicating smog as a meteorological factor affecting the occurrence and density of Yokohama asthma.

As in the case of Los Angeles smog, a great deal more work needs to be carried out, jointly with critical examination of clinical data. The experience, however, is a reminder that there is a wide and unexplored field in the control of air, particularly in industrial regions.

Housing. Little major modification has been made in dwellings over the past several centuries. Construction materials, house design, and housing orientation represent as fertile a field for engineering inquiry as they did in the 1850's. The cynical George Bernard Shaw once observed that: ". . . the house the peasant lives in has not altered as much in a thousand centuries as the fashion of a lady's bonnet in a score of weeks."[5]

Plumbing Deficiencies. In Chicago it is not inappropriate to recall to engineers the continuing problem of controlling the hazards of plumbing deficiencies in buildings in which people live. Of the three epidemic outbreaks of amebiasis in the world, two occurred in Chicago; one in 1936, with 1,050 known cases and 70 deaths; the second in 1934, in the Union Stock Yards fire. The third, involving 118 cases, was among troops at El Paso, Tex., prior to 1933. Reference is made to these situations because there is a still more recent reminder of this ever-present danger in such orthodox items as plumbing.

During the early part of January, 1947, an amebic dysentery epidemic occurred in the Mantetsu Apartment Building in Tokyo, Japan.[6] This structure housed seventy-three family units of American occupation personnel. In all, one hundred sixty-one Americans and two hundred forty-eight Japanese employees were exposed to the threat of amebiasis. The protozoonal infection rate for the Americans was 62.9% for *endameba histolytica;* and for the Japanese employees, 22.2%. The exposures of the Japanese were fewer in the hotel, and their drinking customs were safer than those of the Americans. The epidemiological survey of the situation indicated that the epidemic was water-borne. The brief period of exposure, coupled with the extremely high rates of protozoonal infections, supported by physical investigation, showed a probable connection between the water system and the sewage from the apartment house.

Other Fields. Only limited time prevents detailed comment on new areas of activity carrying challenges to the engineer. The development of aircraft and collateral ground operations lends new force to the necessity for exploring the health aspects of light glare, noise, odor, smoke, dust, insects, rodents, and land and water pollution.[7]

The rapidly evolving atomic energy operations disclose new vistas in the studies of gaseous, liquid, and solid wastes; in the use of radio-isotopes as research tools; and in the search for uses for waste radioactive products. The behavior of man and of materials under the impact of nuclear fission products provides an area for exploration that should inspire the most fertile mind.

One hesitates even to refer to another completely barren field of cooperative investigation, because engineers have so consistently shied away from it. Real opportunities for collaboration are in the physiologist's domain. Only feeble attempts have been made to apply engineering analysis to the orthopedist's problems, to the embryologist's problem of the "pumplike" behavior of the umbilical cord, to the physiologist's problem of the respiratory mechanism, and to the physician's problem of the filtration system of the kidney. The engineer's facility with the analysis of structures and of the dynamics of air and water flow must be applied to these collateral promises for the future. Not all the problems of hydraulics are in cast-iron pipe!

Summary

The English sanitary engineer, A. J. Martin, once said:

> The poorest worker today is far better off than the wealthiest noble in the days of the Plantagenets or the Tudors. His home . . . is much healthier than the castle of a Norman baron.

The engineer in public health should be pleased with the progress in the past. He should be intrigued at the same time by the challenges of the future!

REFERENCES

1. "Plague on Us," by Geddes Smith, Oxford Univ. Press, Oxford, England, 1941, p. 181.
2. *Ibid.*, p. 182.
3. "Aaron Burr," by Samuel H. Wandell and Meade Minnegerode, G. H. Putnam's Sons, 1927, pp. 176–178.
4. "Health Resources in the United States," by George W. Bachman and Associates, The Brookings Institution, Washington, D. C., 1952, p. 199.
5. "Man and Superman," by George Bernard Shaw, Brentano's, Inc., New York, N. Y., August, 1915, Act III, p. 106.
6. "Epidemic Amoebiasis in Occupants of the Mantetsu Apartment Building, Tokyo, Japan," by Lawrence S. Ritchie and Cooper Davis, *The American Journal of Tropical Medicine*, November, 1948, p. 803.
7. "Sanitary and Industrial Hygiene, Engineering Aspects of Master Planning," by Alvin F. Meyer, *The Military Surgeon*, July, 1952, p. 29.

The Engineer and Society*

It has been the fashion of the learned professions in recent years to point out the confusions into which our present society has lapsed. Writers "view with alarm" the breakdown of modern society and search for cures for what they believe to be the modern twin diseases, overgrowth and mechanization. Whether we follow the gloomy banner of a Spengler to world destruction or the aspirations and hopes of the rhythmic Toynbee, the undercurrent is one of pessimism both as to the problems and the solutions of the present day world.

The leaders of the Bar, that is, those above or below the age of seventy, depending upon current alignments, take at least partial responsibility for the collapse of modern society. One of its recent spokesmen, Arthur T. Vanderbilt, chairman of the National Conference of Judicial Council states:

> The future of the Bar is not an isolated problem. . . . An inevitable transformation in our mode of living and our habits of thought is taking place as a result of the impact of our tremendous advances in the realm of the physical sciences on our relative inertia in the field of the social sciences. This presents a sharp challenge to every existing social institution, the Bar included.[1]

* Reprinted from *Johns Hopkins Alumni Magazine*, Vol. XXV, No. 4 (June, 1937), 340–48. Address delivered before the Alumni Association, Feb. 22, 1937.

The distinguished scientist, President Compton of the Massachusetts Institute of Technology, makes the comment: "We have reached the point beyond which further increase in our wealth, population, physical comfort, and cultural opportunity will not depend on discovering new resources by geographical exploration, but by wiser use of the resources that we now have, through scientific exploration." He points out: "This idea is not new, but I doubt if we realize its profound significance; it marks a turning point in the history of the world."[2]

The social science historian joins the procession by the warning: "Let the engineers and the scientists quit and the whole cultured order will revert to that of the eighteenth century agriculture."[3] He assumes that the present state of civilization is due to the tools and technological devices at our command, even though others might prefer a reversion to an eighteenth century agricultural world and hold the engineer responsible for the sufferings of our times.

These rumblings about the deficiencies of modern society have even led certain less timid souls to point out how we may be saved from destruction. Carrel[4] holds out high hopes: "For the first time in the history of humanity a crumbling civilization is capable of discerning the causes of its decay. For the first time, it has at its disposal the gigantic strength of science." It must be confessed, however, that with this flight of hope Dr. Carrel does not become more specific in suggesting how the serious difficulties of the present are to be met. Another noted biologist, Dr. H. S. Jennings, points out, however, with characteristic balance, that it is not the lack of knowledge or of its application that accounts for many or our present deficiencies in the control or development of society. He believes[5] that mankind manages its affairs so badly because there is disagreement as to the ends to be pursued, disagreement as to the individuals or groups for whom desirable ends should be secured, and disagreement as to what knowledge is valid for application to human affairs. Certain characteristics of human behavior result also in failure to use such knowledge as may be available, or to use it wisely.

These observations are unanimous only in the conclusions that there is something wrong with our universe, that the advances of science have had something to do with it and that the engineer in particular was the unfortunate, if unconscious, Satanic Majesty who has cast us all into this pit of despair. So strong are these charges that scores of distinguished orators, usually quite unfamiliar with the scientific field and frequently running for office, have bravely called for complete "intellectual disarmament," for a cessation of research, for a penalty on technological advance, for a return to the Garden of Eden or to the agricultural havens of some of our not distant international neighbors.

These gropings for the "Simple Life" are only partially explained by the depression psychology. They gained force from, but did not originate, with the bank holidays. They rest upon a more solid base. People, both lay and professional, sense a restriction upon their hopes and capacities, which restrictions they believe are somehow linked with pernicious scientific advance. What form this suspicion has assumed is immaterial for the purposes of our discussion. What is important is the inescapable conclusion that science, which has made modern life safe, comfortable, and easy, is conceived to be the enemy rather than the friend of man.

For this reaction against science in general and the engineer in particular, at least part of the responsibility rests upon the engineer. Both the engineer and the scientist have restricted their spheres of usefulness in the past to only two of the three possible opportunities in society. They have combined the functions of applying the fruits of science and of creating and expanding the sciences which makes these applications possible. An intermediate field, however, appears to have been missed. It is a field which has been preempted for the most part by individuals alert to public opinion, active in debate, but extraordinarily deficient in fundamental data. To these men, the engineer has generally been the "subordinate in the waiting-room, not the equal in the council chambers."

The engineer has contributed to the general welfare by reducing drudgery, by providing a new entertainment, by saving time, and by increasing material possessions. His failure, perhaps, has been in the field of "social transfer," in his lack of assuming wider responsibility for fitting scientific contributions into the general social fabric and by participation in those activities which would permit the universal adoption of the fruits of the labor of science with the least dislocation of the social structure.

We submit that a future task must be added to the present accepted functions of the engineering profession. That task is to transform the creations of science into the opportunities of society. The engineer has a peculiar responsibility in this task of conversion, since he has been trained to substitute knowledge for guesswork in dealing with technological problems. When the engineer undertakes the tasks of conversion here suggested, he automatically embraces an activity largely in the field of public service. He must deal with problems which are not only technical in character, but which also involve the knowledge of economics, finance, and above all, an understanding of human relations. The days when an engineer could be only a technical expert in a highly specialized field, are gone. One or two examples of modern engineering problems may be examined at this point. They may serve to clarify suggestions hitherto stated only in general terms.

Most readers have still fresh in mind the recent catastrophic floods in the Ohio and Mississippi Rivers. Probably few, however, have stopped to enumerate the engineering, legal, financial, and administrative problems which these floods dramatize in the technical field. No one doubts that the human and material damages which these floods have caused will be met. Perhaps the public mind may be temporarily satisfied by these concessions. The long term difficulties remain, however, in all of the fields mentioned. Upon their solution, future safety, economy, and public welfare rest.

The Ohio River is a sewer, a source of water supply, an outlet for floods, and a highway. One-seventh of the population of the United States is concerned directly with the waters of the Ohio Basin.

The Ohio River system now furnishes the chief means of disposal for nearly all the waste products of the many communities that line its banks. It provides the water essential to the health of millions of people and to the operations of thousands of industrial plants. Pollution of the main river and some of its tributaries by untreated domestic sewage and industrial wastes is a constant and serious threat to public health. Acid drainage from mines complicates the problem. The sewage produced by 6,500,000 people reaches the Ohio River directly or through tributaries. Less than thirty per cent of the sewage receives any treatment. On days of minimum flow, about one quart in every gallon of water in the main river at certain points has passed through a sewer system. This grossly polluted water after filtration is used as drinking water by 2,500,000 people.

High floods have swept down the Ohio from time to time since the days of earliest settlement along its banks. It has contributed more than any other stream to the devastating floodwaters of the lower Mississippi. Protection against major floods was provided years ago in the Miami drainage area and soon will be afforded in the Muskingum Basin by a system of reservoirs now under construction. A comprehensive plan developed by the Corps of Engineers of the War Department includes some eighty-nine reservoirs for flood control and power production. Much benefit in flood control could be obtained by building thirty-nine of these reservoirs, but only half of these are judged to be economically justified at this time. Fourteen were authorized by the Congress in the Flood Control Act of 1936.

Despite the conflict between the need of reservoir space for storage of floodwaters and for storage of water for other purposes, the integrated use of a system of large reservoirs for control of floodwaters, for augmentation of low flow, for power development, for water supply, and for recreation is possible. A study of such possibilities in the Ohio Basin is essential. Its water problems are complex and inter-related. In few drainage areas, if any, is there greater need of greater opportunity to solve water problems in combination, and to provide simultaneously for multiple uses of water.

The Ohio River and some of its tributaries, notably the Monongahela, carry the heaviest river traffic in the country. Further improvement of the Ohio, including replacement of obsolete dams, changes to facilitate operation of locks and dams, channel dredging, and the like, are desirable. One of the ambitious schemes of recent years for the creation of a new commercial waterway within and near the Ohio Basin calls for a canal through the Beaver, Mahoning, and Grand Rivers to connect Lake Erie with the Ohio River at an estimated cost of some $165,000,000.

This brief description of problems in the Ohio Basin is intended to disclose engineering difficulties, comprehensive in scope and involving hundreds of millions of dollars in cost. More important, however, must be the realization that difficult as the engineering problems are they are still vastly easier to solve than the collateral issues. In the Ohio Valley alone over seventeen million people reside. They engage in every form of enterprise from agriculture to manufacturing. They range in location from New York State through Pennsylvania, Maryland, West Virginia, Ohio, Indiana, Illinois, Tennessee, Kentucky, and Virginia.

The technical solutions and resulting structures in one state have profound effects on one or more adjacent or lower states. In construction, financing, administration, and legislation a remarkable degree of intellectual "tight-rope" walking is required to determine who is to pay for what, who is to be assessed in one area to create the beneficent effects in another area, who is to administer completed undertakings, and what shall be the conditions which shall govern such administration.

The handling of a single resource in this typical basin of the United States dramatizes at once the issues of local versus central financing and administration. Moreover, when the collateral undertakings in land use, involving soil erosion control and forestation, in power, in navigation, water supply and disposal of wastes, and other related factors intrude into the picture, the confusion of governmental agencies, of divisions of responsibility, of assessments of benefits and damages, of overlying responsibility for operation during periods of flood crests and during drought, all rise up to plague those simple minds who cling either to states rights or to Federalism and then retire peacefully to slumber. But more adequate answers involving engineering analysis and conscious translation of complex data into workable social formulae must be provided by those most competent to lead us out of these administrative wildernesses.

Another example of engineering and administrative territory of high risk is recalled to some of us by the first dust storm of 1937 in Texas several weeks ago. This should serve to remind us that the problem of dust and drought on the Great Plains is still with us. Too much water in the wrong places in the east and in the middle west have served to divert the public mind from the recurring problem of the Great Plains drought area.

The Great Plains extend from the foot hills of the Rocky Mountains about three hundred miles east to the mid-continental prairies. They include the eastern parts of Montana, Colorado, and New Mexico, and the western parts of the Dakotas, Nebraska, Kansas, Oklahoma, and Texas. These lands represent the concessions which the unattractive features of pioneering have caused to be made to people of this country. They once supported vast herds of buffalo and had not yet become one of the major "problem children" of the United States. It was only during a period of increased rainfall that these lands were turned into a granary, destined to be blown away during each recurring dry period.

Investigators believe that "the land may bloom again if man once more makes his peace with nature. Careful planting will give him back the foothill trees; terracing will save lush foothill farms; a wise use of the land will restore grass for controlled grazing; fewer and larger farms on scientifically selected sites may yield under the plough a comfortable living."

The Great Plains Committee, recently reporting to the President of the United States, affirmed with conviction that these lands may be converted into an asset. This conversion, however, rests upon an elaborate long term program of cooperation among the Federal Government, the ten states involved, local communities, and the individual farmers and stock men. It must be synchronized also with the broader national program for land and water use and control, already so ably emphasized[6] by Dr. Bowman, our distinguished President.

Here again the problems and solutions are technical in character. They involve the engineer, the lawyer, the administrator, the financier, and the teacher. Rules for action so as to produce the most helpful result are in many instances lacking. Integration and coordination of the various units and levels of government involve highly complex difficulties. While in the Ohio Basin the control and use of too much water at one time and too little at another posed certain issues, in the Great Plains area far too little water for long periods of years is the cue to the difficulty. Here again we must some day attempt to reconcile the desires, prejudices, and greed of individual sections of our country's people to the best advantage of all.

In this new kind of pioneering, as distinct from the simple geographical pioneering with which we are all familiar, the engineer and scientist must take the lead. The adaptation of our natural resources and of our familiar structural machinery of government to new or more complex problems appears to offer a fruitful, important, and challenging field for the scientist of tomorrow. Upon the engineering schools rests the great responsibility of so preparing the intellectual ground of its graduates as to meet these issues with courage, honesty, and ability. These seats of learning must see to it that in their distribution of the tools of knowledge they provide their graduates with the technique and attitude necessary to sustain our cherished liberty by the orderly processes of government and of law.

The engineering schools likewise must extend the horizon of the "departmentalized" mind of the engineer and produce a greater realization of the problems of the times and of the wider duties and responsibilities which these problems will entail upon their calling in the future. The engineer cannot evade assuming jurisdiction for studying the solutions for some of the issues which his contributions have created in the past and will continue to develop in the future. Engineering education must be required to extend its task beyond the technological to the collateral fields of human relations, economics, and finance. It should assume the responsibility of building—in the language of Sir William Bragg—"the men who are quick to apply the knowledge of the time to the needs of the times."

REFERENCES

1. "Past, Present and Future of the Legal Profession." *The Daily Record*, Baltimore, Maryland, January 7, 1937.

2. "Science in an American Program for Social Progress." *The Scientific Monthly*, January, 1937.

3. *The Rise of American Civilization*, by Charles A. Beard and Mary R. Beard. The MacMillan Company, New York, 1937.

4. *Man the Unknown*, by Alexis Carrel. Harper Brothers, New York, 1935.

5. "Biology and Social Reform." *Journal of Social Philosophy*, January, 1937.

6. Our Expanding and Contracting 'Desert'." *Geographical Review*, January, 1935.

Hippocrates Revisited*

Some twenty-five hundred years ago Hippocrates provided the physician with a reasonably broad definition of the relationship between man and his environment. He suggested that one has to have—

> . . . due regard to the seasons of the year, and the diseases which they are observed to produce,—to the states of the wind peculiar to each country, and the qualities of its waters;—marks carefully the localities of towns, and of the surrounding country, whether they are low or high, hot or cold, wet or dry;—neglects not to mark the diet and regimen of the inhabitants and, in a word, all the causes which may produce disorder in the animal economy.

In the centuries which followed, if they are reviewed by the environmentalist, our progress in definition, at least, is marked primarily by semantic evolution and preciousness of expression. For the simplicity of relationships Hippocrates spelled out, we have substituted the words and phrases of ecology, ekistics, the interaction of organism and environment (natural and man-made), and the broad ecosystems encompassing economic, sociologic, political, physical, biological, and psychological stresses. The "holism" of General Smuts and the constellation of causes

* The Herman E. Hilleboe Lecture, New York, N.Y., May 25, 1966.

of diseases of Dubos are all amplifications of the concept that man impinges upon and is affected by his environment.

Throughout the ages, however, conceptual relationships had greater strength than did their scientific validation. Although some optimists, such as Ritchie Calder, in his *After the Seventh Day*, confidently felt that man could remake his environment to suit his needs, the great questions still remain unresolved as to why and how this remaking might best be accomplished. Man has much to his credit in the environmental controls he has instituted over the years in reducing significant communicable diseases. When, however, he moves from these to a confrontation with the diseases of this age, more subtle in origin, more complex in manifestation and detection, and generated over longer time spans, he has greater difficulty in translating the Hippocratic truths into realistic private and public action. Nor is he helped much in this task by the shifting winds of political doctrine which always fan his budgetary papers.

The public health profession today operates in a world of an unreasonable mixture of public hysteria, general desire to enhance the quality of its environment and simultaneously to prevent its further degradation. The profession, sometimes with tongue in cheek, may choose as its slogan one of a multiplicity of descriptions of our present status. One prophet of doom recently suggested that "the United States stands knee-deep in sewage, shooting rockets at the moon!"—much hyperbole, but not much accuracy. A popular journal releases an article on "Our Dying Waters" with the introductory sentence: "This is the story of a national disgrace."

In contrast, a recent Report of the Environmental Pollution Panel of the President's Science Advisory Committee attempts to describe the problem of pollution, to distinguish between what is known and what is not, and to recommend steps necessary to assure the lessening of pollution already about us and to prevent unacceptable environmental deterioration in the future. This document, less lurid than some would desire, but more in keeping with scientific validity, does present the basis of a charter which may guide us in an organized attack upon the objectionable features of the environment.

The health worker is fully aware—or should be—that pollution is anything we do and environmental pollution is an unfavorable alteration of our surroundings, as a by-product of man's actions. These definitions, completely adequate philosophically, naturally bring in their wake a whole series of unresolved issues. In simplest terms, they require the public health worker to distinguish between fact and fancy, between crisis and orderly action, and between his functions either to acquiesce in ephemeral public opinion or to appraise and illuminate public choices. None of these arts are simple, none are likely to produce, except temporarily, winners of popularity contests and none will escape the necessity of much heart and soul searching!

The present exposition rests upon the assumption that we have a current and prospective job of correcting and adjusting the environment so as to protect man against significant deleterious impacts. In pursuit of this precept many issues confront us, in which balanced judgment and assessment should supersede both inertia and hysterical action. Analyses of the issues make up the body of this document. Only incidentally will we concern ourselves with the detailed scientific and technologic evidence underlying them. Focus is directed toward where, when, and how implementation should occur and what the obstacles are to sane and logical official action. The reason for this selection of subject matter lies in an attempt to recapture for the profession its historic role of preceptor and guide to the public for official action.

The Art of Prophecy

The concern of the public—and to some extent of the professional scientist and technologist—rests upon the extrapolation of the present conditions to those of the future in the environment. In general, the argument runs thus: if we have 195 million people now and we produce x tons of sewage sludge, we shall be surrounded by a sea of sludge when we have 225 million people and y tons of sludge. To the thoughtful student, the argument takes no account of current and past sludge reduction or of future technologic advance. The prophecy, however, makes its merry way into newspaper and magazine because its magic numbers are exciting and people have a penchant for drama and doom, especially if quantitatively expressed.

Fortunately, we have some examples in the historical record to warn us against such extrapolations. In 1903 Dr. Paul B. Barringer of Charlottesville, Virginia, published an article entitled, "An Unappreciated Source of Typhoid Infection."[1] At that time he was still blessed with abundant incidence of typhoid fever to play with mathematically. He was concerned with the infection of the roadbed of our American railways through the discharges of typhoid patients traveling over the road while in the infective stage. In the words of Dr. Kenneth F. Maxcy, who reviewed the Barringer document some years ago, Dr. Barringer "through a series of questionable assumptions based upon the current attack rates from typhoid fever, the number of railway tickets sold annually, and the average mileage travelled per passenger, estimated that there were 370 cases travelling over each mile of railroad in the United States each year. From this he theorized that 'in the well-drained but cool and moist soil under the ties and ballast of the modern railway

road bed, baptized day after day and year after year with the albuminous
fluids of human excrement, the *Bacillus typhosus,* once planted in the
natural culture medium will live forever, revitalized at intervals by new
infection, perhaps, but in the meantime facultative enough to meet seasonal and other changes.' Accordingly, he expressed the opinion that
the old trunk lines of the United States were already infected for practically their entire length, and that unless some radical change was made
in dealing with railway excrement, 'the country would ere long be
threaded and traversed in every direction by long and narrow but none
the less deadly zones of enteric infection, a permanent and ever-growing
menace to national health.' "

Regardless of the wisdom of railroad practices, or the lack of it, the
plausible hypothesis received wide acceptance among contemporary
sanitarians. The record, however, shows that a few expressed doubt
as to the validity of the prediction. The interest in the calculation lies
in the fact that the subsequent experience in the United States, Ger-
many, Switzerland, and England showed conclusively that Dr. Barringer's flight into prophecy was completely wrong.

Dr. Barringer at least was dealing with a known disease, of known
modes of transmission. But what of our prophets of 1966 who indulge in
more elaborate, dire predictions, cloaked in the newest of scientific terminology? For example, what does this virologist mean to say to the
people of this country, when he is quoted in the public press in the following words: "He suspects that our water may be a route for a steady,
low-level transmission of a number of diseases, not at a strength that
causes epidemics, but 'seeding of communities with viruses to which
they might not otherwise be exposed,' " What are these unknown diseases, of unknown origin, of unknown symptoms, and of unknown incidence? Should the health officer tell his people to stop drinking water?
Or would he be wiser to suggest that we curb oracular hints about water
until the mysteries of over a hundred viruses have been a little better
penetrated?

The Forgotten Man—The Epidemiologist

One may accept quite fully the dictum that control and correction
of environmental hazard should often run ahead of scientific proof as to
public health risk, either for aesthetic or economic reasons. At the same
time, one must always select objectives for action out of a growing universe of possible insults to man, materials, or other plant and animal
life. Not all environmental threats are equal. Paraphrasing Orwell's
well-known dictum, some threats to health are more equal than others.

Selection of priorities, therefore, for either control or investigation,
remains a primary responsibility. Here default or abdication becomes

increasingly evident. Perhaps, the sheer weight of public pressure drives the official to a reluctant acquiescence in less than convincing public health action.

The road to choice would be made much smoother if the epidemiologist's participation were more frequent in identifying, isolating, and measuring the factors which dominate the impact of the multifaceted environment upon biological reactions. The task is obviously difficult, the subtle aspects of the many forces are confusing and the desire of the investigator to choose simpler areas for study are understandable. Nevertheless, without this help, actions become reckless, wasteful, and even doomed to failure to produce the desired result. Unless the practitioner aims to be all things to all people, and many of us try to be, he must turn to the epidemiologist to help; for example, put "numbers upon the air we breathe, and what happens to us after we breathe it."[2]

Some Fantasies of An Affluent Society

Only the rich can really afford to be foolish. The poor may indulge in the silly, but a built-in restraint of money keeps the area small. The search for "clean air, clean water, clean land" drives our society into strange behaviors.

The belief that cleanliness is an absolute rather than a relative concept makes the health officer's lot not a happy one. Life in a sterile environment—whether physical, chemical, biological, or psychological—is both improbable and undesirable. Yet it is surprising to note how some search for this doubtful utopia because they can afford it and because our environment is now suspect.

In the field of water, striking examples come to light of a Diogenes-like search for purity—often at an amazing economic price. In a New York City department store "Branch Water" is sold in a bottle at a cost of 89 cents for half a gallon. (Parenthetically, safe public water furnished by New York City to its citizens costs less than 30 cents per 1,000 gallons!) The advertisement says that "Branch Water is pure natural, spring water, with very low sodium content and no chlorine or fluoride, uncontaminated by air pollution, sold solely for internal consumption,—drink Branch Water for good taste."

Lest public health workers lose heart, let me hasten to add that in Los Angeles supermarkets you may buy bottled water *with* or *without* fluorides—and with or without almost any of the mineral constituents familiar to us. Some of the dairies in that same area now deliver a bottle of water and a bottle of milk. How successful the Madison Avenue technique has become in scaring people to death!

It has been suggested that a modicum of zinc in a water increases the virility of the male. How soon will it be before we see on the shelf bottles of water, with a pinch of zinc, marked "His." For public health reasons alone, the adjoining shelf with bottles marked "Hers" will contain water with a contraceptive pill. Heaven forbid that we shall ignore the threat of the "population typhoon!"

The charge that the people run ahead of the health worker is true, but we are interested not only in how fast he runs but also to where he is running. Public opinion is an ingredient of high significance in every public decision. Public education geared to intelligent policy decision becomes, therefore, one of the unceasing responsibilities of the health worker. Otherwise, society slips into the curious route of decision-making aptly described as "the peanut-butter syndrome." Congressional hearings on matters of great public health import, are fine forums for educating both statesmen and the public. They are not, by themselves, the arenas of last resort on the setting of standards for either materials or for therapeutic practices. The temptation is great to decide either or both of these by democratic acclamation—in which the public, the representatives, and the professional health worker vie with each other for dramatic television appearances. It is unlikely that such processes, applied, for example, to polio virus, to fluoridation of water, to B.C.G. vaccination, will lead to the most fruitful protection of the public. Public policy-making often veers away from scientific judgment—and sometimes wisely. It should be developed knowingly, however, with the full benefit of scientific and technological information, unharnessed to self-interest and self-service.

Creative Federalism

The happy phrase, creative federalism, recently revived by President Johnson is pointed toward an official relationship between the federal and state governments. Conceptually, it has major implications in the field of environmental health. The acceptance of the responsibility for isolating the environmental determinants of community well-being and acting upon their adjustments involves every level of government. Historically, the involvement concerned only the state and the federal governments. In the last quarter of a century, however, the country has changed demographically. Once a largely rural society with a few conurbations, it has now become predominantly an urban complex. The population growth, the industrialization, and unprecedented urbanization create within the states new problems and new centers of action. These great population centers, in theory the creatures of the state, are remote from it politically and philosophically. By and large, the states prefer to ignore their reality.

While this demographic revolution was in the making, a parallel and equally dramatic shift to federal power structure was taking place. The shift is easy to understand, because the tax money began to flow in floods to Washington. It is an old axiom that where the money is, there lies the power. The environment, however, is local, notwithstanding the vociferous insistence that its problems are national. That the issues are of national interest is, of course, true. Their solutions for the most part have their roots in the states and in their local subdivisions. Aside from this salient fact, much of the strength of our country stems from the grass roots participation in policy decision making.

A quarter of a century ago, creative federalism was truly at work in the field of health. Since that time, joint interest and action have been eroded away. Strangely enough, this erosion has been led by the very representatives of the states and local areas. The congressman and senator, the presumed protectors of local autonomy and responsibility, have become the major protagonists of central government control—always, of course, with pious declarations for preservation of state virility.

Their declared basis for legislative erosion is that the states have defaulted in their general and specific responsibilities. Hence, the federal government must step in, gently at first and before long militantly, when federal agencies take over. Is the charge against the states true? Unfortunately, it is sufficiently accurate to warrant taking steps to do something about it.

The route for correcting the weaknesses charged, lies dominantly within the states, because the federal measures essentially cure the disease by gradually killing the patient. Can state health departments, for example, recognize in reorganization that cities, metropolitan areas, and regional sectors are so large, so autonomous, and so complex that new ways must be found for them to use more flexible procedures in meeting their problems? New relationships to the state must be developed to provide more rapid attacks upon environmental problems.

The states in turn must acknowledge that in the field of which we speak, the last 20 years have shown a decline in interest, in manpower, in budget, and in leadership. Creative federalism could still have much promise and great value, provided leaders at all the levels of government paid more than lip service to its implications. The states must be strengthened rather than debilitated by their own federal representatives, and must be reconstructed within their own confines. The federal agencies must stop the brain drain from the states, while they complain of the resulting states' leukemias. The Congress must reverse the flow of money in part, so that the sinews of state and local government might be strengthened. The aphorism is true that the problems are in the urban areas and the money is in Washington. Statesmen can change this and can make creative federalism work, if they have a mind to do so.

The management of the environment waits upon money, technological advance, institutional reconstruction, research, and development.

In all of these, the federal government might well resume its great functions of stimulator, investigator, and innovator while truly encouraging the states toward more active and effective participation in restoring the quality of our environment.

The Traffic in Grants-in-Aid

A natural consequence of efforts to meet the challenges of the environment, within the framework of the government structure we have created, is the proliferation of grants-in-aid. Some thirty of these in the fields of air, water, and land pollution abatement were operative at the end of 1965. By now, more have been added. If to these, we add those of state origin, we find ourselves in a situation of over-abundant riches in categories, if not in absolute dollars.

The evolution of grants-in-aid, first at a slow pace, and in the last few years at a crisis, breakneck pace, is well explained by the Congressional desire to make the environment over. Motivation is high. Administrative machinery grows necessarily rapidly to implement by these devices the same high motives which prompted them. All levels of government become the victims of a process of application, grant, financial review, and reports. Project proposals force the development of amazing strategies, confusing to the participants, no matter how well-intentioned they may be. The art of "grantsmanship" and "multiple convergence" has recently been spelled out before "bemused" congressmen at hearings held in April, 1966.

This traffic is not new to the health officer. It was delineated with care by the American Public Health Association in 1965, in a memorandum to the Congress. Health directors have elaborated upon the theme by describing grantsmanship "as a well-established specialty and by no means a simple one;" "goals are now being defined not in output terms of reduction of public problems but primarily in terms of services to be provided. This puts a premium on activity rather than accomplishment."

"Multiple convergence" resulted from the fact that it is easier to create new job titles on the federal level. A simple state agency may be the target for not a single counterpart federal agency but for a group or teams which may sometimes appear to be in competition with one another. These phenomena will increase in number in 1966 as additional reorganizations proceed in Washington.

Within the last month, the Maryland State Department of Planning issued a 332-page book entitled: *Manual of Federal Aid Programs*. The publication lists 223 separate sources of federal funds available to state and local governments. It took a year and a half to prepare. It will take several months more and a supplement to include the aid programs approved in 1965 and 1966. After that, a full-time employee will be required to keep the aid list up-to-date. The Maryland *Manual* is the first to be published. It will undoubtedly be followed by many other states.

With the proliferation of grants-in-aid, for categorical programs, it becomes well-nigh impossible for any orderly plan or program to ensue. In the universal scramble for money, as the number of objectives rapidly mounts, it is not surprising that logical and balanced public health programs succumb to a scattered array of miscellaneous projects.

The responsibility for the difficulties of administration cannot be placed upon the federal agencies, which are themselves the victims of Congressional directives. As a matter of fact, notably by the Department of Health, Education, and Welfare, strenuous efforts have been made to simplify processes and to reduce excessive checking of groups receiving grants-in-aid. This has been particularly true with HEW participation in financing projects at university and other research centers. The granting agencies cannot release funds completely without detailed scrutiny or they would jeopardize their own assigned responsibilities.

Are There Better Ways?

Among the proposals for simplification, in which the health worker has prime interest, was the suggestion put forward two or three years ago by Walter Heller, economic advisor to the late President Kennedy. Under it, the federal government would return to the states a proportion of federal personal income and corporate taxes—2 per cent of the take in the first year and gradually building up to 10 per cent.

The system would result in less restrictive grants to the states than now exist—even though general purposes would be specified, such as, for example, reducing water and air pollution. The states benefitting from such general funds would be prohibited from reducing their own taxes and would be required to apply current federal laws where federally financed programs are undertaken.

Resistance in principle to such proposals, or variants thereof, are bound to arise, particularly with many federal officials who do not trust the states as instruments of service to social and economic needs. Those who desire speed in all correctives share this mistrust of the states. Yet the realistic fact remains that improvement of state government is a matter of increasing urgency—if one believes, as I do, that the states are an essential foundation of our whole system of federalism.

Fortunately, we have a strong political ally in President Johnson, who said in 1964: "The national Government, as a constructive partner in creative federalism should help restore fiscal balance and strengthen state and local governments by making available for their use some part of our great and growing federal tax revenues."

It is to be hoped that the recent proposal, in the same vein, by a Republican party task force will not kill serious discussion of the basic scheme. The task force has unanimously indorsed the principle of federal-state revenue sharing.

Summary

A review of the environmental determinants of community well-being soon discloses that any ecosystem in which man works, plays, fights, or thinks poses hazards to himself and to his environment. It is apparent, also, that the universal eradication of hazards as a guiding principle is untenable and impractical. The parallel suggested by some with the eradication of smallpox and malaria is faulty.

The health profession, therefore, is confronted with less than total eradication measures. It then must select and appraise those routes which promise most beneficial results at minimum social costs. In this process of selection and appraisal, it often must decide between those choices coming out of public ignorance and clamor and those of more evident scientific validity. It must at the same time pursue such research as will clarify debatable effects, where scientific evidence is lacking.

The difficult and sensitive occupation in which he finds himself is not new, but his contributions to society's well-being are long and impressive. The search for truth cannot be used as a shield for inaction. Many things need to be curbed, if for no other reason than decent housekeeping. The dumping of abandoned automobiles, refrigerators, washing machines, and newest nonrefillable beer bottles should be eliminated and prevented. This practice is inexcusable, not because it causes disease x (which it does not), but because it is a violation of decency. It is an example of what H. L. Mencken once called the American "libido for uglification." An all-too prevalent disease!

In other areas of control, however, balanced approaches do require thought. The design of a safe automobile is desirable, but it may be less important than a program for reducing the total emission problem of this master of modern society. And the control of the driver may be more significant than either of the above measures, if one keeps one's sights focused upon tens of thousands of automobile deaths and millions of disabilities annually. It is true that one should attack all of these features, but let the public in on the relative merits and probable results. Our interest is still in lives saved and in disabilities avoided.

With a great task before us, reorientation in our total machinery for action is indicated. Orthodox institutional structure needs to be modified.

Fiscal changes are essential for implementation of objectives. The position of cities, metropolitan areas, and regional complexes vis-à-vis the state and the federal governments needs re-appraisal. The relationship of health departments to other social agencies needs strengthening. Certainly, the next 5 years should be full, with renewed emphasis on the two guiding principles of (1) the epidemiologic determination of the causation of disease so that preventive measures can be soundly based and (2) the assessment of the efficiency of prophylactic and therapeutic measures.

REFERENCES
1. *Medical Record*, December 19, 1903.
2. William A. Reinke.

Principal Professional Experience to 1968

1913   U.S. Public Health Service, Studies in Stream Pollution.

1914–22 Maryland State Department of Health.

1921–27, 1936–37 Lecturer in Sanitary Engineering, School of Hygiene and Public Health, The Johns Hopkins University.

1921–37 Editor in Chief, *Journal American Water Works Association*.

1922–39 Chief Engineer, Maryland State Department of Health.

1923–27 Associate Editor, *American Journal of Public Health*.

1924   Editor, *Manual of Water Works Practice*.

1925   Chairman, Public Health Engineering Section, American Public Health Association.

1925   Advisory Committee on the Oyster Industry to Surgeon General, U.S. Public Health Service.

1927   Chairman, Potomac River Flood Control Committee, Cumberland, Md.

1927–29 Consulting Engineer, Baltimore County Metropolitan District.

1929–30 Chairman, Conference of State Sanitary Engineers.

1929–30 Consulting Engineer to State of New Jersey in U.S. Supreme Court Case re: Delaware River, New Jersey vs. New York, N.Y.

1930–67 Water Works Practice Committee, American Water Works Association.

1931 to date Consulting Engineer on Water Supply, Sewerage, and Refuse Disposal, Baltimore City Department of Public Works.

1933–34 State Engineer, Federal Emergency Administration of Public Works, Maryland.

1933 to date Advisory Committee on Sanitation, Baltimore City Health Department.

1934–36 Chairman, Committee on Public Education, American Society of Civil Engineers.

1934–37 Acting State Director, Federal Emergency Administration of Public Works, Maryland and Delaware.

1934–45 Chairman, Maryland State Planning Commission.

1935–41 Chairman, Water Resources Committee, National Resources Planning Board.

1935–64 Chairman, National Water Supply Committee, American Water Works Association.

1935–43 Allegheny Forest Research Advisory Council, U.S. Department of Agriculture.

1936–43 Chairman, Stream Pollution Committee, Construction League of America.

1937–59 Professor of Sanitary Engineering, The Johns Hopkins University.

1937–44 Consulting Engineer, U.S. Public Health Service and U.S. Corps of Engineers, Investigations of Ohio River Pollution.

1937   Consulting Engineer, State of Pennsylvania Water and Power Resources Board and State Department of Health (future water supply of Harrisburg).

1938–40 Chairman, Bridge Supervisory Committee, Maryland.

1938–39, 1945, 1948, 1956–67 Consulting Engineer, Washington Suburban Sanitary Commission.

1939   President, American Public Health Association.

1939–44 Board of Directors, American Water Works Association.

1939   Planning Committee, Conference on Children in a Democracy.

1939   Advisory Committee to the Department of Sanitation of New York City.

1939–40 Commission on City Plan, Baltimore, Maryland.

1939–40 Medical Continuation Committee of the Conference on Inter-American Relations in the Field of Education, U.S. State Department.

1939–45 Consultant, U.S. Public Health Service.

1939–41 Consulting Engineer on Sewage Disposal, Portland, Oregon.

1939, 1940, 1943 Consulting Engineer, Water and Sewerage, Richmond, Virginia

1939 to date Consulting Engineer, The Tennessee Valley Authority.

1939–49 Chairman, Executive Board, American Public Health Association.

1939–45 Advisory Board, Bureau of Control Surveys and Maps, Maryland.

1940–64 Consulting Engineer, Bethlehem Steel Company, Water Supply, Sparrows Point, Maryland.

1940–50 Federal member, Potomac River Commission.

1941–49 National Technological Committee, Advisory to the Secretary of War.

1942   President, American Water Works Association.

1942   Advisory Committee on Public Health and Public Health Engineering, Office of Civilian Defense.

1942   Board of Directors, American Society of Planning Officials.

1942–45   Board of Procurement and Assignment, War Manpower Commission.

1942–60   Chairman, Advisory Committee on Sanitary Engineering and Environment, Division of Medical Sciences, National Research Council.

1942–45   Committee on Post-War Planning, Maryland.

1942–45   Committee on Sanitation of the Environment, Office of Foreign Relief and Rehabilitation Operations.

1942 to date Chairman, Permanent Sanitary Engineering Committee, Pan American Sanitary Bureau.

1943–45   Consultant War Production Board, Washington, D.C.

1943–45   Chief Consultant to the Director of War Utilities, War Production Board, Washington, D.C.

1943–46   Chairman, Interdepartmental Board for Sanitary Control and Protection of Public Water Supply of New York City.

1943   Consultant, Committee on Medical Research, Office of Scientific Research and Development, Washington, D.C.

1943 to date Advisor, U.S. Geological Survey.

1943–45   Vice-Chairman, Maryland Commission on Post-War Reconstruction and Development.

1943–50   Chairman, Committee on Water and Sewage Works Development, American Water Works Association.

1944   Public Utilities Committee Mission to the United Kingdom, Combined Production and Resources Board.

1944–48   Consulting Engineer, Water Supply and Sewerage, Seattle, Washington.

1944–54   Consultant to Surgeon General, U.S. Army.

1945–56   Chairman, Board of Consultants, Jordan River Project, Israel.

1945–49   Chairman, Sanitary Engineering Division, Advisory Board on Health Services of the American Red Cross.

1946–50   Advisory Committee on Biological Action of Chemical Agents, National Research Council.

1946–56   Consultant Director on Sanitation Research, Association of American Railroads, Baltimore, Maryland.

1946–50   Chairman, Expert Committee on Environmental Sanitation, World Health Organization.

1947–60   Atomic Energy Commission, Reactor Safeguards Committee, Safety and Industrial Health Advisory Board; Chairman, Stack Gas Working Group.

1950–51   Board of Consultants, New York City Water Supply.

1950–51   Consultant, U.S. Dispersal of Federal Buildings.

1951–57   Chairman, Advisory Council, Maryland State Roads Program and Policy.

1951   Chairman, Committee on Water Rates, Baltimore City.

1951   Commission on Administrative Organization of the State of Maryland.

1952–53   Consulting Engineer, Kansas River Basin Study.

1953   Consulting Engineer on Sewerage, Jacksonville and Sanford, Florida.

1953–56 and 1967 to date Chairman, Board of Consultants, Middlesex County Sewerage Authority, New Jersey.

1954–59 Consulting Engineer, West Virginia Pulp and Paper Company.

1955   Editor, *American Journal of Public Health.*

1955   Consultant, National Science Foundation.

1955   Consultant, National Defense Department.

1955   Consultant to Government of Ceylon, World Health Organization.

1955   Chairman, Committee on Mass Transportation, Baltimore City.

1956–57 International Mission, Organization of Government of Argentina.

1956–57 Board of Consultants, Detroit Metropolitan Regional Water Supply.

1956 to date Consultant, Miami Conservancy District.

1957–60 National Advisory Committee on Radiation, U.S. Public Health Service.

1957   Board of Consultants, Indianapolis Water Company.

1957   Consultant, International Cooperation Administration, Santiago, Chile.

1958 to date Consultant, Water Development, Israel.

1958   U.S. Delegate to Geneva Conference on Peaceful Uses of Atomic Energy.

1959   Mission to South America, International Cooperation Administration.

1959   Chairman, Board of Consultants on Calcutta Water Supply, World Health Organization.

1959   Consultant, Patuxent River Valley Regional Sewerage Study.

1959–61 Consultant, Senate Select Committee on National Water Resources.

1960   Chairman, Brazil Evaluation, The Johns Hopkins University team, International Cooperation Administration.

1960   Consultant, Metropolitan Washington Pollution Study.

1961   Chairman, Mission to Taiwan (Formosa) Republic of China, Community Water Supplies, World Health Organization.

1961   President's Conference on Occupational Safety.

1961   Vice-President, National Health Council.

1962–66 Chairman, Panel on Water Resources, Agency for International Development.

1963–66 Southeastern Michigan Sewerage and Drainage Study, National Sanitation Foundation, Detroit.

1963   Consultant, Greater Buenos Aires Area, Pan American Health Organization.

1963–68 Consultant on Sao Paulo Metropolitan Area, Agency for International Development.

1963–67 Committee to Study the Department of Public Works, Baltimore City.

1963–67 Maryland Water Study Commission.

1964 to date Special Water and Sewer Study, Baltimore Metropolitan Area.

1964 to date Board of Consultants, Regional Sanitary Advisory Board, Metropolitan Council of Governments, Washington, D.C.

1966 to date National Academy of Engineers.

1966–67 Planetary Biology Advisory Subcommittee of the Space Science Steering Committee, Washington, D.C.

1966 to date Board of Consultants, North Atlantic Regional Water Resources Study, Corps of Engineers, Washington, D.C.

1966 to date Expert, National Council on Marine Resources and Engineering Department, Washington, D.C.

1966 to date Consultant, Development Committee for Greater Columbus, Columbus, Ohio.

Chronological List of Published Works

1. "Standards of Mechanical Filtration Plant Performance," *American Journal Public Health*, Vol. 6. No. 11 (September 1916), 1,153–61.

2. "The Quality of Water and Confirmatory Tests for B. Coli," *Journal of the American Water Works Association*, Vol. 4, No. 2 (June 1917), 200–205.

3. "A Modification of the McCrady Method of the Numerical Interpretation of Fermentation Tube Results," with Herbert L. Weaver, *Journal of Infectious Diseases*, Vol. 21, No. 3 (September 1917), 287–92.

4. "A Preliminary Analysis of the Degree and Nature of Bacterial Removal in Filtration Plants," *Journal of the American Water Works Association*, Vol. 5, No. 3 (September 1918), 272–78.

5. "The Practicability of Adopting Standards of Quality for Water Supplies," with Robert B. Morse, *Journal of the American Water Works Association*, Vol. 6, No. 3 (September 1918) 198–228.

6. "Chlorine Absorption and Chlorination of Water," with Linn H. Enslow, *Journal of Industrial and Engineering Chemistry*, Vol. 11, No. 3 (March 1919), 206–13.

7. "Index Numbers and Scoring of Water Supplies," Parts I and II, *Journal of the American Water Works Association*, Vol. 6, No. 3 (September 1919), 444–56, and Vol. 7, No. 6 (November 1920), 927–30.

8. "Sanitary Effect of Water Storage in Open Reservoirs," with S. T. Powell,

Engineering News-Record, Vol. 83, No. 18 (October 30 and November 6, 1919), 804–805.

9. "An Inquiry into the Effect of Meteorological Conditions Upon the Efficiency of Storage, Filtration and Chlorination Based Upon a Study of the Hagerstown Water Supply," *Journal of the American Water Works Association*, Vol. 7, No. 3 (May 1920), 352–63.

10. "The Statistical Method in Problems of Water Supply Quality," *Quarterly Publication of the American Statistical Association*, Vol. 8, New Series No. 130 (June 1920), 188–202.

11. "Cooperative Research in Problems of Water Purification," *Engineering News-Record*, Vol. 85, No. 1 (July 1, 1920), 10–11.

12. "The Surface Shrinkage of Rapid Sand Beds," with S. T. Powell, *Engineering News-Record*, Vol. 85, No. 5 (July 29, 1920), 210–16.

13. "*Water Chlorination Control by the Absorption Method*," *Engineering News-Record*, Vol. 86, No. 15 (April 14, 1921), 639–41.

14. "Residual Aluminum Compounds in Water Filter Effluents," with Frank Hannan, *Chemical and Metallurgical Engineering*, Vol. 24, No. 17 (April 27, 1921), 95–115.

15. "The Small Plant Operator as Scientist," *Journal of the American Water Works Association*, Vol. 8, No. 4 (July 1921), 359–61.

16. "A Plan for Meeting Water Supply and Sewerage Costs," with Robert B. Morse, *Engineering News-Record*, Vol, 86, No. 22 (June 21, 1921), 944–47.

17. "Further Observations on pH in Natural Waters," with Frank Hannan, *Chemical and Metallurgical Engineering*, Vol. 25, No. 11 (September 14, 1921), 116–27.

18. "Hygienic Aspects of the Use of Sewage Sludge for Fertilizer," *Engineering News-Record*, Vol. 92, No. 5 (January 31, 1924), 198–202.

19. "The Training for the Sanitarian of Environment," *Journal of the American Public Health Assocation*, Vol. 14, No. 6 (June 1924), 472–73.

20. "Sand Bed Studies at Montebello Filters, Baltimore; Sand Size Cause of Troubles," with S. T. Powell, *Engineering News-Record*, Vol. 92, No. 26 (June 26, 1924), 1,094–1,095.

21. "Metropolitan District Planning in Maryland," *Public Works*, Vol. 55, No. 8 (August 1924), 242–45.

22. "Sanitary Engineering Progress in Maryland 1923–1924," *American Journal of Public Health*, Vol. 14, No. 8 (August 1924), 681–87.

23. "Values in the Control of Environment," *Journal of the American Public Health Association*, Vol. 15, No. 3 (March 1925), 189–94.

24. "The Occurrence of Tastes and Odors in Hyattsville Water District System after Painting Elevated Tank," *Engineering Bulletin*, Maryland State Department of Health, Vol. 1, No. 2 (September 1925), 90–92.

25. "Study of Sewage Pollution of Sinepuxent Bay," with A. E. Goodrich and W. N. Spring, *Engineering Bulletin*, Maryland State Department of Health, Vol. 1, No. 2 (September 1925), 162–68.

26. "Values in the Control of Environment," *Engineering Bulletin*, Maryland State Department of Health, Vol. 1, No. 2 (September 1925), 6–14.

27. "Hygienic Aspects of the Use of Sewage Sludge for Fertilizer," *Engineering Bulletin*, Maryland State Department of Health, Vol. 1, No. 2 (September 1925), 15–32.

28. "Metropolitan District Planning," *Engineering Bulletin*, Maryland State Department of Health, Vol. 1, No. 2 (September 1925), 169–78.

29. "Notes on Role of Iron in the Activated Sludge Process," *Engineering News-Record*, Vol. 98, No. 5 (February 3, 1927), 202–204.

30. "Municipal Water and Sewerage Costs in Maryland," *Journal of New England Water Works Association*, Vol. 41, No. 4 (1927), 439–48.

31. "The Hughes Report on the Great Lakes Levels Controversy," *Journal of the American Water Works Association*, Vol. 19, No. 4 (January 1928), 36–42.

32. "A Statistical Summary of the Oyster Findings in the Chesapeake Bay and its Tributaries," *Engineering Bulletin*, Vol. 1, No. 3, Maryland State Department of Health (April 1928), 6–15.

33. "Water Consumption Varies with Standards of Living and Fluctuations in Industrial Conditions," *Engineering News-Record*, Vol. 102, No. 24 (June 13, 1929), 943–48.

34. "Permanent Sources of Water Supply for those Sections of Maryland near the District of Columbia," with Robert B. Morse, in *Washington Capital Park and Planning Commission Supplementary Data*. Washington, D.C.: 1930. Pp. 97–109.

35. "Recent Progress in the Art of Water Treatment," with Wellington Donaldson and Linn H. Enslow, *Journal of the American Water Works Association*, Vol. 22, No. 9 (September 1930), 1,161–77.

36. "The Significance of Waterborne Typhoid Fever Outbreaks—1920–1930," with A. E. Gorman, *Journal of the American Water Works Association*, Vol. 23, No. 2 (February 1931), 160–201.

37. "Waterborne Typhoid Still a Menace," with A. E. Gorman, *Journal of the American Public Health Association*, Vol. 21, No. 2 (February 1931), 115–29.

38. "Filter Sand and Effective Size—A Symposium. 'Accurate Statistical Index,'" *Engineering News-Record*, Vol. 16, No. 19 (May 7, 1931), 770–71.

39. "Sportsman, Industrial, Sanitarian View of Stream Pollution," *Chemical and Metallurgical Engineering*, Vol. 38, No. 9 (September 1931), 504–505.

40. "The Water Resources Commission of Maryland," *Journal of the American Water Works Association*, Vol. 24, No. 8 (August 1932), 1,147–56.

41. "Fact and Fancy in Sewerage Financing," *Sewage Works Journal*, Vol. 5, No. 2 (March 1933), 302–308.

42. "Controlling Corrosion of Distribution Systems," *Journal of the American Water Works Association*, Vol. 25, No. 7 (July 1933), 947–55.

43. "Research in Sewage Chemistry and Sewage Treatment, A Critical Review of the Literature of 1932," with J. W. Bugbee, W. S. Mahlie, W. Rudolfs, and Earle B. Phelps, *Sewage Works Journal*, Vol. 5, No. 4 (July 1933), 567–94.

44. "Research in Sewage Chemistry, Sewage Treatment and Stream Pollution: A Critical Review of the Literature of 1933," with Wellington Donaldson, Linn H. Enslow, Samuel A. Greeley, W. S. Mahlie, Willem Rudolfs, and Earle B. Phelps, *Sewage Works Journal*, Vol. 6, No. 2 (March 1934), 169–207.

45. "Public Works and Water Supply Construction," *Journal of the American Water Works Association*, Vol. 26, No. 10 (October 1934), 1,363–73.

46. "Can you Live Without Water?" *Scientific Monthly*, Vol. 39, No. 6 (December 1934), 551–53.

47. *"Report to Public Improvement Commission of the City of Baltimore on Future Sources of Water Supply and Appurtenant Problems,"* with John H. Gregory and G. J. Requardt. Baltimore City, 1935.

48. "State Planning," *Bulletin of the Maryland Branch, The National Economy League*, February 1936.

49. "Discussion of Paper by George D. Clyde on 'Control and Use of Small Streams,'" *Headwaters Control: Proceedings of Upstream Engineering Conference*. Washington, D.C.: Soil Conservation Service, U.S. Department of Agriculture, 1937. Pp. 175–78.

50. "Recent Trends in Public Health Engineering Practice," *Journal of the American Public Health Association*, Vol 27, No. 1 (January 1937), 43–49.

51. "What Progress in Stream Sanitation?" *Municipal Sanitation*, January 1937, 40–41.

52. "Drainage Basin Problems and Programs," *Engineering News-Record*, April 1, 1937, 476–79.

53. "Problems in Developing a National Flood-Protection Policy," *Proceedings American Society of Civil Engineers*, Vol. 63, No. 3 (March 1937), 429–39.

54. "The Engineer and Society," *The Johns Hopkins University Alumni Magazine*, Vol. 25, No. 4 (June 1937), 340-48.

55. "Progress in Federal Conservation of Water Resources," *Journal of the American Water Works Association*, Vol. 29, No. 7 (July 1937), 915–41.

56. "Changing Public Health Practices and Problems," *Journal of the American Public Health Association*, Vol. 27, No. 10 (October 1937), 1,029–1,035.

57. "What can we do about Stream Pollution?" *Proceedings American Society of Civil Engineers*, Vol. 64, No. 1 (January 1938), 64–67.

58. "State and Other Governmental Functions in the Control and Abatement of Water Pollution in the United States," *Modern Sewage Disposal*, anniniversary book of the Federation of Sewage Works Association, 1938, 285–97.

59. "The Trend of Civil Engineering Since Franklin," *Journal of the Franklin Institute*, Vol. 226, No. 3 (September 1938), 413–28.

60. "Flood Control, Irrigation and Drainage," *Public Works Engineers Yearbook*, 1938, 156–70, 81–90.

61. "A Century in Arrears," *Journal of the American Public Health Association*, Vol. 29, No. 12 (December 1938), 1,369–75.

62. "Waterborne Typhoid Fever, 1920–1936," with A. E. Gorman, *Journal of the American Water Works Association*, Vol. 31, No. 2 (February 1939), 225–373.

63. "The National Health Program, How Far? How Fast?" *American Journal of Public Health*, Vol. 29, No. 6 (June 1939), 628–32.

64. "Water Planning in Southeastern Florida," *Proceedings 5th Annual Southeastern Planning Conference*, December 1939, 2–10.

65. "The National Health Program—Present Status," *American Journal of Public Health*, Vol. 30, No. 1 (January 1940), 1–8.

66. "Pollution Control—Where Does it Stand?" *Municipal Sanitation*, January 1940, Vol. 11, No. 2 (February 1940), 64–66.

67. "Dentistry in Public Health, A Problem in Research," *Proceedings of the National Dental Centenary Celebration*, March 1940, 453–58.

68. "The Construction of Sewage Treatment Works and Its Relation to the National Economy," *Water Works and Sewage*, Vol. 87, No. 5 (May 1940), 201–204.

69. "An Inquiry into Standards Proposed for Stream Cleanliness," *Sewage Works Journal*, Vol. 12, No. 6 (November 1940), 1,116–20.

70. "The Education and Training of Personnel Other than Physicians," *American Journal of Public Health*, Vol. 30, No. 12 (December 1940), 1,452–55.

71. "Manganese in the Loch Raven Reservoir," with Robert B. Stegmaier, Jr., *Journal of the American Water Works Association*, Vol. 32, No. 12 (December 1940), 2,015–2,037.

72. "Environmental Sanitation," in *Administrative Medicine*. New York: Thomas Nelson, 1941. Pp. 471–87.

73. "Development and Trends in Sewerage Practice," with Alfred H. Fletcher, *Water Works and Sewerage*, Vol. 88, No. 2 (February 1941), 45–59.

74. "Bacteriological Quality of Water from Small Filtration Plants Treating Surface Waters," with Herbert M. Bosch, *Journal of the American Water Works Association*, Vol. 33, No. 5 (May 1941), 913–25.

75. "The Public Health Engineer and the City Health Officer," *American Journal of Public Health*, Vol. 31, No. 5 (May 1941), 436–40.

76. "Planning the Use of Water Resources," in *Planning for America*. New York: Henry Holt, 1941. Pp. 109–126.

77. "The American Public Health Association 1940–1941," *American Public Health Association Year Book*, 1941, 32–37.

78. "Regional Water Supplies," *Journal of the American Water Works Association*, Vol. 33, No. 11 (November 1941), 1,875–1,896.

79. "For Whom the Bell Tolls," *Journal of the American Public Health Association*, Vol. 31, No. 12 (December 1941), 1,243–48.

80. "Future Sources of Water Supply," *Report to the Public Improvement Commission of the City of Baltimore*, with Gustav J. Requardt. Baltimore City, 1942.

81. *Hampton Roads Regional Water Supply*, with John C. Geyer and Willard F. Day. Washington, D.C.: National Resources Planning Board, 1942.

82. "Treatment of Distillery Wastes," with Abraham Wallach, *Sewage Works Journal*, Vol. 14, No. 2 (March 1942), 382–402.

83. *Baltimore City Future Water Supply*, with Gustav J. Requardt. Baltimore City, 1942. Pp. 1–47.

84. "The Post-War Role of the Sanitary Engineer," *Sewage Works Journal*, Vol. 15, No. 3 (May 1943), 445–52.

85. "The Opportunity for the Engineer in the Field of Housing," with Alfred H. Fletcher, *Journal of the American Public Health Association*, Vol. 33, No. 6 (June 1943), 701–705.

86. "Post-War Water Works to Cost $200,000,000," *Water Works Engineering*, Vol. 96, No. 14 (July 14, 1943), 790–92.

87. "Planning the Post-War Water Supply Program," *Journal of the American Water Works Association*, Vol. 35, No. 7 (July 1943), 861–68.

88. *The Report on the Water Supply and the Cedar River Watershed of the City of Seattle, Washington*, with Carl E. Green and Bror L. Grondal, City of Seattle, 1944.

89. "Favorable and Adverse Development in the School Environment," with Wilmer H. Schulze and Alfred H. Fletcher, *Journal of the American Public Health Association*, Vol. 34, No. 5 (May 1944), 484–88.

90. "Geographical Directives in Urban Planning," *Report of Urban Planning Conference*. Baltimore, Md.: The Johns Hopkins Press, 1944. Pp. 3–12.

91. "The Effect of Sewage Treatment on Maryland Streams," with Albert B. Kaltenbach, *Sewage Works Journal*, Vol. 16, No. 6 (November 1944), 1,193–215.

92. *Report to the Mayor and City Council of the City of Baltimore on Refuse Collection and Disposal*, with Gustav J. Requardt and Hiram W. Woodward. Baltimore City, 1944, 116 pp.

93. "Landmarks of 1944," *American Journal of Public Health*, Vol. 35, No. 1 (January 1945), 1–7.

94. "Public Health Problems in Impounding Water in the Tennessee Valley," with S. Leary Jones, *Journal of the American Water Works Association*, Vol. 37, No. 4 (April 1945), 327–44.

95. "Some Sanitary Engineering Developments During the War," *Boletín de la Oficina Sanitaria Pan Americana*, Vol. 25, No. 4 (April 1946), 320–25.

96. "Proposed Plan of Irrigation and Hydro-Electric Power Development for

Palestine," with James H. Hays and A. E. Barrekette, *Technion Journal*, Vol. 5 (June 1946), 37–41.

97. "Responsibility for Industrial and Municipal Wastes," *Journal of the American Water Works Association*, Vol. 38, No. 7 (July 1946), 883–87.

98. "Wanted—A National Water Policy," *State Government*, Vol. 29, No. 9 (September 1946), 215–217, 239.

99. "The Sanitary Engineer Looks Forward," *Journal of the American Water Works Association*, Vol. 38, No. 11 (November 1946), 1,219–25; *American Journal of Public Health*, Vol. 36, No. 11 (November 1946), 1,273–78; *Water and Sewage Works*, Vol. 93, No. 11 (November 1946), 409–12.

100. "Fluorine and The Public Water Supply," in *Dental Caries and Fluorine*. Washington, D.C.: American Association for the Advancement of Science, 1946. Pp. 108–111.

101. "The Compact of 1785." *Geographical Review*, Vol. 37, No. 3 (July 1947), 521–22.

102. "State Responsibility in Stream Pollution Abatement," *Industrial and Engineering Chemistry*, Vol. 39 (May 1947), 561–65.

103. "Should Public Water Supplies Be Used for Mass Medication?" *Journal American Water Works Association*, Vol. 39, No. 9 (September 1947), 834–43.

104. "Industrial Water Supply from Processed Sewage Treatment Plant Effluent at Baltimore, Maryland," *Sewage Works Journal*, Vol. 20, No. 1 (January 1948), 15–19.

105. "Human Waste Disposal from Railroad Passenger Cars," with Lloyd K. Clark, *American Journal of Public Health*, Vol. 38, No. 5 (May 1948), 652–63.

106. "Nuclear Fission Operations and the Sanitary Engineer," with Arthur E. Gorman, *Sewage Works Journal*, Vol. 21, No. 1 (January 1949), 63–74.

107. "Lemuel Shattuck—Still a Prophet—Sanitation of Yesterday—But What of Tomorrow?" *American Journal of Public Health*, Vol. 39, No. 2 (February 1949), 145–150.

108. "Some Public Health Problems in Nuclear Fission Operations," with Arthur E. Gorman, *American Journal of Public Health*, Vol. 39, No. 4 (April 1949), 443–53.

109. "Utilization of Surface, Underground and Sea Water," introductory paper prepared for Section Meeting on Water Supply and Pollution Problems, *Proceedings, United Nations Scientific Conference on the Conservation and Utilization of Resources*. Geneva, Switz., April 11, 1949.

110. "Bacterial Standards for Natural Waters," *Sewage and Industrial Wastes*, Vol. 22, No. 3 (March 1950), 346–52.

111. "Some Problems in General Sanitation in Railroad Transportation," with Lloyd K. Clark, *Proceedings, 30th Annual Meeting, Medical and Surgical Section, Association of American Railroads*, April 24–25, 1950, 21–31.

112. "Some Biochemical Problems in Sanitary Engineering," in *In Research*

in Medical Science, ed. D. E. Green and W. E. Knox. New York: Macmillan, 1950. Pp. 479–92.

113. "Ionizing Radiation Materials as an Air Pollutant," *Industrial Hygiene and Occupational Medicine,* Vol. 2, No. 2 (August 1950), 134–36.

114. "Public Health Aspects of Atomic Energy," *American Journal of Public Health,* Vol. 40, No. 12 (December 1950), 1,502–507.

115. "Waste Materials in the United States Atomic Energy Commission," with Arthur E. Gorman, in *Industrial and Safety Problems of Nuclear Technology,* ed. M. H. Shemos and S. G. Roth. New York: Harper Brothers, 1950. Pp. 268–302.

116. "Railroad Sanitation," with Lloyd K. Clark, *Modern Sanitation,* Vol. 3, No. 2 (February 1951), 27–31.

117. "Water Policy as the Engineer Sees It," *Journal American Water Works Association,* Vol. 43, No. 6 (June 1951), 401–408.

118. "Better Ground Water Management," in Harold E. Thomas, *Conservation of Ground Water.* New York: McGraw-Hill, 1951. Pp. 277–90.

119. "Man as a Resource," *The Land,* Vol. 10, No. 1 (1951), 34–38.

120. "Future Water Sources of the City of New York," with L. R. Howson, W. W. Horner, T. Saville, in *Report of Engineering Panel on Water Supply to Mayor's Committee on Management Survey of the City of New York.* New York: Tabard Press, 1951. Pp. 1–81.

121. "Characteristics and Problems of Industrial Water Supply," *Journal American Water Works Association,* Vol. 44, No. 4 (April 1952), 279–86.

122. "The Complexities of a National Water Policy," *Edison Electric Institute Bulletin,* July 1952, 248–50.

123. "Effects of Ionizing Radiation in Air Pollution," in Louis C. McCabe, *Air Pollution.* New York: McGraw-Hill, 1952. Pp. 489–92.

124. "Financing Sanitary Works in the Tropics—A Challenge," *American Journal of Tropical Medicine and Hygiene,* Vol. 2, No. 4 (July 1953), 557–64.

125. "Water and the Atomic Energy Industry," with Arthur E. Gorman, *Journal of the Institution of Water Engineers,* Vol. 7, No. 4 (July 1953), 319–46.

126. "Flood Protection in Kansas River Basin," with N. T. Veatch, Louis E. Howson, *Journal American Water Works Association,* Vol. 45, No. 7 (July 1953), 685–93.

127. "Contributions of Engineering to Health Advancement," Paper No. 2611, *Transactions of the American Society of Civil Engineers, Centennial Transactions,* Vol. CT, 1953, 579–87.

128. "World Health: The Optimists v. the Pessimists," *WHO Newsletter,* Vol. 6, No. 8 (September 1953).

129. "Unfinished Business and New Forces in Environmental Health Orthodoxy," *Public Health Reports,* Vol. 68, No. 10 (October 1953), 962–67.

130. "Disposal of Radioactive Wastes," with Arthur E. Gorman, *American Society of Mechanical Engineers,* July 30, 1954, Paper No. 54 a/2.

131. "Providing Reasonable Water Service," *Journal American Water Works Association*, Vol. 47, No. 1 (January 1955), 1–8.

132. "Management and Disposal of Wastes," with Arthur E. Gorman, *Proceedings of the International Conference on the Peaceful Uses of Atomic Energy*, Geneva, Switz., 1955. New York: United Nations, 1956. Pp. 9–16.

133. "Extension of Public Services to Suburban Areas," *Journal American Water Works Association*, Vol. 47, No. 10 (October 1955), 945–47.

134. "Disposal of Man's Wastes," in *Man's Role in Changing the Face of the Earth*, ed. William L. Thomas. University of Chicago Press, 1956. Pp. 807–16.

135. "Committee on Sanitary Engineering and Environment," *News Report*, National Academy of Sciences, Vol. 5, No. 6 (November-December 1955), 93–96.

136. *A Report Upon a National Policy for the Development and Use of the Water Resources of Ceylon*. Ceylon: Government Press, 1956, 27 pp.

137. "75 Years of Improvement in Water Supply Quality," *Journal American Water Works Association*, Vol. 48, No. 8 (August 1956), 905–914.

138. "Long-Range Planning for Water Service," *Journal American Water Works Association*, Vol. 48, No. 12 (December 1956), 1,457–62.

139. "Disposal of Radioactive Wastes," *Journal American Water Works Association*, Vol. 49, No. 5 (May 1957), 505–511.

140. "Basic Principles of a National Water Policy, Report of AWWA Committee 1130," *Journal American Water Works Association*, Vol. 49, No. 7 (July 1957), 825–33.

141. *A Clean Potomac River in the Washington Metropolitan Area*, with John C. Geyer and Edwin E. Pyatt. Washington, D.C.: Interstate Commission on the Potomac River Basin, 1957.

142. "Elements of a State Water Program," *State Government*, Vol. 31, No. 2 (February 1958), 23–26.

143. "A Fresh Approach to Water Law," *Journal American Water Works Association*, Vol. 50, No. 10 (October 1958), 1,279–84.

144. "Radiation and the Health Officer," *Yale Journal of Biology and Medicine*, Vol. 31, No. 4 (February 1959), 231–46.

145. "Philosophy for Water Utility Managers," *Journal American Water Works Association*, Vol. 51, No. 5 (May 1959), 555–60.

146. "Technical, Financial and Administrative Aspects of Water Supply in the Urban Environment in the Americas," *Ingeniería Sanitaria*, November 1959, 1–31.

147. "Las Radiaciones y el Funcionario de Salud Pública," *Boletín de la Oficina Sanitaria Panamericana*, Vol. 47, No. 6 (December 1959), 487–98; also, "Radiation and the Health Officer," *Yale Journal of Biology and Medicine*, Vol. 31, No. 4 (1959), 231–46.

148. *Report on The Sanitary Facilities of the Greater Calcutta Area*, with

H. F. Cronin, Luther Gulick, and R. Pollitzer. Calcutta: Government of India, 1960.

149. *Present and Prospective Means for Improved Reuse of Water,* with E. F. Gloyna, J. B. Wolff and J. C. Geyer, Committee Print No. 30, 86th Congress, 2d Session. Washington, D.C.: Select Committee on National Water Resources, 1960. 54 pp.

150. "Water and Society," *Public Health Reports,* November 1960, 296–300.

151. "Technical and Administrative Considerations in the Management of Radioactive Wastes," with Joseph A. Lieberman, in *Disposal of Radioactive Wastes,* Proceedings of the Scientific Conference on the Disposal of Radioactive Wastes, Monaco, November 16–21, 1959. Vienna, Austria: International Atomic Energy Agency, 1960. Pp. 554–61.

152. "Physical Aspects of the Environment," *Industrial Medicine and Surgery,* Vol. 30, No. 9 (September 1961), 390–92.

153. "Bonfires, Cannons and Disease," *The Sinai Hospital Journal,* Vol. 11, No. 1 (May 1962), 13–22.

154. "Concepts of Policy in the Formulation of So-called Standards of Health and Safety," *Journal American Water Works Association,* Vol. 52, No. 11 (1960), 1,343–48.

155. "Impact of Desalinization on the Water Economy," *Journal American Water Works Association,* Vol. 53, No. 2 (1961), 119–24.

156. "Desalted Sea Water Is No Bargain," *The American City,* February 1961, 140–41.

157. "Man and His Changing Environment," *American Journal of Public Health,* Vol. 51, No. 11 (November 1961), 1,631–37.

158. "New Directions for Public Health," *International Development Review,* Vol. 3, No. 3 (October 1961), 22–25.

159. "Water Resources," *A Report to the Committee on Natural Resources,* Publication 1000B. Washington, D.C.: National Academy of Sciences, 1962.

160. *A Report to the World Health Organization on the Community Water Supplies of Taiwan, Republic of China,* with Luther Gulick and Noel Wood. Taiwan: Republic of China, 1962.

161. "Formulation of National Water Resources Policy in Israel," with Aaron Wiener, *Journal American Water Works Association,* Vol. 54, No. 3 (March 1962), 257–63.

162. "A Luta Pela Agua," *Revista Departamenta de Aguas e Esgotos de Sao Paulo,* No. 45, Ano 23 (July 1962), 77–80.

163. "Environmental Problems in Expanding Metropolitan Areas," *Maryland State Department of Health Monthly Bulletin,* Vol. 14, No. 9 (September 1962), 1–4.

164. "Salud y Desarrollo Internacional," *Boletín de la Oficina Sanitaria Panamericana,* Vol. 53, No. 4 (October 1962), 290–96.

165. "Remarks to Formosan Engineers on World Water Supply," *Journal*

American Water Works Association, Vol. 54, No. 12 (December 1962), 1,543–47.

166. "What is Good Water and How Should it be Paid For?" *Journal of the American Water Works Association*, Vol. 55, No. 1 (January 1963), 4–26.

167. "US Water Supply Lessons Applicable to Developing Countries," with Herbert M. Bosch, *Journal American Water Works Association*, Vol. 55, No. 8 (August 1963), 946–56.

168. "Engineering and Economic Problems in Re-Use of Water in Stream Systems," *Ohio State University Publication*, 1962–63.

169. "Status of Water Resources Use, Control and Planning in the US," *Journal of the American Water Works Association*, Vol. 55, No. 10 (October 1963), 1,253–72.

170. "Water Composition and Cardiovascular Health," with John H. Dingle, Oglesby Paul, W. H. Sebrell, Jr., William H. Strain, and James R. Wilson, *Illinois Medical Journal*, Vol. 125, No. 1 (January 1964), 25–31, and *Journal American Water Works Association*, Vol. 56, No. 4 (April 1964).

171. "The Last 15 Years in Cardiovascular Diseases," Second National Conference on Cardiovascular Diseases, in *Research*, ed. E. Cowles Andrus, Vol. 1 of *The Heart and Circulation*. Washington, D.C.: Federation of American Societies for Experimental Biology, 1964. Pp. 30–36.

172. "New Directions for Public Health," in *Dynamics of Development*, ed. Gove Hambidge, New York: Praeger, 1964, 261–68.

173. "The Engineer and Israel Society," *Technion Pamphlet Series P-1*. Haifa: Israel Institute of Technology, 1964.

174. "Water—Economics and Politics," *Journal Water Pollution Control Federation*, Vol. 37, No. 2 (February 1965), 145–50.

175. "La Experiencia de Estados Unidos en Materia de Abastecimiento de Agua y su Aplicación a los Países en Vías de Desarrollo," with Herbert M. Bosch, *Boletín de la Oficina Sanitaria Panamericana*, Vol. 58, No. 4 (April 1965), 329–39.

176. "Effects of Population Changes on Environmental-Health Problems and Programs," *Journal American Water Works Association*, Vol. 57, No. 7 (July 1965), 811–18.

177. "The Metabolism of Cities," *Scientific American*, Vol. 213, No. 3 (September 1965), 179–90.

178. "We Have Enough Water," in *Challenges and Choices*, special supplement to the St. Louis *Post-Dispatch*, September 26, 1965, pp. 37–38.

179. "Pollution of Water, Air and Food," in *Ciba Foundation Symposium on Health of Mankind*, ed. Gordon Wolstenholme and Maeve O'Connor. London: J. & A. Churchill, 1967. Pp. 164–72.

180. "Administration of International River Basins," with Northcutt Ely, in *The Law of International Drainage Basins*, ed. A. H. Garretson, R. D. Hayton and C. J. Olmstead. Dobbs Ferry, N.Y.: Oceana Publications, 1967. Chap. 4. Pp. 124–59.

181. "This Environment—Friend or Foe?" *Special Report No. 1.* Urbana: Water Resources Center, University of Illinois, 1968.

182. "Air Pollution—Time for Appraisal," Proctor Award Address, Research Society of America, New York City, December 29, 1967, *Science,* Vol. 159, No. 3822 (March 29, 1968), 1, 437–40.

183. "Pollution as an International Issue," *Foreign Affairs,* Vol. 47, No. 1, Autumn (October 1968), 164–75.

184. "Environmental Issues in the Arctic," *Archives of Environmental Health,* Vol. 17 (October 1968), 649–52.